B R I T A

WHERE TO STAY

Camping &
Caravan Parks

England • Northern Ireland
Scotland • Wales

CONTENTS

Front cover:
Haggerston Castle Holiday Park,
near Berwick on Tweed,
Northumberland.

Information Pages

Key to symbols
Inside back cover flap

COMPETITION - Win a week's family break at an award-winning holiday park. See pages 14-15.

CONCOURS - Gagnez un séjour d'une semaine pour toute la famille dans un parc de vacances primé. Voir en page 14-15.

PREISAUSSCHREIBEN - Gewinnen Sie einen einwöchigen Familienurlaub in einem preisgekrönten Ferienpark. Siehe Seiten 14-15.

PRIJSVRAAG - Win een vakantie van een week voor het hele gezin op een bekroond vakantiepark. Zie pagina's 14-15.

CONCORSO - Vincete una vacanza di una settimana per tutta la famiglia in un premiatissimo parco vacanze. Vedere pagine 14-15.

3

TOURING BRITAIN

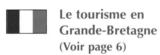 **Le tourisme en Grande-Bretagne (Voir page 6)**

 **Unterwegs in Großbritannien (Lesen Sie Seite 8)**

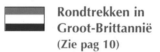 **Rondtrekken in Groot-Brittannië (Zie pag 10)**

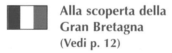 **Alla scoperta della Gran Bretagna (Vedi p. 12)**

Britain is a country of beautiful landscapes and historic interest where the traveller can enjoy great variety of scenery within short distances. Camping or caravanning is a good way to see Britain. You can go as you please without sticking to a set programme, enjoy the country air and have a lot of fun. Wherever you stay, you can use your park as a base for sightseeing and touring the surrounding area.

As the birthplace of camping, Britain has a large number of parks of every kind - from small quiet parks to big lively parks offering a wide range of facilities and entertainment. Many have a restaurant, bar, nightclub, regular barbecues and evening entertainment (eg dinner dance, cabaret).

An increasing number of parks now make ideal centres for an activity holiday. Fishing, sailing and golfing are just three of the more

popular activities offered by more and more parks. Many also have indoor swimming pools, tennis courts, games room and provide a wide range of facilities and activities to keep the children amused.

Most parks admit tents, touring and motor caravans and provide a wide range of central facilities for the tourer. Many have caravan holiday homes for hire. These are often very spacious, luxurious and well equipped with two to three good sized bedrooms, a lounge with comfortable furnishings and a separate dining area. Many have modern conveniences such as colour televisions, fridges, hot showers, en-suite bathrooms and microwaves. In addition to caravan holiday homes, many parks also have chalets and lodges for hire designed and equipped to the same standard. All are truly a home from home giving you the facilities and freedom you need to enjoy your holiday.

To help you select the type of park to suit you, with the facilities and standards you require, the British Graded Holiday Parks Scheme symbols, featured in the entries, will be of great assistance. Each park involved in this scheme has been visited by an independent inspector and graded according to the standard and quality of the facilities available. An explanation of these symbols can be found on page 17.

Many parks are open all year and can be an excellent way to have a short break in the spring, autumn and even in the winter months. Prices will be cheaper than during the main season and many facilities will still be available (although it might be wise to check).

If you intend to stay in a popular holiday area during the main season (June to September), you are advised to book in advance. It is essential either to send written confirmation of any reservations made or to arrive very early at your chosen park.

 La Grande-Bretagne est un pays qui abonde en panoramas superbes et en sites d'intérêt historique, où les touristes n'ont pas besoin de parcourir des kilomètres pour pouvoir admirer des paysages très variés. Le camping et le caravaning sont d'excellents moyens d'explorer la Grande-Bretagne. On peut aller où on le désire sans adhérer à un plan fixe, profiter du bon air de la campagne et se divertir. Quelle que soit la région où se trouve le terrain dans lequel on séjourne, on peut s'en servir comme point de chute pour faire du tourisme et rayonner dans la région.

C'est en Grande-Bretagne qu'est né le camping, on y trouve donc un grand nombre de terrains de toutes sortes, allant de petits terrains tranquilles à de grands parcs pleins d'animation proposant une vaste gamme d'équipements et de distractions. Un grand nombre de terrains possèdent des restaurants, bars, night-clubs, et organisent régulièrement des barbecues et des distractions nocturnes (par ex. dîners dansants, spectacles de cabaret).

Les terrains de camping sont des endroits merveilleux pour passer des vacances à thème, et un nombre de plus en plus important de terrains proposent cette formule. La pêche, la navigation de plaisance et le golf, entre autres, font partie des activités les plus populaires qu'on peut pratiquer dans des terrains de plus en plus nombreux. Un grand nombre de terrains mettent également à la disposition des vacanciers des piscines couvertes chauffées, des courts de tennis, des salles de jeux, et proposent une large gamme d'installations et d'activités destinées aux enfants.

La plupart de terrains acceptent les tentes, les caravanes de tourisme et les camping-cars, et mettent un vaste éventail d'équipements à la disposition des vacanciers. Un grand nombre de terrains louent des caravanes fixes, qui sont souvent très spacieuses, luxueuses et bien aménagées, comportant deux ou trois belles chambres à coucher, un salon confortable et un coin salle à manger séparé. Un grand nombre de ces logements de vacances ont tout le confort moderne: télévision couleur, réfrigérateur, douche avec eau chaude, salle de bains et four à micro-ondes. En plus des caravanes de vacances, de nombreux terrains louent également des chalets et des pavillons, conçus et équipés avec le même soin et dotés du même confort. Vous vous sentirez

comme chez vous dans tous ces terrains et vous y trouverez les aménagements et la liberté dont vous avez besoin pour profiter au mieux de vos vacances.

Pour vous aider à choisir le genre de terrain qui vous convient (ceux qui proposent les équipements et le niveau de confort que vous désirez), les signes conventionnels du British Graded Holiday Parks Scheme qui figurent dans les descriptions des terrains, vous seront très utiles. Tous les terrains participant à ce système ont été examinés par un inspecteur indépendant et classés selon le niveau et la qualité des équipements offerts. Vous trouverez la légende de ces signes conventionnels en page 20.

De nombreux terrains sont ouverts toute l'année, et permettent ainsi de prendre quelques jours de vacances agréables au printemps, en automne et même en hiver. Les tarifs sont moins élevés que pendant la haute saison, et de nombreux équipements sont encore à la disposition des vacanciers (il est toutefois prudent de vérifier).

Si vous avez l'intention de séjourner, en haute saison (de juin à septembre), dans une région de villégiature très fréquentée, nous vous conseillons de réserver à l'avance. Il est indispensable soit de confirmer toute réservation par écrit, soit d'arriver très tôt au terrain de votre choix.

Großbritannien ist reich an schönen Landschaften und historischen Stätten, und die Natur zeigt sich dem Besucher innerhalb weniger Kilometer von ihrer abwechslungsreichsten Seite. Die Übernachtung auf dem Campingplatz oder im Wohnwagen eignet sich gut, um Großbritannien kennenzulernen. Sie können nach Lust und Laune ins Blaue fahren, die würzige Landluft genießen und viel Interessantes erleben. Wo Sie sich auch aufhalten mögen, Ihr Platz ist stets ein idealer Ausgangsort für Besichtigungstouren und Ausflüge in die Umgebung.

Großbritannien ist der Geburtsort des Zeltens und bietet eine große Anzahl an Plätzen jeder Art - von kleinen, ruhigen bis zu großen, lebhaften Plätzen mit einer großen Auswahl an Einrichtungen und einem reichen Unterhaltungsprogramm. Zahlreiche Plätze verfügen über ein Restaurant, eine Bar, einen Nachtklub und veranstalten regelmäßige Grillpartys und Abendunterhaltung (z.B. Abendessen mit Tanz, Kabarett).

Das Zeichen des British Graded Holiday Parks Scheme, das neben den Eintragungen zu finden ist, hilft Ihnen bei der Wahl eines Platzes, der Ihren Anforderungen an Einrichtungen und Qualität entspricht. Jeder im Rahmen dieses Programms beurteilte Platz wird von einem unabhängigen Inspektor besucht und gemäß der Qualität der angebotenen Einrichtungen eingestuft. Eine Erklärung der Zeichen findet sich auf Seite 24.

Zahlreiche Plätze sind ganzjährig geöffnet und ideal für Kurzurlaube im Frühling, Herbst oder auch Winter. Die Preise sind während der Nebensaison billiger als während der Hochsaison, und zahlreiche Einrichtungen sind immer in Betrieb (es ist jedoch ratsam, sich zuerst zu erkundigen).

Immer mehr Plätze sind ideale Ferienorte für Aktivferien. Angeln, Segeln und Golf, nur drei der beliebtesten Aktivitäten, werden von einer wachsenden Zahl von Plätzen angeboten. Viele verfügen auch über ein Hallenbad, Tennisplätze, Spielzimmer und bieten eine große Auswahl an Einrichtungen und Aktivitäten für Kinder.

Die meisten Plätze sind für Zelte, Wohnwagen und Wohnmobile eingerichtet und bieten dem Besucher eine Reihe von Einrichtungen. Zahlreiche Plätze vermieten Wohnwagen. Diese sind oft äußerst geräumig,

luxuriös und gut ausgestattet und verfügen über zwei oder drei Schlafzimmer, ein Wohnzimmer mit komfortablen Möbeln und einen getrennten Eßbereich. Viele bieten auch Farbfernseher, Kühlschrank, Dusche mit warmem Wasser, Bad und Mikrowellenherd. Zusätzlich zu den Wohnwagen gibt es auf zahlreichen Plätzen auch Chalets und Hütten mit demselben Komfort. Alle sind in der Tat ein zweites Zuhause und bieten die Einrichtungen und die Unabhängigkeit, die für erfolgreiche Ferien unerläßlich sind.

Falls Sie während der Hochsaison (Juni bis September) eine beliebte Feriendestination wählen, ist es ratsam, im voraus zu buchen. Sie müssen die Buchung entweder schriftlich bestätigen oder sehr früh auf dem Platz Ihrer Wahl eintreffen.

slechts drie mogelijkheden die steeds meer terreinen organiseren. Vaak vindt u ook overdekte zwembaden, tennisbanen, spellenkamers en allerlei faciliteiten en activiteiten om de kinderen bezig te houden.

Op de meeste terreinen worden tenten, trekcaravans en kampeerauto's toegelaten en vindt u een groot aantal centrale faciliteiten voor de trekker. Ook

In Groot-Brittannië vindt u prachtige landschappen en een interessante geschiedenis. De reiziger treft op korte afstand van elkaar allerlei verschillende gebieden aan, en kamperen met de tent of de caravan is de ideale manier om echt van Groot-Brittannië te genieten. Ga en sta waar u wilt, zonder aan een programma vast te zitten, geniet van de frisse lucht en maak plezier! Waar u ook bent, u kunt uw kampeerplaats uw basis maken en in het omliggende gebied rondtrekken.

Groot-Brittannië is het geboorteland van het kamperen, en wij hebben dan ook een groot aantal terreinen in allerlei soorten en maten: vanaf kleine rustige terreintjes tot en met grote gezellige parken met allerlei faciliteiten en amusement. Vele hebben een restaurant, bar, nachtclub, en organiseren regelmatig barbecues en amusement 's avonds (zoals diner dansant, cabaret).

Steeds meer parken vormen tegenwoordig een ideaal centrum voor een actieve vakantie. Vissen, zeilen en golfen zijn

zijn er vaak stacaravans te huur: deze zijn vaak zeer ruim, luxueus en goed uitgerust, met twee of drie ruime slaapkamers, een

zitkamer met gerieflijk meubilair en een aparte eetkamer. Vaak vindt u er ook moderne gemakken zoals kleuren t.v., ijskast, warme douches, en-suite badkamers en magnetronovens. Vele parken bieden niet alleen stacaravans maar ook huisjes te huur, die al net zo goed zijn ingericht en uitgerust. Geniet van de faciliteiten en de vrijheid om echt vakantie te vieren.

Wij maken bij de vermeldingen gebruik van de symbolen van het zgn. British Graded Holiday Parks-inspectieprogramma, om u te helpen bij het vinden van een kampeerterrein dat aan uw

wensen tegemoetkomt. Ieder terrein dat aan dit programma meedoet is door een onafhankelijke inspecteur bezocht en ingedeeld naarmate de standaard en de kwaliteit van de beschikbare faciliteiten. Op blz 28 vindt u een uitleg van de symbolen.

Vele parken zijn het hele jaar open en bieden de ideale manier om er even tussenuit te gaan in de lente, herfst of zelfs in de winter. De prijzen zijn dan lager dan in het hoogseizoen, terwijl toch vele faciliteiten beschikbaar zijn (het is wel raadzaam dit van te voren na te gaan).

Als u in een populair vakantiegebied denkt te verblijven in het hoogseizoen (juni tot september), raden wij u aan van te voren te reserveren. Bevestig de reservering schriftelijk of kom zeer vroeg aan op het terrein.

La Gran Bretagna è uno stupendo paese di grande interesse storico che offre un'ampia varietà di paesaggi. Il campeggio in tenda o roulotte è uno dei modi più efficaci di visitare la Gran Bretagna, dato che consente di viaggiare quando e dove si vuole, senza dover rispettare un itinerario prestabilito, divertendosi e respirando l'aria fresca della campagna. Ovunque si decida di andare, il campeggio può servire da base dalla quale il turista può visitare la zona circostante.

Il campeggio è un'invenzione britannica, ne consegue che in Gran Bretagna vi sono numerosissimi campeggi di tutti i tipi: da quelli piccoli e tranquilli a quelli grandi e animatissimi che offrono un'ampia gamma di strutture e intrattenimenti. Molti campeggi offrono anche ristoranti, bar, locali notturni, banchetti all'aperto con barbecue e spettacoli serali (p.es. serate di ballo, cabaret).

Molti campeggi sono ideali per trascorrere periodi di vacanza di tipo più dinamico, dato che un numero sempre maggiore di essi offre la possibilità, ad esempio, di pescare, praticare la vela o giocare al golf. Molti dispongono di piscine, campi da tennis e palestre al coperto e di numerose strutture e attività per il divertimento dei bambini.

Molti dei campeggi sono aperti tutto l'anno e sono dunque ideali per trascorrere una breve vacanza anche in primavera, in autunno o in inverno, stagioni in cui i prezzi sono più bassi che durante i mesi di alta stagione, anche se restano disponibili molte delle strutture (consigliamo comunque di controllare prima dell'arrivo).

La maggior parte dei campeggi accetta tende, campers e roulottes e offre un'ampia gamma di strutture centralizzate per il campeggiatore. Molti offrono anche roulottes a noleggio Queste roulottes sono spesso spaziosissime, lussuose e ben attrezzate con due o tre camere doppie, un salotto comodamente ammobiliato e una sala da pranzo separata. Molte offrono anche altre moderne comodità come televisioni a colori, frigoriferi, docce calde, camere con bagno e forni a microonde. Oltre alle roulottes a noleggio, molti campeggi offrono anche chalet e casette a noleggio progettate e attrezzate con gli stessi criteri. Sono tutte abitazioni dove ci si sente come a casa propria, e che offrono libertà e tutte le attrezzature necessarie a godersi la propria vacanza.

Per aiutare il visitatore a scegliere il tipo di campeggio più appropriato, che offra le strutture e i livelli di qualità desiderati, le inserzioni recano i simboli di classificazione del British Graded Holiday Parks Scheme. Ogni campeggio che aderisce al programma di classificazione è stato visitato da un ispettore indipendente, e classificato in base alla qualità delle strutture disponibili. A pagina 32 viene data una spiegazione di questi simboli.

Si consiglia a chi intenda trascorrere una vacanza in una delle località turistiche più frequentate durante i mesi di alta stagione (da giugno a settembre) di prenotare in anticipo. È essenziale confermare la prenotazione per iscritto o arrivare molto presto al campeggio prescelto.

BRITISH HOLIDAYS

WIN A ONE WEEK FAMILY HOLIDAY *OR* ONE OF 5 RUNNER UP FAMILY BREAKS AT HAGGERSTON CASTLE HOLIDAY PARK

Britain: Camping & Caravan Parks

In association with British Holidays, *Where to Stay: Camping and Caravan Parks* is offering you the chance to win a full 7-day family holiday in luxury accommodation at an award-winning holiday park or one of 5 runners up family breaks of either a 3-night weekend break or a 4-night mid-week break. All prize winners will stay at Haggerston Castle Holiday Park near Berwick on Tweed.

Toweringly different, Haggerston Castle enjoys an imaginative setting around lakes and trees, whilst offering families the choice of a host of fun-packed activities. All this and a location in Northumbria, renowned for its glorious sandy beaches, historic towns and ancient castles.

You'll be staying in a British Holidays five-star caravan holiday home, which sleeps 2 to 8 people and gives you outstanding comfort and style. This top quality holiday home provides: Duvets for all bedrooms ☼ Pillows and blankets ☼ Fully-fitted kitchen with fridge and cooker ☼ Colour TV ☼ Fully-fitted bathroom with shower and toilet ☼ PLUS free gas and electricity.

This amazing prize also includes **free** entry for all the family to a world of entertainment and activities including: Bradley Bear Kids Club ☼ TC Teen Challenge Club ☼ Indoor swimming pool ☼ Outdoor heated pool ☼ Waterslide ☼ Jacuzzi ☼ Tennis courts ☼ Bowls ☼ Football ☼ Children's play area

HOW TO ENTER

All you have to do to enter is answer these five questions on some of Northumbria's splendid attractions. You'll find all the answers in the Northumbria Where to Go and What to See section on pages 57 to 61 of *Camping and Caravan Parks*.

1. **Which architect converted Lindisfarne Castle into a private home in 1903?**

2. **Where can you go on a journey under the North Sea?**

3. **Which saint's tomb is in Durham Cathedral?**

4. **High Force Waterfall is on which river?**

5. **Who was the 'King of Smugglers'?**

Write your answers on a postcard with your full name, address and telephone number and return it by 30 September 1997 to:

BTA Competition/ Attention Sandra
British Holidays,
Normandy Court, 1 Wolsey Road,
Hemel Hempstead,
Hertfordshire HP2 4TU, England

All correct entries received will be entered in a prize draw to take place on 14 October 1997.

USE YOUR *i*'S

Tourist Information *i*

When you're in Britain and would like further information about what to see and do - call in to one of over 800 Tourist Information Centres across the country.

There's one in most towns, and in many of the villages throughout Britain. Look out for the Tourist Information sign.

You'll be able to pick up maps and guides, as well as information on special events and attractions in the region.

If you are visiting Britain from overseas and would like more information before you travel, contact your nearest BTA office. A list of these can be found on page 237.

BRITAIN: Camping and Caravan Parks

Published by: British Tourist Authority, Thames Tower, Black's Road, Hammersmith, London W6 9EL.
ISBN 0 7095 6625 5
Managing Editor: Jane Collinson
Technical Manager: Marita Sen
Compilation & Production: Guide Associates, Croydon
Design and illustrations: Jackson Lowe Marketing, Lewes, East Sussex
Colour Photography: Mike Williams (front cover)
Cartography: Colin Earl
Typesetting: Reed Technologies and Information Services, London and Jackson Lowe Marketing, Lewes
Printing and Binding: Bemrose Security Printing, Derby
Advertisement Sales: Guide Associates, Croydon
Telephone: 0181 681 1099
© British Tourist Authority (except where stated)

Important:
The information contained in this guide has been published in good faith on the basis of information submitted to the British Tourist Authority by the proprietors of the premises listed, who have paid for their entries to appear. The British Tourist Authority cannot guarantee the accuracy of the information in this guide and accepts no responsibility for any error or misrepresentation. All liability for loss, disappointment, negligence or other damage caused by reliance on the information contained in this guide, or in the event of bankruptcy, or liquidation, or cessation of trade of any company, individual or firm mentioned, is hereby excluded. Please check carefully all prices and other details before confirming a reservation.

HOW TO USE THIS GUIDE
REFER TO SYMBOLS ON BACK COVER FLAP

Most parks listed here have accommodation for touring caravans or tents or both and most welcome motor caravans. Many parks also have caravan holiday homes to let.

Sure Signs of Quality

The British Graded Holiday Parks Scheme is operated by the Scottish, English, Wales and Northern Ireland Tourist Boards in conjunction with the British Holiday and Home Parks Association and National Caravan Council. All holiday caravan, chalet and camping parks displaying the 'Q' for quality symbol are graded by tourist board inspectors every year. Parks featured in *Where to Stay Britain: Camping and Caravan Parks* have been inspected or have applied for inspection under the British Graded Holiday Parks Scheme.

Each participating park has been visited by a trained inspector to ensure the highest standard of facilities, and enable the visitor to select a holiday with confidence. All aspects of the park have been assessed for their quality, and particular emphasis has been placed on the standard of cleanliness throughout. The quality standard of a park's facilities is indicated by **One** to **Five Ticks**. You will find a 'Q' rating after the park's name in most entries in *Camping and Caravan Parks*; where no rating appears, the park was awaiting inspection at the time of going to press. Below is an explanation of the standard you can expect for each rating.

✓✓✓✓✓ Facilities provided and maintained to an excellent standard.

✓✓✓✓ Facilities provided and maintained to a very good standard.

✓✓✓ Facilities provided and maintained to a good standard.

✓✓ Facilities provided and maintained to a fair standard.

✓ Facilities provided and maintained to an acceptable standard.

Facilities

Facilities are indicated by means of the at-a-glance symbols explained on the fold-out back cover flap.

Prices

Prices given for touring pitches are based on the minimum and maximum charges for one night for 2 persons, car and either caravan or tent. It is more usual in Britain to charge simply for the use of the pitch, but a number of parks charge separately for car, caravan or tent, and for each person. Some parks charge extra for caravan awnings and this is stated when applicable. Minimum and maximum prices for caravan holiday homes are given per week. Prices quoted are those supplied to us by the park operators concerned, and are intended to give an indication of the prices which will be charged during the currency of this publication. Prices are shown in pounds (£) and pence (p). VAT (Value Added Tax) at 17.50% is included in the prices shown. In order to avoid misunderstandings, it is particularly advisable to check prices with the park concerned when making reservations.

Making a Booking

When enquiring about accommodation, as well as checking prices and other details, you will need to state your requirements clearly and precisely - for example:

- arrival and departure dates with acceptable alternatives if appropriate.
- the accommodation you need.
- tell the management about any particular requirements.

Misunderstandings can occur very easily over the telephone so we recommend that all bookings be confirmed in writing if time permits. Remember to include your name and address and please enclose a stamped addressed envelope or an international

reply coupon (if writing from outside Britain) for each reply.

Deposits and Advance Payments

In the case of caravan, camping and chalet parks and holiday centres the full charge has often to be paid in advance. This may be in two instalments - a deposit at the time of booking and the balance by, say, two weeks before the start of the booked period.

Cancellations

When you accept offered accommodation, in writing or on the telephone, you are entering into a legally binding contract with the proprietor of the establishment. This means that if you cancel a reservation, fail to take up the accommodation or leave prematurely (regardless of the reasons) the proprietor may be entitled to compensation if it cannot be relet for all or a good part of the booked period. If a deposit has been paid it is likely to be forfeited and an additional payment may be demanded.

It is therefore in your interest to advise the management immediately if you have to change your travel plans, cancel a booking or leave prematurely.

Electric hook-up points

Most parks now have electric hook-up points for caravans and tents. Voltage is generally 240v AC, 50 cycles, although variations between 200v and 250v may still be found. An adaptor for use with hook-ups may be necessary. Parks will usually charge extra for this facility, except where otherwise stated, and it is advisable to check rates when making a booking.

The International Camping Carnet is rarely recognised in Britain except at parks organised by the major clubs.

Finding Your Park

Parks in this guide are listed England (by region), Scotland, Wales and Northern Ireland. They are listed alphabetically under the name of the town in or near which they are situated. The Town Index on page 254 and colour location maps at the back of the guide show all cities, towns and villages with park listings in this guide. Use these as a quick and easy way to find suitable accommodation. If you know which park you wish to stay at, check under the Index to Parks on page 249.

If the place you wish to stay is included in the Town Index, turn to the page number given to find the parks available there. The town names appear in black on the maps at the back of the guide as indicated by the map reference in the entry. Also check on the colour maps to find other places nearby which also have parks listed in this guide.

If the place you want is not in the town index - or you only have a general idea of the area in which you wish to stay - use the colour location maps. Some areas appear on more than one map, but town names (printed in black on the maps) are shown only once.

The positions of parks on the map should be taken simply as a general guide. Directions supplied by the park operators are included under each entry and if you have any difficulties finding a particular park, we suggest that you ask for final directions within the neighbourhood.

The International Direction Signs shown above are in use in Britain and are designed to help visitors find their park. They have not yet been erected for all parks and do not display the name of any particular one. They do show, however, whether the park is for tents or caravans or both.

Boundary Changes

In April 1996 the boundaries and names of many counties and regions in Britain were changed as the result of local government reorganisation. Changes that had been announced at the time of compiling the 1997 edition have been reflected in the maps and town descriptions within the guide. Further changes are planned for April 1997 which have yet to be confirmed.

London is a great attraction to many visitors, so the camping and caravan parks in the Greater London area tend to become full very quickly, and early booking is required. Parks are also available at most ports of entry to the country and many of these are listed in this guide and marked on the maps at the back.

Park Finding Services
Tourist Information Centres throughout Britain (see end pages) are able to give campers and caravanners information about parks in their areas.

Some Tourist Information Centres have camping and caravanning advisory services which provide details of park availability and often assist with park booking. At present, in England, these advisory Tourist Information Centres cover areas in **London**, London Tourist Board and Convention Bureau, Victoria Station; **Peak District**, (01629) 814341; **New Forest**, (01703) 283771; and **Cornwall**, (01872) 74057. In Wales, many Tourist Information Centres can supply information on pitch availability in their area from the end of May to the end of August.

Avoiding peak season problems
In the summer months of June to September, parks in popular areas such as North Wales, Cumbria, the West Country or the New Forest in Hampshire may become full. Campers should aim to arrive at parks early in the day or, where possible, should book in advance. Some parks have overnight holding areas for visitors who arrive late. This helps to prevent disturbing other campers and caravanners late at night and means that fewer visitors are turned away. Caravans or tents are directed to a pitch the following morning.

Other Caravan and Camping Places

If you enjoy making your own route through Britain's countryside, it may interest you to know that the Forestry Commission operates forest camp parks in Britain's seven Forest Parks as well as in the New Forest. Some offer reduced charges for youth organisations on organised camping trips, and all enquiries about them should be made, well in advance of your intended stay, to the Forestry Commission.

Camping Barns

These are usually redundant farm buildings which have been converted to provide simple accommodation, for up to 15 visitors, at a reasonable cost. Facilities are basic with somewhere to sleep, eat and prepare food, a supply of cold running water and flush toilet.

The Youth Hostels Association has a network of camping barns stretching from the Forest of Bowland in Lancashire, through Durham and into North Yorkshire. Further information and bookings details can be obtained from the YHA, Trevelyan House, 8 St Stephen's Hill, St Albans, Hertfordshire AL1 2DY. Tel: (01727) 855215.

Camping barns are also available in the Peak National Park. Further information and details can be obtained from Peak National Park, Losehill Hall, Castleton, Derbyshire S30 2WB.

Pets
Many parks will accept guests with dogs but we advise you to confirm this at the time of booking, when you should also enquire about any extra charges.

Taking Animals to Britain

RABIES warning: Because of quarantine requirements (for instance six months for dogs and cats) it is not a practical proposition to bring an animal with you on holiday to Britain. If you do you must have an import licence, obtainable at least six weeks in advance from Ministry of Agriculture, Fisheries and Food,

Hook Rise South, Tolworth, Surbiton, Surrey KT6 7NF. Tel: (0181) 330 4411. If you do not obtain a licence you will be breaking the law. Any illegally imported animal is liable to be destroyed.

Drugs Warnings for Incoming Tourists

The United Kingdom has severe penalties against drug smuggling. Drug traffickers may try to trick travellers. If you are travelling to the United Kingdom avoid any involvement with drugs. Never carry luggage or parcels through customs for someone else.

Legal Points

The best source of legal advice for motorists in Britain will be your motoring organisation. What the caravanner or camper needs to know in addition is relatively simple.

If you are towing a caravan or camping trailer you must not exceed 60 mph (96 km) on dual carriageways and motorways, 50 mph (80 km) on single carriageways, and on a motorway with three lanes each side you must not enter the third (fastest) lane. Do not light cooking stoves in motorway service areas.

In most towns parking is restricted both by regulations and practical difficulties. Cars with trailers may not use meter-controlled parking spaces, and many town car parks are designed with spaces for single vehicles only. However, a number can accommodate long vehicles as well as cars.

At night a trailer or a car attached to a trailer, if parked on the roadway, must show two front and two rear lights even where a car by itself would be exempt.

The brakes, lights, weight etc. of foreign vehicles do not have to comply with British technical requirements. However, a trailer must not exceed the British size limits - 23 feet (7 metres) long and 7 feet 6 inches (2.3 metres) wide. They must carry your national identification plates. Do not stop overnight on roadside grass verges or lay-bys, because these are considered by law to be part of the road.

Finally, it is important to find out the time you are expected to vacate your pitch on your departure day. You should then leave in good time in the morning, or you may be asked to pay an extra day's charge.

Advice for Visitors

The British Tourist Authority welcomes your comments on any aspects of your stay in Britain, whether favourable or otherwise. We hope that you will have no course to complain, but if you do, the best advice is to take up the complaint immediately with the management of the enterprise concerned: for example the park, shop or transport company. If you cannot obtain satisfaction in this way, please let us know and we ourselves may investigate the matter or suggest what action you might take.

You may bring currency in any denomination and up to any amount into Britain and there is no restriction on the number of travellers' cheques you can change. If you need to change money when the banks are closed you can do so at some large hotels, travel agents and stores or at independent bureaux de change. **Be sure to check in advance the rate of exchange and the commission charges**. All large shops, department stores and most hotels and restaurants will accept the usual internationally recognised credit cards. If you go shopping in local street markets, patronise only the large, recognised ones, and examine goods carefully.

Always ask the price of goods and services before committing yourself. Beware of pick-pockets in crowded places.

If your possessions are stolen or if you are involved in an accident or fire, telephone 999 (no charge will be made) and ask for the police, the ambulance service or the fire brigade.

Every effort has been made by the British Tourist Authority to ensure accuracy in this publication at the time of going to press. The information is given in good faith on the basis of information submitted to the British Tourist Authority by the promotors of the caravan parks listed. However, BTA cannot guarantee the accuracy of this information and accepts no responsibility for any error or misrepresentation. All liability for loss, disappointment, negligence or other damage caused by the reliance on the information contained in this guide or in the event of the bankruptcy or liquidation of any company, individual or firm mentioned, or in the event of any company, individual or firm ceasing to trade, is hereby excluded. It is advisable to confirm the information given with the establishments concerned at the time of booking.

All parks in this guide conform to Tourist Board Standards. A list of these Standards for Camping and Caravan Parks may be found on page 221.

All the establishments listed have paid for inclusion in this guide.

MODE D'EMPLOI DU GUIDE

La plupart des terrains répertoriés ici possèdent des emplacements pour les caravanes de tourisme ou les tentes, ou les deux, et la plupart accueillent volontiers les camping-cars De nombreux terrains ont aussi des caravanes fixes à louer.

Des labels de qualité auxquels on peut faire confiance

Le système de classification des parcs de vacances britanniques (British Graded Holidays Parks Scheme) est utilisé par les offices de tourisme d'Écosse, d'Angleterre, du Pays de Galles et d'Irlande du Nord en parallèle avec la British Holiday and Home Parks Association et le National Caravan Council. Tous les campings, caravanings et parcs de chalets affichant le label de qualité "Q" sont classés par des inspecteurs de l'office de tourisme chaque année. Les terrains figurant dans la brochure *Where to Stay Britain: Camping and Caravan Parks* ont été inspectés ou ont demandé à être inspectés dans le cadre du système de classement mentionné ci-dessus.

Chaque terrain classé a été visité par un inspecteur qualifié afin d'assurer des installations du plus haut niveau et de permettre au visiteur de choisir sa destination de vacances en toute confiance. Tous les aspects du terrain ont été évalués quant à leur qualité et on a accordé une importance particulière à l'hygiène dans tous les domaines. Le niveau de qualité des installations d'un terrain est indiqué par le nombre de **coches, de une à cinq**. Vous trouverez le label "Q" après le nom du terrain dans la plupart des entrées de la section Campings et Caravanings. Lorsque aucun label n'est indiqué, cela signifie que le terrain attendait d'être inspecté à la date de mise sous presse. Vous trouverez ci-dessous une description du niveau correspondant à chaque classification.

✓✓✓✓✓ Installation offertes et maintenues dans un excellent état.
✓✓✓✓ Installations offertes et maintenues dans un très bon état.

✓✓✓ Installations offertes et maintenues en bon état.
✓✓ Installations offertes et maintenues dans un état relativement bon.
✓ Installations offertes et maintenues dans un état acceptable.

Equipements

Les installations sont indiquées au moyen de symboles illustratifs, dont la légende est donnée ici.

Signes conventionnels

M Membre d'un Office de tourisme régional

BH& British Holiday & Home Parks
HPA (voir page 35)

NCC National Caravan Council (voir page 35)

🚐 Caravanes admises (suivi du nombre d'emplacements et des tarifs)

🚐 Camping-cars admis (suivi du nombre d'emplacements et des tarifs). Dans certains cas, les emplacements pour camping-cars sont compris dans le total des emplacements pour caravanes

▲ Tentes admises (suivi du nombre d'emplacements et des tarifs)

🏠 Nombre de caravanes disponibles pour la location (voir la rubrique "emplacements" ci-dessous)

🏠 Location de bungalows et logements similaires

🚗 Place de parking à côté de l'unité

P Parking dans le terrain

🏠 Aire de séjour d'une nuit

🔌 Branchements électriques pour caravanes (voir la rubrique "alimentation électrique pour caravanes" ci-dessous)

🚿 Douches

🚰 Eau chaude à tous les lavabos

🔦 Eclairage dans les compartiments WC, etc.

🚽 Décharge pour WC chimiques

🔥 Service de remplacement des bouteilles de gaz butane ou propane

🛒 Magasin d'alimentation fixe/itinérant

✕ Café/restaurant

🍸 Club/bar/magasin avec vente de boissons alcoolisées

📺 Salle de télévision

☎ Cabine(s) teléphonique(s)

🧺 Laverie

💨 Dispositifs de séchage du linge

🔌 Matériel de repassage

⊙ Prises électriques pour rasoirs

🎱 Salle de jeux

🛝 Aire de jeux pour les enfants

🏊 Piscine couverte chauffée sur le terrain

🏊 Piscine de plein air sur le terrain

🤿 Installations de plongée sous-marine (avec compresseur)

🎿 Ski nautique depuis le terrain

🛶 Canotage/canoë sur le terrain

⛵ Voile depuis le terrain

🐎 Equitation/randonnée à dos de poney depuis le terrain

🎾 Tennis sur le terrain

🎣 Pêche sur le terrain

⛳ Golf sur le terrain ou à proximité

🏹 Chasse privée

🐕 Les chiens ne sont PAS acceptés

🎵 Distractions nocturnes

🏛 Terrain situé dans le domaine d'un édifice historique

⚓ Réservations recommandées l'été

Ⓣ Les réservations peuvent s'effectuer par l'intermédiaire d'une agence de voyages

⚙ Agréé "Welcome Host"

Tarifs

Les tarifs indiqués pour les emplacements sont établis sur la base du tarif minimum et du tarif maximum pour une nuitée et pour 2 personnes accompagnées d'une voiture et d'une tente ou d'une caravane La pratique générale veut qu'en Grande-Bretagne on ne fasse payer que l'emplacement, mais certains terrains de camping pratiquent des tarifs séparés pour la voiture, la tente ou la caravane ainsi que pour chaque personne. Certains terrains appliquent des suppléments pour les auvents de caravanes, auquel cas cela est bien précisé. Les tarifs minimum et maximum de location des caravanes sont donnés par semaine. Les prix indiqués nous ont été fournis par les responsables des terrains concernés, et ont pour but de donner une idée des prix en vigueur au moment de la publication de ce guide. Les prix sont libellés en livres (£) et pence (p). La T.V.A. (Taxe à la Valeur Ajoutée) de 17,5% est comprise dans les tarifs indiqués Afin d'éviter tout malentendu, il est fortement conseillé de vérifier les prix auprès du terrain de camping concerné au moment d'effectuer les réservations.

Modalités de Réservation

Lorsque vous vous renseignerez sur l'hebergement offert ainsi que sur les tarifs et autres détails, vous devrez énoncer avec clarté et précision quels sont vos besoins, notamment ;

- dates d'arrivée et de départ, avec dates de remplacement acceptables le cas échéant.
- type d'hebergement requis.
- autres besoins particuliers à signaler à la direction.

Les malentendus sont très courants par téléphone, aussi vous est-il recommandé de confirmer par écrit toutes vos réservations si les délais vous le permettent. N'oubliez pas de mentionner votre nom et votre adresse et prenez soin de joindre une enveloppe timbrée avec adresse ou un coupon-réponse international (si vous écrivez depuis l'étranger) pour la réponse.

Arrhes et paiements anticipés

Les terrains de camping, de caravaning, ou avec bungalows, ainsi que les centres de vacances exigent souvent le versement intégral du paiement à l'avance. Celui-ci peut s'effectuer en deux fois: vous devez payer des arrhes lors de la réservation et vous acquitter du solde deux semaines avant le début de la période de location, par exemple.

Annulations

Lorsque vous acceptez l'hébergement qui vous est offert par écrit ou par téléphone, bous êtes lié par contrat avec le propriétaire de l'établissement. Cela signifie que si vous annulez une réservation, si vous ne venez pas prendre possession du logement ou si vous partez plus tôt que prévu (quelle qu'en soit la raison), le propriétaire est en droit d'exiger un dédommagement s'il ne peut pas relouer pour la durée totale ou une grande partie de la location. Si vous avez versé des arrhes, vous ne serez probablement pas remboursé, et l'on peut vous demander de payer une somme supplémentaire.

Vous avez donc intérêt à aviser immédiatement la direction si vous devez changer vos projets de voyage, annuler une réservation ou partir plus tôt que prévu.

Point de branchement électrique: La plupart des terrains ont à présent des points de branchement électrique pour les caravanes et les tentes. Le voltage est en général de 240v 50Hz en courant alternatif, bien qu'on puisse encore trouver des courants variant entre 200v et 250v. Il se peut qu'un adaptateur soit nécessaire pour le branchement. En général, sauf avis contraire, les terrains font payer un supplément pour ce service, et il est conseillé de se renseigner sur les tarifs en vigueur au moment de la réservation.

L'International Camping Carnet est rarement reconnu en Grande-Bretagne sauf dans les terrains gérés par les grands clubs.

Comment choisir un terrain

Les terrains sont répertoriés dans ce guide en plusieurs sections : Angleterre (par région), Écosse, Pays de Galles et Irlande du Nord. Dans chaque section, ils sont répertoriés par ordre alphabétique selon le nom de la ville la plus proche. L'Index des Villes en page 254 ainsi que les cartes en couleur au dos du guide vous indiquent toutes les villes et villages pour lesquels un terrain apparaît dans ce guide. Utilisez-les pour trouver un terrain rapidement et très facilement. Si vous savez quel est le terrain où vous voulez séjourner, vous le trouverez immédiatement en consultant l'index des terrains en page 249.

Si le lieu où vous désirez séjourner figure dans l'index des villes, reportez-vous au numéro de page indiqué pour voir quels terrains y sont disponibles. Le nom de la ville est indiqué en noir sur les cartes au dos du guide à l'endroit indiqué par la référence carte donnée dans chaque entrée. Consultez également les cartes en couleur pour trouver des lieux proches pour lesquels des terrains sont également répertoriés dans ce guide.

Si le lieu où vous désirez séjourner ne figure pas dans l'index des villes (ou bien si vous avez seulement une idée générale du lieu dans lequel vous désirez séjourner), utilisez les cartes en couleur. Certaines régions apparaissent sur plus d'une carte mais les noms de villes (imprimés en noir sur les cartes) sont indiqués une fois seulement.

La localisation des terrains sur la carte n'est donnée qu'à titre indicatif. Chaque rubrique comporte l'adresse fournie par les exploitants du terrain et si vous avez des difficultés pour trouver un terrain donné, nous vous suggérons de demander votre chemin une fois que vous serez vous trouvez dans le voisinage.

Pour aider les visiteurs à trouver leur terrain de camping, La Grande-Bretagne emploie les panneaux de signalisation internationaux ci-dessus. Tous les terrains ne sont pas encore signalés de cette manière et les panneaux n'affichent pas le nom de terrains particuliers. Ces panneaux indiquent en revanche si le terrain peut accueillir des tentes, des caravanes ou les deux.

Modifications des limites de région

En avril 1996, les limites et le nom de nombreux comtés et de nombreuses régions en Grande-Bretagne ont été modifiés suite à la réorganisation des autorités locales. Les modifications déjà annoncées lors de la préparation de l'édition 1997 de ce guide sont prises en compte dans les cartes et descriptions des villes données ici. D'autres modifications sont prévues pour avril 1997 mais elles n'ont pas encore été confirmées.

Londres attire de nombreux visiteurs, aussi les terrains de Camping-caravaning du Grand Londres ont-ils tendance à se remplir tres rapidement. Des terrains sont également disponibles dans la plupart des ports d'entrée du pays: bon nombre d'entre eux sont répertoriés dans ce guide et indiqués sur les cartes en fin de guide.

Services-conseils disponibles

Les Centres d'Information Touristique de toute la Grande-Bretagne (voir dernières pages) sont en mesure de donner aux campeurs et aux caravaniers des renseignements sur les terrains de leur région.

Certains Centres d'Information Touristique possèdent des services-conseils pour le camping-caravaning qui vous donneront des détails sur les terrains disponibles et pourront souvent vous aider à effectuer votre réservation. A l'heure actuelle, en Angleterre, ces Centres d'Information Touristique couvrent les régions suivantes: **Londres** (London Tourist Board and Convention Bureau, Victoria Station; **Peak District**, (01629) 814341; **New Forest**, (01703) 283771; et **Cornouailles**, (01872) 74057. Au Pays de Galles, de nombreux Centres d'Information touristique peuvent fournir des

renseignements sur les emplacements disponibles dans leur région depuis la fin du mois de mai jusqu'à la fin du mois d'août.

Précautions à prendre en haute saison

Lors des mois d'été, de juin à septembre, les terrains situés dans des régions très fréquentées comme le Nord Gallois, le Cumbria, le Sud-Ouest de l'Angleterre ou la New Forest, dans le Hampshire, risquent d'être complets. Les campeurs doivent s'efforcer d'arriver sur les terrains de bonne heure dans la journée ou, si c'est possible, de réserver à l'avance. Certains terrains ont des aires de séjour temporaire ou les visiteurs arrivant tard le soir peuvent passer la nuit. Cela permet de ne pas déranger les autres campeurs et caravaniers pendant la nuit et d'accepter un plus grand nombre de vacanciers. Les caravanes et les tentes se voient attribuer un emplacement le lendemain matin.

Autres terrains de camping-caravaning

Si vous souhaitez suivre votre propre itinéraire dans la campagne britannique, il peut vous être utile de savoir que la Forestry Commission gère des terrains de camping en forêt dans les sept Parcs forestiers de Grande-Bretagne ainsi que dans la New Forest. Certains terrains offrent des tarifs réduits pour les organisations de jeunesse effectuant des séjours de groupes: il vous est conseillé de vous renseigner à ce sujet auprès de la Forestry Commission très à l'avance.

Granges aménagées pour le camping (Camping Barns)

Ce sont en général des bâtiments de ferme aujourd'hui superflus qui ont été aménagés pour permettre d'héberger - en toute simplicité - jusqu'à 15 personnes, à un prix raisonnable. Les installations sont ce qu'il y a de plus simple: un endroit pour dormir, manger et préparer les repas, l'eau froide et les WC avec chasse d'eau. La Youth Hostels Association exploite un réseau de granges aménagées pour

le camping qui va de la région de Forest Bowland dans le Lancashire au North Yorkshire, en passant par Durham. Pour obtenir de plus amples renseignements et des détails sur la façon de réserver, veuillez vous adresser à: YHA, Trevelyan House, 8 St Stephen's Hill, St Albans, Hertfordshire ALI 2DY. Tel: (01727) 855215.

On peut également séjourner dans des granges aménagées pour le camping dans le Peak National Park. Pour obtenir de plus amples renseignements et des détails, veuillez vous adresser auprès du Peak National Park, Losehill Hall, Castleton, Derbyshire S30 2WB.

Animaux domestiques

De nombreux terrains acceptent les visiteurs accompagnés de chiens, mais nous vous conseillons de vous le faire confirmer lors de la réservation et de demander également si un supplément est perçu à ce titre.

Importation d'animaux

Réglementation contre la rage: En raison des prescriptions en matière de quarantaine (par exemple, six mois pour les chiens et les chats), il n'est pas possible sur le plan pratique d'emmener votre animal avec vous en vacances en Grande-Bretagne. Si vous souhaitez l'emmener, vous devez vous procurer un permis d'Importation à demander au moins six semaines a l'avance au Ministry of Agriculture, Fisheries and Food, Hook Rise South, Tolworth, Surbiton, Surrey KT6 7NF. Tél: (0181) 330 4411. Si vous n'êtes pas en possession d'un permis, vous vous trouverez en infraction. Tout animal Importé de manière illégale risque d'être abattu.

Réglementation contre la drogue

Le Royaume-Uni applique des sanctions sévères contre la contrebande de la drogue. Les trafiquants de drogue peuvent essayer de duper les voyageurs. Si vous voyagez à destination du Royaume-Uni, ne soyez pas mêlé au trafic de drogue.

Ne passez jamais de bagages ou de colis pour autrui par les douanes.

Aspects juridiques

La meilleure source de renseignements juridiques pour les automobilistes voyageant en Grande-Bretagne reste l'association des automobilistes de leur pays d'origine. Les détails supplémentaires que doivent connaître le campeur ou le caravanier sont relativement simples.

Si vous tractez une caravane ou une remorque de camping, vous ne devez pas dépasser 96 km/h sur les voies express ou sur les autoroutes, 80 km/h sur les routes à deux voies; en outre, sur les autoroutes ayant trois voies dans chaque direction, vous ne devez pas rouler sur la troisième voie (la plus rapide). N'allumez pas de réchauds à gaz sur les aires de service des autoroutes.

Dans la plupart des villes, le stationnement est limité à la fois par la réglementation et par le manque de place. Les voitures dotées de remorques ne peuvent pas occuper les espaces de stationnement limité à parcmètres et de nombreux parcs de stationnement de ville ne sont conçus que pour accueillir des véhicules indépendants. Toutefois, certains parcs peuvent accueillir des véhicules plus longs en plus des voitures.

La nuit, les remorques ou les voitures dotées de remorques, lorsqu'elles sont en stationnement au bord de la route, doivent avoir les deux feux avant et les deux feux arrière allumés même dans le cas où cela n'est pas jugé nécessaire pour une voiture seule.

Les freins, l'éclairage, le poids, etc. des véhicules étrangers n'ont pas à respecter les prescriptions techniques britanniques. Toutefois, une remorque ne doit pas dépasser les limites dimensionnelles britanniques: 7m de long et 2,3m de large. Elle doit être munie de votre plaque d'immatriculation nationale. Vous ne devez pas vous arrêter pour la nuit sur les accotements ou sur les petites aires de stationnement des bas-côtés car la loi stipule que ces emplacements font partie de la route.

Enfin, il est important de vous renseigner sur l'heure à laquelle il vous est demandé de libérer votre emplacement le jour du départ. Vous devrez prévoir de partir assez tôt, sans quoi vous risquez d'avoir à payer une journée de location supplémentaire.

Conseils aux visiteurs

L'Office de Tourisme de Grande-Bretagne vous invite à formuler vos observations sur tout aspect de votre séjour en Grande-Bretagne, qu'elles soient favorables ou non. Nous espérons que vous n'aurez pas lieu de vous plaindre, mais dans l'affirmative, il vous est conseillé de faire part de votre mécontentement immédiatement auprès de la direction de l'établissement concerné comme par exemple : camping, magasin ou société de transport. Si vous ne pouvez pas obtenir satisfaction de cette manière, veuillez nous le faire savoir et nous examinerons la question nous-mêmes ou nous vous suggérerons une procédure éventuelle à suivre.

Vous pouvez emporter en Grande-Bretagne les devises de votre choix en quantité illimitée et aucune restriction ne s'applique à la quantité de chèques de voyage changés. Si vous avez besoin de devises britanniques pendant les heures de fermeture des banques, vous pouvez vous les procurer dans certains grands hôtels, agences de voyages, grands magasins ou dans les bureaux de change indépendants. **Ne manquez pas de vérifier à l'avance le taux de change et la commission appliqués**.

Tous les grands magasins et boutiques et la plupart des hôtels et restaurants accepteront les cartes de crédit usuelles reconnues dans le monde entier. Si vous aimez faire vos achats au marché, limitez-vous aux grands marchés de rue officiels et examinez toujours les articles soigneusement.

Demandez toujours le prix des marchandises avant de vous engager. Prenez garde aux pickpockets en cas d'affluence. Si l'on vous vole des objets personnels ou si vous vous trouvez sur le lieu d'un incendie ou d'un accident, composez le 999 (numéro gratuit) et demandez la police, les services

d'ambulance ou les pompiers.

L'Office de Tourisme de Grande-Bretagne (BTA) a pris toutes les dispositions nécessaires pour assurer l'exactitude des Informations contenues dans la présente publication au moment de mettre sous presse. Ces Informations sont fournies en toute bonne foi sur la base des renseignements donnés à la BTA par les exploitants des terrains de camping répertoriés. Toutefois, la BTA ne peut pas garantir l'exactitude de ces renseignements et décline toute responsablité en cas d'erreur ou de déformation des faits. Toute responsabilité est également déclinée pour toutes pertes, déceptions, négligences ou autres dommages que pourrait subir quiconque se fie aux renseignements contenus dans le présent guide, pour les cas de faillite ou de liquidation de toute personne morale ou physique mentionnée, et pour les cas de cessation d'activités de toute personne morale ou physique. Il est conseillé de se faire confirmer les renseignements fournis par les établissements concernés lors de la réservation.

Tous les terrains répertoriés dans le présent guide sont conformes aux normes de l'Office de Tourisme de Grande-Bretagne. On trouvera à la page 221 une liste de ces normes relatives aux terrains de camping-caravaning.

Tous les établissements répertoriés figurent dans le présent guide à titre payant.

BENUTZUNG DIESES REISEFÜHRERS

Die meisten der hier aufgelisteten Plätze verfügen über Standplätze für Wohnwagen oder Zelte oder beides, und die meisten nehmen auch Wohnmobile auf. Viele Parks vermieten auch Ferienwohnwagen.

Ein sicheres Zeichen für Qualität

Das "British Graded Holiday Parks Scheme" ist eine Initiative der Tourist Boards von Schottland, England, Wales und Nordirland, die in Zusammenarbeit mit der British Holiday and Home Parks Association und dem National Caravan Council durchgeführt wird. Alle Ferienwohnwagen, Chalets und Campingparks, die das Qualitätszeichen "Q" führen, werden jedes Jahr von den Inspektoren der Tourist Boards eingestuft. Ferienparks, die in *"Where to Stay in Britain: Camping and Caravan Parks"* aufgeführt sind, wurden entweder bereits inspiziert oder haben im Rahmen des "British Graded Holiday Parks Scheme" eine Inspektion beantragt.

Alle Parks, die an dieser Initiative teilnehmen, wurden von einem geschulten Inspektor besichtigt, um das höchste Niveau der vorhandenen Einrichtungen zu gewährleisten und Besucher in die Lage zu versetzen, ohne Bedenken einen Urlaubsort zu wählen. Alle Gesichtspunkte des Parks wurden auf die Qualität hin überprüft. Dabei wird stets besonders großer Wert auf Sauberkeit gelegt. Das Qualitätsniveau der Einrichtungen eines Parks ist mit **einem bis fünf Häkchen** bezeichnet. Bei den Camping- und Wohnwagenparks steht nach dem Namen des betreffenden Parks in den meisten Fällen eine "Q"-Einstufung. Ist diese Einstufung nicht vorhanden, so bedeutet das, daß eine Inspektion des Parks zur Zeit der Drucklegung noch ausstand. Nachstehend wird erläutert, welches Niveau Sie bei den einzelnen Einstufungen erwarten können.

✓✓✓✓✓ Einrichtungen und Service von höchstem Standard.

✓✓✓✓ Einrichtungen und Service von sehr gutem Standard.

✓✓✓ Einrichtungen und Service von gutem Standard.

✓✓ Einrichtungen und Service von zufriedenstellendem Standard.

✓ Einrichtungen und Service von annehmbarem Standard.

Einrichtungen

Die Einrichtungen sind mittels der Symbole auf einen Blick, die an dieser Stelle erläutert sind, bezeichnet.

Zeichenerklärung

M	Mitglied eines regionalen Tourist Board
BH& HPA	British Holiday & Home Parks (siehe Seite 35)
NCC	National Caravan Council (siehe Seite 35)
⊕	Wohnwagen zugelassen (mit Anzahl der Stellplätze und Preisen)
⊕	Wohnmobile zugelassen (mit Anzahl der Stellplätze und Preisen)
Å	Zelte zugelassen (mit Anzahl der Stellplätze und Preisen)
⊡	Anzahl der vermietbaren Ferienwohnwagen (mit Anzahl und Preisen)
⊞	Bungalows, Chalets, Wohnkabinen zum Vermieten
⊕	Parkmöglichkeit neben der Wohneinheit
P	Parkplatz auf dem Gelände
⊞	Auffangstelle für spät im Park eintreffende Gäste
⊕	Stromschluß für Wohnwagen und Zelte
⋔	Duschen
⚲	Heißes Wasser für alle Waschbecken

♨	Beleuchtung im Toilettenbau
⬤	Chemische Toiletten
⟳	Umtauschstelle für Butan-oder Propangaszylinger
⚐	Lebensmittelgeschäft/Wagen für Lebensmittelverkauf
✕	Restaurant
⚑	Klub mit Alkoholausschank Bar
TV	Fernsehraum
☏	Öffentliche Fernsprechzellen
⬚	Wäscherei
∥	Wäschetrockner
⬛	Bügelmöglichkeiten
☺	Anschlüsse für Elektrorasierer
⚒	Hallenspiele
⚠	Kinderspielplatz
⚲	Hallenbad
⚲	Freibad
⚓	Tauchen
⚓	Wasserski vom Park aus
⚓	Bootsfahrten/Kanufahrten
△	Segeln
∪	Reiten/Ponyreiten in der Nähe
Q	Tennis
J	Angeln
⏷	Golf im Park oder in der Nähe
✓	Private Jagdrechte
✕	Hunde NICHT erlaubt
♫	Abendunterhaltung
⊞	Park auf dem Gelände eines Gebäudes von historischem, literarischem oder architektonischen Interesse
⚐	Im Sommer Reservierung empfohlen
T	Buchung durch Reisebüros möglich
◉	Welcome Host

Preise

Die Preise für Stellplätze beruhen auf den Mindest- und Höchstgebühren pro Nacht für zwei Personen, einen Wagen und einen Wohnwagenanhänger oder ein Zelt. Im allgemeinen wird in Großbritannien einfach der Preis für einen Stellplatz berechnet. Einige Parks berechnen jedoch getrennte Gebühren für Wagen, Wohnwagenanhänger oder Zelt und für jede Person. Einige Parks berechnen eine zusätzliche Gebühr für Sonnenzelte. Wo das zutrifft, wird es angegeben. Die Mindest- und Höchstpreise für Ferienwohnwagen werden pro Woche angegeben. Die Preise wurden von den Besitzern zur Verfügung gestellt und sind nur ein Anhaltspunkt für die tatsächlich berechneten Preise während der Gültigkeit dieser Veröffentlichung. Die Preise werden in Pfund Sterling (£) und Pence (p) angegeben. Die Mehrwertsteuer (VAT = 17,5% Value Added Tax) ist im Preis enthalten. Um Mißverständnissen vorzubeugen wird empfohlen, bei der Buchung nach den genauen Preisen zu fragen.

Buchungen

Bei Anfragen über Unterkunftsmöglichkeiten, Preise und andere Einzelheiten sollten Sie Ihre Wünsche genau angeben, zum Beispiel:

- Datum der Ankunft und der Abreise und, falls zutreffend, andere mögliche Daten.
- Die benötigte Unterkunft
- Irgendwelche besonderen Wünsche.

Mißverständnisse sind bei Telefongesprächen leicht möglich. Deshalb empfehlen wir, alle Buchungen schriftlich zu bestätigen, wenn dazu die Zeit ausreicht. Denken Sie bitte daran, Ihren Namen und Ihre Anschrift anzugeben. Fügen Sie bitte einen Freiumschlag oder bei Anfragen aus dem Ausland einen internationalen Antwortschein bei.

Anzahlungen

Für Wohnwagen-, Camping- und Ferienparks muß häufig der gesamte Betrag im voraus gezahlt werden. Die Zahlung kann in zwei Teilzahlungen verlangt werden: Eine Anzahlung bei der Buchung und der Restbetrag zwei Wochen vor dem Beginn des Aufenthalts.

Rücktritte

Wenn Sie eine angebotene Unterkunft schriftlich oder telefonisch akzeptieren, kann das als ein rechtlich bindender Vertrag mit dem Besitzer angesehen werden. Das hat zur Folge, daß der Besitzer, wenn Sie eine Reservierung stornieren, nicht antreten oder wenn Sie die Unterkunft vorzeitig verlassen (gleichgültig aus welchen Gründen), berechtigt sein kann, Schadenersatz zu verlangen, wenn er nicht in der Lage ist, die Unterkunft für den ganzen oder einen Teil des gebuchten Zeitraums wieder zu vermieten. Wenn eine Anzahlung geleistet wurde, kann sie hierfür angerechnet werden, und zusätzliche Zahlung kann notwendig werden.

Es ist daher in Ihrem Interesse, den Besitzer sofort zu benachrichtigen, wenn Sie Ihre Reisepläne ändern, eine Buchung stornieren oder die Unterkunft vorzeitig verlassen möchten.

Anschluß ans Stromnetz: Die meisten Plätze verfügen über Netzanschlußstellen für Wohnwagen oder Zelte. Es handelt sich um Wechselstrom mit einer Spannung von gewöhnlich 240 V, 50 Schwingungen, es können jedoch Spannungsschwankungen zwischen 200 und 250 V auftreten. Unter Umständen benötigen sie einen Adapter. Es wird gewöhnlich eine Gebühr erhoben, und es ist ratsam, sich bei der Buchung über deren Höhe zu erkundigen.

Der **internationale Campingausweis** wird in Großbritannien meistens nur von Parks anerkannt, die von größeren Klubs verwaltet werden.

So finden Sie Ihren Park

In der vorliegenden Broschüre sind die einzelnen Parks jeweils nach der

Überschrift England (nach Region), Schottland, Wales und Nordirland aufgeführt. Sie sind in alphabetischer Reihenfolge unter dem Namen der Ortschaft, in der oder in deren Nähe sie liegen, verzeichnet. Im Verzeichnis der Ortschaften auf Seite 254 und auf den farbigen Lagekarten am Ende dieses Führers sind alle Städte, Ortschaften und Dörfer aufgeführt, die in dieser Broschüre mit einem Park vertreten sind. Anhand des Verzeichnisses und der Karten können Sie schnell und leicht eine passende Unterkunft finden. Wenn Sie schon wissen, in welchem Park Sie wohnen möchten, schlagen Sie im Verzeichnis der Parks auf Seite 249 nach.

Wenn die Ortschaft, in der Sie übernachten möchten, im Verzeichnis der Ortschaften aufgeführt ist, schlagen Sie auf der angegebenen Seite nach, wo die dort vorhandenen Parks verzeichnet sind. Die Namen der Ortschaften sind laut Kartenverweis beim Eintrag schwarz gedruckt auf den Karten am Ende des Führers verzeichnet. Sehen Sie auch auf den farbigen Lagekarten nach, um Ortschaften in der Nähe zu finden, wo sich ebenfalls Parks befinden, die in diesem Führer aufgeführt sind.

Falls die Ortschaft, in der Sie übernachten möchten, nicht im Verzeichnis der Ortschaften aufgeführt ist, oder Sie nur eine ungefähre Vorstellung von der Gegend haben, in der Sie übernachten möchten, so benutzen Sie die farbigen Lagekarten. Einige Gegenden sind auf mehreren Karten verzeichnet, aber die Namen der Ortschaften (schwarz gedruckt) tauchen nur einmal auf.

Die Lage der Camping-, Wohnwagen- oder Ferienparks auf den Karten gilt nur als Anhaltspunkt. Die von den Besitzern gelieferten Beschreibungen über die Anreise werden bei jeder Eintragung wiedergegeben. Sollten Sie Schwierigkeiten haben, einen bestimmten Park zu finden, wenden Sie sich bitte an die Einheimischen um Rat.

Die obigen internationalen Hinweisschilder, die in Großbritannien vielfach zu finden sind, erleichtern Ihnen das Auffinden eines Parks. Sie sind jedoch noch nicht für alle Camping-, Wohnwagen- oder Ferienparks vorhanden und geben nicht den Namen des Platzes an. Sie weisen Sie jedoch auf einen Platz für Zelte, Wohnwagen oder beide Übernachtungsmöglichkeiten hin.

Änderung der Bezirksgrenzen

Im April 1996 wurden im Rahmen einer Umstrukturierung der Gemeinden die Bezirksgrenzen und Namen vieler Grafschaften und Regionen in Großbritannien geändert. Die Änderungen, die bis zum Redaktionsschluß der Ausgabe für 1997 bekannt waren, wurden in den Karten und Ortsbeschreibungen des vorliegenden Reiseführers berücksichtigt. Für April 1997 sind weitere Änderungen vorgesehen, die jedoch noch nicht bestätigt sind.

Da London ein großer Anziehungspunkt für Besucher ist, sind die Camping-, Wohnwagen- oder Ferienparks im Gebiet von Groß-London schnell ausgebucht. Rechtzeitige Buchung wird daher empfohlen. Camping-, Wohnwagen- oder Ferienparks sind auch in den meisten Einreiseorten vorhanden. Viele von ihnen wurden in diese Veröffentlichung aufgenommen und sind auf den Karten zu finden.

Informationsdienste
Die Touristeninformationszentren in allen Teilen Großbritanniens (auf den letzten Seiten aufgeführt) geben Ihnen gerne Auskunft über die Camping-, Wohnwagen- oder Ferienparks in ihrem Gebiet.

Einige besitzen besondere Beratungsdienste, die über freien Platz Auskunft geben und oft Buchungen vornehmen können. Zur Zeit sind die folgenden Beratungsdienste vorhanden:

London, London Tourist Board and Convention Bureau, Bahnhof Victoria; **Peak District**, (01629) 814341; **New Forest**, (01703) 283771; und **Cornwall**, (01872) 74057. Viele Touristeninformationszentren in Wales können Ihnen Auskunft über von Ende Mai bis Ende August verfügbare Stellplätze in ihrem Gebiet geben.

Umgehen von Problemen in der Hochsaison
In den Sommermonaten Juni bis September sind die Camping-, Wohnwagen- oder Ferienparks in den beliebten Feriengebieten, wie Nordwales, Cumbria, West Country oder New Forest in Hampshire schnell ausgebucht. Treffen Sie daher frühzeitig am Tage in dem Camping-, Wohnwagen- oder Ferienpark ein oder buchen Sie nach Möglichkeit im voraus. Einige Camping-, Wohnwagen- oder Ferienparks verfügen über Auffangstellen für spät eintreffende Gäste. Auf diese Weise werden die bereits schlafenden Gäste nicht gestört, und es werden weniger Reisende abgewiesen. Es wird Ihnen dann am nächsten Morgen ein Stellplatz zugewiesen.

Andere Camping- und Wohnwagenplätze

Wenn Sie Ihre eigene Route für Reisen durch ländliche Gegenden in Großbritannien planen möchten, dürften Sie an den Campingplätzen in den Waldgebieten interessiert sein, die von der Forestry Commission verwaltet werden. Hierzu gehören sieben Forest Parks und der New Forest. In einigen erhalten auf Reisen befindliche Jugendorganisationen Preisermäßigungen. Alle diesbezüglichen Anfragen müssen im voraus an die Forestry Commission gerichtet werden.

Camping in der Scheune

Es handelt sich hier um ehemalige Scheunen, die in einfache, günstige Unterkünfte für bis zu 15 Personen umgebaut wurden. Die Einrichtungen sind anspruchslos. Es hat eine Schlaf-, Koch- und Eßstelle, kaltes Wasser und ein Spülklosett.

Die Youth Hostels Association verfügt über ein Netz von Camping-Scheunen, das sich von Forest Bowland in Lancashire über Durham bis nach North Yorkshire erstreckt. Für weitere Informationen und Buchungen wenden Sie sich an die YHA, Trevelyan House, 8 St Stephen's Hill, St Albans, Hertfordshire ALI 2DY. Tel: (01727) 855215.

Camping-Scheunen sind auch im Peak Nationalpark zu finden. Für weitere Auskünfte wenden Sie sich an den Peak National Park, Losehill Hall, Castleton, Derbyshire S30 2WB.

Haustiere
Viele Camping-, Wohnwagen- oder Ferienparks nehmen Hunde auf. Wenn Sie aus dem Ausland einreisen, müssen Sie jedoch unbedingt die gesetzlichen Bestimmungen über die Einfuhr von Tieren beachten.

Das Mitbringen von Haustieren nach Großbritannien

Tollwutwarnung:
Das Einführen von Hunden und anderen Haustieren nach Großbritannien ist ohne Einfuhrgenehmigung nicht gestattet. Auf Grund gesetzlicher Bestimmungen müssen alle mitgebrachten Tiere in eine lange Quarantäne gegeben werden (Hunde und Katzen für 6 Monate), um das Einschleppen von Tollwut zu verhindern. Einfuhrgenehmigungen müssen mindestens sechs Wochen vor der Einreise beantragt werden. Schreiben Sie an: Ministry of Agriculture, Fisheries and Food, Hook Rise South, Tolworth, Surbiton, Surrey KT6 7NF. Tel: (0181) 330 4411. Bei Zuwiderhandlungen werden sehr hohe Strafen verhängt. Unberechtigt eingeführte Tiere werden eingeschläfert.

Warnung wegen Rauschgift

Großbritannien geht gegen Rauschgiftschmuggel sehr scharf vor. Rauschgifthändler versuchen häufig, unschuldige Reisende in ihre Geschäfte zu verwickeln. Seien Sie daher sehr auf der Hut, und tragen Sie niemals Gepäckstücke für andere Personen durch die Zollkontrolle.

Rechtliche Gesichtspunkte

Wenden Sie sich am besten vor Beginn der Reise an Ihren Automobilverband, der Ihnen gerne Auskunft über alle rechtlichen Fragen in bezug auf Reisen in Großbritannien geben wird. Als Besitzer von Wohnwagen müssen Sie weiterhin folgendes beachten.

Haben Sie einen Wohnwagen oder einen Wohnwagenanhänger im Schlepp, dürfen Sie auf Fernstraßen mit zweispurigen Fahrbahnen und auf Autobahnen nicht schneller als mit 96 km/h (60 Meilen /Stunde) fahren. Für Fernstraßen mit einer Fahrbahn in jeder Richtung beträgt die Höchstgeschwindigkeit 80 km/h (50 Meilen/Stunde). Auf Autobahnen mit drei Fahrbahnen in jeder Fahrtrichtung dürfen Sie niemals auf der innersten Fahrbahn, auch nicht zum Überholen, fahren. Auf den Raststätten an der Autobahn dürfen Sie keine Kochöfen benutzen.

In den meisten Städten ist das Parken durch gesetzliche Bestimmungen stark eingeschränkt oder praktisch sehr schwierig. Autos mit Anhängern dürfen nicht an Stellen mit Parkuhren parken. Ferner nehmen die meisten Parkplätze nur Wagen ohne Anhänger auf. Jedoch sind einige Parkplätze vorhanden, die lange Fahrzeuge und Fahrzeuge mit Anhängern zulassen.

In der Nacht muß ein Anhänger und ein Auto mit Anhänger, wenn sie am Straßenrand geparkt werden, vorn und hinten mit zwei Lampen beleuchtet werden, und zwar auch dann, wenn ein einzelnes Auto davon ausgenommen wäre.

Die britischen Vorschriften über Bremsen, Beleuchtung, Gewicht und andere technische Punkte gelten nicht für ausländische Fahrzeuge. Ein Anhänger muß jedoch die britischen Vorschriften erfüllen und darf nicht länger als 7 m und nicht breiter als 2,30 m sein. Anhänger müssen mit den amtlichen Zulassungsschildern Ihres Heimatlandes versehen sein. Übernachten Sie nicht auf dem Grasrand einer Straße oder in einer Ausweichstelle, weil diese Teile als zur Straße gehörig angesehen werden.

Abschließend sei bemerkt, wie wichtig es ist, daß Sie sich erkundigen, wann Sie den Stellplatz in einem Camping-, Wohnwagen- oder Ferienpark am Abreisetag räumen müssen. Reisen Sie morgens rechtzeitig ab, sonst müssen Sie vielleicht die Gebühr für einen weiteren Tag bezahlen.

Ratschläge für Besucher

Die British Tourist Authority bittet um Ihre Meinung über alle Punkte Ihres Aufenthaltes in Großbritannien, ganz geich, ob sie positiv oder negativ ist. Wir hoffen sehr, daß Sie keinen Grund für Beschwerden haben. Falls Sie aber doch zu Klagen Anlaß haben, dann ist es am besten, sich sofort an die Leitung des entsprechenden Unternehmens zu wenden, z. B. des Parks, des Geschäfts oder der Verkehrsgesellschaft. Sind Sie mit der Behandlung, die Sie dann erfahren, nicht zufrieden, lassen Sie es uns wissen, und wir werden der Angelegenheit selbst nachgehen oder Ihnen raten, welche Maßnahmen Sie einleiten können.

Sie können Währungen jeder Art in beliebiger Höhe nach Großbritannien mitbringen und auch wieder ausführen. Reiseschecks werden in beliebiger Höhe eingelöst. Wenn Ihnen das Bargeld ausgeht, wenn die Banken geschlossen sind, können Sie Geld in einigen großen Hotels, Reisebüros und in Geldwechselstellen wechseln. **Prüfen Sie vor dem Geldumtausch nach, welcher Wechselkurs zu Grunde gelegt wird und wie hoch die Bearbeitungsgebühr ist.** Alle größeren Geschäfte, Kaufhäuser und die meisten Hotels und Restaurants akzeptieren international gültige Kreditkarten als Zahlungsmittel. Wenn Sie nicht in Kaufhäusern oder Geschäften einkaufen, gehen Sie nur auf die größeren zugelassenen Straßenmärkte.

Erkundigen Sie sich stets vor dem Kauf nach dem Preis der Waren oder Dienstleistungen. Achten Sie in Menschenmengen auf Taschendiebe.

Sind Sie in einen Diebstahl, einen Unfall oder ein Feuer verwickelt, wählen Sie den Notruf unter der Nummer 999 (kostenloser Anruf) und verlangen Sie die Polizei (police), einen Krankenwagen (ambulance) oder die Feuerwehr (fire brigade).

Die British Tourist Authority hat alle Anstrengungen unternommen, die Richtigkeit der in dieser Veröffentlichung enthaltenen Angaben bei Drucklegung sicherzustellen. Die Informationen werden in gutem Glauben erteilt und beruhen auf den Angaben, die der British Tourist Authority von den aufgeführten Camping-, Wohnwagen- oder Ferienparks erteilt wurden. Die British Tourist Authority erteilt jedoch keine Garantie über die Genauigkeit dieser Informationen und übernimmt keine Haftung für Fehler oder falsche Darstellungen. Die British Tourist Authority übernimmt ferner keine Haftung für Verluste, nicht erfüllte Erwartungen, Fahrlässigkeit oder andere Schäden, die sich daraus ergeben, daß sich der Leser auf die Informationen in dieserVeröffentlichung verlassen hat, oder die sich daraus ergeben, daß in der Veröffentlichung genannte Unternehmen, Firmen oder Einzelpersonen Bankrott anmelden, in Liquidation gehen oder ihre Geschäftstätigkeit einstellen. Es wird empfohlen, sich die in dieser Veröffentlichung enthaltenen Angaben bei der Buchung von den jeweiligen Stellen bestätigen zu lassen.

Alle in dieser Veröffentlichung genannte Camping-, Wohnwagen- oder Ferienparks erfüllen die Standardbedingungen der Tourist Boards. Ein Verzeichnis der Standardbedingungen befindet sich auf Seite 221.

Für die Aufnahme in diesen Führer wurde eine Gebühr entrichtet.

HOE U DEZE GIDS MOET GEBRUIKEN

Op de meeste vermelde terreinen zijn trekcaravans, tenten of kampeerauto's of alledrie welkom. Bij de meeste zijn vakantiecaravans te huur.

Een teken van kwaliteit

Het British Graded Holiday Parks-inspectieprogramma wordt uitgevoerd door de toeristenraden van Schotland, Engeland, Wales en Noord-Ierland, in samenwerking met de British Holiday and Home Parks Association en de National Caravan Council. Alle caravanparken, vakantieparken en campings die het kwaliteitssymbool 'Q' vertonen, worden ieder jaar door inspecteurs van de toeristenraad geïnspecteerd. Parken die in *Where to Stay Britain: Camping and Caravan Parks* voorkomen, zijn geïnspecteerd, of hebben inspectie aangevraagd, onder het British Graded Holiday Parks-inspectieprogramma.

Alle deelnemende parken zijn bezocht door een gekwalificeerde inspecteur die controleert of aan de hoogste normen van faciliteiten wordt voldaan, zodat de bezoeker met vertrouwen van het park gebruik kan maken. Alle aspecten van het park komen onder beschouwing, met speciale aandacht voor hygiëne en properheid. De kwaliteitsstandaard wordt aangegeven door **één tot en met vijf vinkjes** in de Q. Bij de meeste vermeldingen in Camping and Caravan Parks bevindt de Q-gradatie zich achter de naam van het park. Is deze afwezig, dan betekent het dat de inspectie hangende was tijdens het ter perse gaan. Hieronder vindt u een aanduiding van de te verwachten kwaliteit bij het aantal vinkjes.

✓✓✓✓✓ Faciliteiten en onderhoud van uitstekend niveau.
✓✓✓✓ Faciliteiten en onderhoud van zeer goed niveau.
✓✓✓ Faciliteiten en onderhoud van goed niveau.
✓✓ Faciliteiten en onderhoud van redelijk niveau.
✓ Faciliteiten en onderhoud van aanvaardbaar niveau.

Faciliteiten

De faciliteiten worden aangeduid d.m.v. de hieronder in het kort verklaarde tekens.

Verklaring van de tekens

M lid van een regionale toeristenraad

BH& British Holiday & Home Parks
HPA (zie blz 35)

NCC National Caravan Council (zie blz 35)

🚐 caravans toegestaan (met aantal staanplaatsen en tarieven)

🚚 kampeerauto's toegestaan (met aantal staanplaatsen en tarieven) In sommige gevallen is het aantal plekjes voor kampeerauto's opgenomen in het totaal voor toercaravans

▲ tenten toegestaan (met aantal plekjes en tarieven)

🏚 aantal vakantiecaravans te huur *(Zie 'Vakantiecaravans')*

🚍 bungalows/chalets/huisjes te huur

🚗 parkeerplaats naast staanplaats

P parkeerruimte op terrein

🚘 terrein voor late aankomers op het park

🔌 elektrische aansluiting voor caravans (zie 'Elektriciteit. Elektrische aansluiting voor caravans)

🚿 douches

🚰 alle wastafels hebben warm water

💡 verlichting in toiletten, etc.

🚽 lozing van chemische toiletten mogelijk

🔄 omwisseling van butaan- en propaangasflessen

🛒 levensmiddelenwinkel/rijdende winkel

✕ café/restaurant

🍷 klub/barwinkel met vergunning

📺 televisiekamer

📞 openbare telefoons

🔲 wasserette op terrein aanwezig

✂ drogen van wasgoed mogelijk

🗜 strijken van wasgoed mogelijk

☉ stopcontacten voor scheerapparaten

🎱 recreatiekamer

🛝 speeltuin

🏊 verwarmd binnenbad op park

🏊 openluchtbad op park

🤿 onderwaterzwemmen op terrein (zuurstofflessen verkrijgbaar)

🎿 waterskiën op terrein

⛵ boten/kano's op terrein aanwezig

⛵ zeilen op terrein

🐴 manège (paard/pony) op terrein

🎾 tennis op terrein

🎣 vissen op terrein

⛳ golf op of bij park

🔫 particuliere jachtvergunning

🐕 honden NIET toegestaan

🎵 amusement's avonds

🏛 park op het terrein van een historisch gebouw

🌞 raadzaam voor de zomermaanden te boeken

T kan geboekt worden bij reisbureaus

◎ Welcome Host

Prijzen

De vermelde tarievan zijn de minimale en maximale prijzen voor een overnachting voor 2 personen, auto plus caravan of tent. Over het algemeen berekent men in Groot-Brittannië voor de staanplaats, maar een aantal terreinen belast u apart voor de auto, caravan of tent, en elke persoon. Bij sommige parken moet u extra betalen voor een tent of voortent die aan een caravan vastgebouwd is, maar dat staat dan apart aangegeven. Minimale en maximale tarieven voor vakantiecaravans zijn per week. Vermelde prijzen werden verstrekt door de terreinbeheerders en dienen als richtlijn voor de prijzen die tijdens de geldendheid van dit boekje gerekend zullen worden. Vermelde prijzen zijn in ponden (£) en pence (p). VAT (BTW) à 17.5% is bij de prijzen inbegrepen. Om misverstanden te vermijden, raden wij u dringend aan de prijzen te controleren als u een reservering maakt.

Reserveren

Bij het maken van een reservering, of het inwinnen van inlichtingen, moet u vooral duidelijk en precies aangeven wat u wilt - bij voorbeeld:

- aankomst- en vertrekdata met mogelijke alternatieven.
- gewenste accommodatie.
- vertel de beheerder vooral wat voor speciale wensen of eisen u heeft.

Misverstanden kunnen heel gemakkelijk voorkomen over de telefoon en wij raden u daarom aan alle reserveringen, als de tijd dat toelaat, schriftelijk te bevestigen. Vergeet vooral niet uw naam en adres te vermelden en een aan uzelf geadresseerde envelop met postzegel of internationale antwoordcoupon (als u uit het buitenland schrijft) in te sluiten voor elk antwoord.

Aan- en vooruitbetalingen

Campings, caravanterreinen, bungalow- en vakantieparken moeten meestal van tevoren geheel betaald worden. Dit kan gedaan worden in tweeën - een aanbetaling bij de reservering en betaling van het saldo bijvoorbeeld twee weken voor de aanvang van de geboekte periode.

Annuleren

De aanvaarding van geboden accommodatie, hetzij schriftelijk of telefonisch, wordt over het algemeen beschouwd als een wettelijk bindend contract. Dit betekent dat als u annuleert, niet verschijnt op het park, of vroegtijdig het park verlaat (het geeft niet om welke reden), de eigenaar compensatie van u kan verlangen als de staanplaats voor het overgrote deel van de geboekte periode niet opnieuw verhuurd kan worden. Als u een aanbetaling gedaan heeft, kan deze vervallen worden verklaard en een aanvullend bedrag van u verlangd worden.

Het is daarom in uw eigen belang de bedrijfsleiding onmiddellijk in kennis te stellen, als u uw reisplannen moet wijzigen, een boeking moet annuleren, of voortijdig moet vertrekken.

Elektrische aansluiting: De meeste parken hebben elektrische aansluitpunten voor caravans en tenten. De voltage is meestal 240v AC, 50Hz, hoewel nu steeds voltages tussen 200v en 250v kunnen worden aangetroffen. Het kan zijn dat u een adaptor nodig heeft voor de aansluiting. Meestal moet u extra betalen voor deze faciliteit, behalve indien anders staat aangegeven. Het is raadzaam de tarieven na te vragen voor u reserveert.

Het Internationale Kampeerkarnet wordt maar weinig in Groot-Brittannië erkend, behalve op terreinen die beheerd worden door de grote clubs.

Het vinden van een park of terrein

De parken in dit gidsje zijn ingedeeld in: Engeland (per regio), Schotland, Wales en Noord-Ierland. Zij staan in alfabetische volgorde onder de naam van de meest nabijgelegen plaats. De index van plaatsen op blz. 254 en de gekleurde lokatiekaarten achterin de gids vertonen alle steden, plaatsen en dorpen met parken die in deze gids voorkomen. Zo kunt u snel en gemakkelijk ergens een park vinden. Als u al weet op welk park u wilt

staan, kunt u de index van parken raadplegen op blz. 249.

Als uw bestemming in de index van plaatsen voorkomt, raadpleeg dan de gegeven bladzij, waar de aldaar gevestigde parken worden vermeld. De plaatsnamen staan in zwart op de kaarten achterin het gidsje, aangeduid met coördinaten bij de vermelding. Ook kunt u de kleurenkaarten raadplegen om nabijgelegen plaatsen te vinden die ook in de gids voorkomende parken hebben.

Als uw bestemming niet in de index van plaatsen voorkomt, of als u alleen een vaag idee heeft van het gebied dat u wilt bezoeken, kunt u eveneens de kleurenkaarten raadplegen. Sommige gebieden komen op meer dan één kaart voor, maar de plaatsnamen (zwartgedrukt op de kaarten) worden slechts eenmaal vertoond.

De ligging van de parken op de kaart moet men slechts als een algemene aanduiding beschouwen. Wegwijzingen, verschaft door de beheerders, vindt u bij elke vermelding en als u moeite heeft een bepaald park te vinden, raden wij u aan in de buurt om verdere aanwijzingen te vragen.

De hierboven vermelde internationale verkeersborden worden in Groot-Brittannië gebruikt en zijn speciaal ontworpen voor het gebruik van de parkbezoekers en kampeerders. Ze zijn nog niet bij alle parken opgesteld en vermelden niet altijd de naam van een park of camping. Ze duiden echter wel aan of het park geschikt is voor caravans, tenten of beide.

Wijzigingen in provinciegrenzen

In april 1996 zijn, als gevolg van de reorganisatie van plaatselijke overheden, de grenzen en namen van vele provincies en regio's in Groot-Brittannië gewijzigd. Wijzigingen die vóór de afronding van de editie voor 1997 werden aangekondigd, zijn opgenomen in de kaarten en stadsbeschrijvingen van het gidsje. In april 1997 zullen er verdere wijzigingen plaatsvinden. Deze zijn echter nog niet officieel bevestigd.

Londen is een grote trekpleister voor toeristen en daarom raken de campings en caravanterreinen in de streek van Greater London erg snel vol en boeking ver van tevoren is daarom noodzakelijk. Bij de meeste aankomsthavens zijn ook campings te vinden en de meeste worden vermeld in deze gids en aangeduid op de kaarten achterin.

Hulp bij het vinden van een park
De Toeristische Informatiecentra over heel Groot-Brittannië (zie aan het einde van deze gids) kunnen kampeerders en caravaneigenaars informatie verschaffen over lokale parken en terreinen. Een aantal Toeristische Informatiecentra biedt ook een adviesdienst, die inlichtingen kan geven over mogelijke plaats op campings en vaak kan helpen met het maken van een reservering. Momenteel beslaan de volgende TIC's in Engeland de streken: **Londen**, London Tourist Board and Convention Bureau, Victoria Station; **Peak District**, 01629-814341; **New Forest**, 01703-283771; en **Cornwall**, 01872-74057. In Wales kan tussen mei en eind augustus een groot aantal Tourist Information Centres inlichtingen verstrekken over beschikbare staanplaatsen in hun streek.

Vermijding van problemen in het hoogseizoen
In de zomermaanden juni t/m september kunnen parken in populaire gebieden, zoals Noord-Wales, Cumbria, de West Country en het New Forest in Hampshire bijzonder vol raken. Bezoekers moeten proberen zo vroeg mogelijk op de dag bij het park aan te komen, of nog beter, van tevoren boeken. Een aantal parken heeft een speciaal terrein voor bezoekers die laat in de avond arriveren. Dit is om te voorkomen dat andere bezoekers in hun slaap gestoord worden en minder kampeerders weggestuurd worden. De

volgende morgen worden de caravans en tenten dan een juiste plek gegeven.

Andere mogelijkheden voor caravans en tenten

Als u ervan houdt om door landelijke streken in Groot-Brittanië te trekken, vindt u het misschien interessant te weten, dat de Forestry Commission (staatsbosbeheer) bos-kampeerterreinen in zeven van Groot-Brittanië's Forest Parks en het New Forest beheert. Sommige bieden gereduceerde tarieven voor jeugdorganisaties op georganiseerde kampeertochten, en alle inlichtingen hierover moeten ver van tevoren ingewonnen worden bij de Forestry Commission.

Kampeerschuren

Dit zijn meestal niet meer in gebruik zijnde boerengebouwen die zijn verbouwd tot simpele logies voor een groep tot 15 personen, tegen redelijke prijs. De faciliteiten zijn eenvoudig: u kunt er slapen, eten, en eten bereiden, er is koud stromend water en een doortrek w.c. De Jeugdherberg Vereniging heeft een heel netwerk van kampeerschuren, van de Forest of Bowland in Lancashire tot en met Durham en Noord-Yorkshire. Meer informatie bij de YHA, Trevelyan House, 8 St Stephen's Hill, St Albans, Hertfordshire AL1 2DY. Tel: 01727-855215.

Kampeerschuren zijn ook in het Peak National Park beschikbaar. Meer informatie verkrijgbaar bij Peak National Park, Losehill Hall, Castleton, Derbyshire S30 2WB.

Huisdieren
Op vele parken zijn honden toegestaan, maar het is raadzaam dit te controleren tijdens het reserveren. U kunt dan ook navragen of er extra wordt berekend voor een huisdier.

Het meenemen van huisdieren naar Groot-Brittannië

Hondsdolheid waarschuwing: vanwege de quarantaine-

voorschriften (b.v. zes maanden voor honden of katten) is het niet praktish om dieren mee te nemen op een vakantie in Groot-Brittannië. Indien u dit toch wilt doen, moet u een invoervergunning (minstens zes weken voor de aanvang) verkrijgen bij het Ministry of Agriculture, Fisheries and Food, Hook Rise South, Tolworth, Surbiton, Surrey KT6 7NF. Tel: 0181-330 4411. Indien u deze vergunning niet verkrijgt, overtreedt u de wet. Elk illegaal ingevoerd dier kan afgemaakt worden.

Drugswaarschuwing voor inkomende toeristen

In het Verenigd Koninkrijk staan er zware straffen op het illegaal invoeren van drugs. Drugshandelaars proberen onschuldige reizigers te misleiden en wij raden u daarom aan alle betrokkenheid met drugs te vermijden. Draag nooit pakjes of bagage door de douane die niet van uzelf zijn.

Wettelijke bepalingen

De allerbeste bron van wettelijk advies voor automobilisten is een Club voor Automobilisten (b.v. ANWB). Wat de kampeerder of caravaneigenaar nog meer moet weten is betrekkelijk eenvoudig. Als u een caravan of kampeerwagentje achter de auto heeft, mag u niet meer dan 60 mijl (96 km) per uur rijden op tweebaanswegen of snelwegen, 50 mijl (80 km) per uur op eenbaanswegen, en op snelwegen met drie banen aan elke kant mag u niet in de derde (snelste) baan. Kooktoestellen mogen niet bij een wegrestaurant met benzinestation aangestoken worden.

In de meeste steden is parkeren beperkt, zowel door wettelijke bepalingen als uit praktische overwegingen. Auto's met aanhangende caravans mogen niet parkeren bij een parkeermeter en vele stadsparkeerterreinen zijn alleen geschikt voor auto's zonder aanhangende caravans of kampeerwagentjes.

's Nachts moet een kampeerwagen, of

een auto verbonden met een aanhangwagen, die aan de weg geparkeerd staat, zowel z'n twee voorlichten als z'n achterlichten aanhebben, terwijl een auto alleen dit niet hoeft.

De remmen, lampen, het gewicht, etc. van buitenlandse voertuigen hoeven niet te voldoen aan de Britse technische voorschriten. Hoe dan ook, een aanhangwagen mag de Britse wettelijke afmetingsbepalingen - 23 feet (7m) lang en 7 feet 6 inches (2,3m) breed - niet overschrijden. Ze moeten het internationale kenteken (NL of B) voeren en niet overnachten in de berm of op de parkeerhavens, daar deze wettelijk onderdeel uitmaken van de weg.

Tenslotte is het ook heel belangrijk van tevoren uit te vinden hoe laat u op de dag van vertrek moet opbreken. U moet zich daar aan houden, anders kan men u een extra dag in rekening brengen.

Advies aan bezoekers

De BTA stelt er prijs op uw op- of aanmerkingen op uw verblijf in Groot-Brittannië te vernemen. wij hopen dat u geen reden tot klagen heeft, maar mocht dit toch het geval zijn, raden wij u dringend aan om uw klacht onmiddellijk kenbaar te maken aan de leiding van het desbetreffende park, de winkel of vervoersmaatschappij. Indien u hieruit geen genoegdoening verkrijgt, laat u ons dit dan weten, zodat wij zelf een onderzoek kunnen instellen, of u kunnen adviseren over eventuele verder te nemen stappen.

U mag het geeft niet hoeveel geld, en in welke munteenheid dan ook, meenemen en er bestaan geen beperkingen op het aantal inwisselbare reischeques. Als u geld wilt wisselen als de banken gesloten zijn, kunt u dit doen bij de grotere hotels, reisbureaus en warenhuizen of bij onafhankelijke wisselkantoren. **Controleer vooral van tevoren de berekende wisselkoers en commissietarieven.**

Alle grote winkels, warenhuizen, en de meeste hotels en restaurants accepteren de gebruikelijke, internationaal erkende credit cards. Als u ook graag op markten winkelt, koop dan alleen op grote, erkende markten, en bekijk de artikelen eerst zorgvuldig.

Vraag altijd wat de prijs is voor u tot de aankoop overgaat. Pas op voor zakkenrollers in drukke menigten.

Indien u bestolen bent, of betrokken bent bij een ongeval of brand, ben dan 999 (waarvoor geen geld nodig is) en vraag om de 'police' (politie), 'ambulance service' (ambulance) of de 'fire brigade' (brandweer).

De British Tourist Authority heeft alle pogingen in het werk gesteld om deze publicatie bij het ter perse gaan van nauwkeurigheid te verzekeren. **De informatie werd in goed vertrouwen verstrekt, gebaseerd op inlichtingen gegeven aan de British Tourist Authority door de organisatoren van de vermelde caravanparken en campings. De BTA kan echter niet garanderen dat deze informatie correct is en kan geen verantwoording aanvaarden voor foute of onjuiste voorstellingen. De BTA kan beslist niet verantwoordelijk worden gesteld voor verlies, teleurstelling, nalatigheid of enige andere schade die voortvloeit uit het vertrouwen in de informatie in deze gids, of problemen voortkomend uit het faillisement of liquidatie van enige vermelde maatschappij, individu of bedrijf, of indien een maatschappij, individu of bedrijf ophoudt handel te drijven. Het is daarom raadzaam de gegeven informatie bij het maken van een reservering goed te controleren.**

Alle in deze gids vermelde parken en terreinen voldoen aan de eisen van de Tourist Board. Een lijst van de aan de campings en caravanparken gestelde eisen kunt u vinden op pagina 221.

All genoemde instellingen hebben betaald voor hun vermelding in deze gids.

COME USARE QUESTA GUIDA

I campeggi elencati in questa guida sono per la maggior parte aperti sia alle roulottes che alle tende e molti di essi accolgono anche i camper e le motorhome. Molti campeggi dispongono anche di roulottes a noleggio.

Segni certi di qualità

Il British Graded Holiday Parks Scheme è gestito dagli Enti Turistici scozzese, inglese, gallese, e nord-irlandese in collaborazione con la British Holiday and Home Parks Association and National Caravan Council. Tutti i campeggi per roulotte, chalet e tende che espongono la "Q", simbolo di qualità, ricevono ogni anno una classificazione da parte degli ispettori dell'ente turistico. I campeggi presentati in Where to Stay in Britain: Camping and Caravan Parks, sono stati ispezionati o hanno almeno richiesto un'ispezione secondo le norme del British Graded Holiday Parks Scheme.

Ogni campeggio che prende parte al progetto è stato visitato da un ispettore qualificato per assicurare il più elevato livello di strutture, e permettere al visitatore di scegliere con fiducia una vacanza. Tutti gli aspetti del campeggio sono stati valutati per la loro qualità, e un'importanza particolare è stata attribuita al livello generale di igiene. Il livello di qualità delle strutture di un campeggio viene indicato con dei simboli, da uno a cinque. Nella maggior parte dei casi in Camping and Caravan Parks troverete una classificazione in "Q"; dove non appaiono classificazioni, il campeggio era in attesa d'ispezione al momento di andare in stampa. Troverete di seguito una spiegazione del livello di strutture che vi potrete attendere per ogni classificazione.

✓✓✓✓✓ Strutture fornite e mantenute in ottimo stato.

✓✓✓✓ Strutture fornite e mantenute in uno stato molto buono.

✓✓✓ Strutture fornite e mantenute in buono stato.

✓✓ Strutture fornite e mantenute in uno stato abbastanza buono.

✓ Strutture fornite e mantenute in uno stato accettabile.

Strutture

Le strutture vengono indicate per mezzo di simboli, comprensibili a prima vista, spiegati qui di seguito.

Spiegazione dei Simboli

M   Socio del Regional Tourist Board

BH&   British Holiday & Home Parks
HPA   (v. pagina 35)

NCC   National Caravan Council (v. pagina 35)

🚐   Roulottes ammesse (con numero di posteggi e prezzi)

🚍   Camper/motorhome ammessi (con numero di posteggi e prezzi) In alcuni casi il numero di posteggi per camper/motorhome è compreso nel numero di posteggi per roulottes

Å   Tende ammesse

🏠   Numero di roulottes a noleggio (v. posteggi per roulottes a noleggio a seguito)

🏠   Bungalow/chalet/casette a noleggio

🚗   Parcheggio vicino all'alloggio

P   Parcheggio sul post

🏕   Zona di pernottamento temporaneo

🔌   Allacciamento elettrico per roulottes (v. Alimentazione elettrica: prese di allacciamento per roulottes)

🚿   Docce

🛁   Aqua calda per tutti i lavandini

🌓   Illuminazione dei WC ecc.

🚽   WC a trattamento chimico

🔥   Cambio di bombole di gas butano o propano

🛒   Negozio/negozio ambulante di alimentari

✕   Bar/ristorante

🍸   Club/bar/negozio autorizzato alla vendita di bevande alcoliche

📺   Sala con televisione

📞   Telefono pubblico

🧺   Lavanderia sul posto

//   Attrezzature per asciugare la biancheria

🔲   Attrezzature per stirare i vestiti

⊙   Prese per rasoi elettrici

🎱   Sala giochi

🛝   Zona giochi per i bambini

🏊   Piscina riscaldata al coperto sul posto

🏊   Piscina all'aperto sul posto

🤿   Strutture per gli sport subacquei sul posto (comprese le bombole di ossigeno)

🎿   Sci d'acqua sul posto

🚣   Imbarcazioni/canottaggio sul posto

⛵   Vela sul posto

🐎   Equitazione/escursioni a dorso di pony partendo dal campeggio

🎾   Tennis sul posto

🎣   Pesca sul posto o nelle vicinanze

⛳   Golf sul posto o nelle vicinanze

🔫   Galleria per armi da fuoco privata

🚫   NON si ammettono cani

🎵   Spettacoli/intrattenimenti serali

🏛   Campeggio nel parco di un edificio storico

🔔   Si consiglia di prenotare in estate

⊤   Prenotazione possible tramite agenzie di viaggio

⚙   Welcome Host

Prezzi

I prezzi indicati per i posteggi sono il prezzo minimo e il prezzo massimo di un pernottamento per 2 persone, un'automobile e una tenda o una roulotte. I campeggi britannici preferiscono in genere includere tutto in un solo prezzo, benché in alcuni vi siano prezzi separati per automobili, roulottes o tende e per ogni persona. In alcuni campeggi vi sono tariffe supplementari per i tendoni delle roulottes, il che viene indicato. I prezzi minimi e massimi delle roulottes a noleggio sono i prezzi per settimana. I prezzi indicati sono quelli forniti dagli esercenti dei campeggi in questione, e sono un'indicazione dei prezzi che verranno praticati per il periodo di validità di questa pubblicazione. I prezzi indicati sono in sterline (£) e pence (p). L'IVA (Imposta sul Valore Aggiunto) al 17,5% è compresa nei prezzi indicati. Per evitare qualsiasi equivoco, si consiglia vivamente di controllare i prezzi al momento di effettuare la prenotazione.

Prenotazione

Nel richiedere informazioni sulle possibilità di sistemazione, è necessario, oltre a controllare il prezzo, dire chiaramente quali siano le proprie esigenze, per esempio:

- date di arrivo e partenza, e se possibile date alternative;
- il tipo di sistemazione richiesto;
- qualsiasi particolare esigenza.

Quando si prenota per telefono c'è sempre il rischio di errori. Tempo permettendo, si consiglia dunque di confermare sempre le prenotazioni per iscritto. Ricordarsi di indicare il proprio nome e indirizzo e di accludere, per ogni risposta, una busta preindirizzata e preaafrancata o un buono internazionale per riposta pagata.

Anticipi

Per la prenotazione di posti nei campeggi per tende, roulottes e chalets, il prezzo intero va normalmente versato in anticipo. Il versamento può normalmente essere effettuato in due rate: un anticipo al momento della prenotazione e il saldo circa due settimane prima dell'inizio del periodo prenotato.

Annullamenti

Nel Regno Unito, l'accettazione di un alloggio offerto, sia per iscritto che per telefono, equivale per legge alla firma di un contratto vincolante tra l'inquilino e il proprietario dell'alloggio. Ciò significa che se l'inquilino annulla la propria prenotazione, non prende domicilio o parte prima del previsto (per qualsiasi ragione), il proprietario potrebbe avere diritto a un risarcimento qualora non riesca a riaffittare l'alloggio per tutto o parte del periodo prenotato. Se è stato versato un anticipo, è probabile che venga ritenuto dal proprietario, il quale potrebbe anche esigere un ulteriore addebito.

È consigliabile dunque avvisare immediatamente il proprietario sia di qualsiasi cambiamento di itinerario, sia dell'intenzione di annullare una prenotazione o di partire prima del previsto.

Prese di allacciamento elettrico: I campeggi dispongono, per la maggior parte di prese di allacciamento alla rete di distribuzione dell'energia elettrica adoperabili sia per la roulottes che per le tende. La tensione è di 240V circa e 50Hz, benché in alcuni casi possa ancora variare tra 200V e 250V. In alcuni campeggi potrebbe essere necessario un adattatore per l'allacciamento. La fornitura di energia elettrica è normalmente soggetta ad un addebito supplementare, a meno che non venga indicato il contrario, e si consiglia di controllare la tariffa al momento di effettuare la prenotazione.

Il carnet internazionale del campeggiatore è raramente riconosciuto in Gran Bretagna, salvo nei campeggi organizzati dai principali club.

Come trovare il campeggio prescelto

I campeggi in questa guida sono divisi a seconda che si trovino in Inghilterra (per regione), Scozia, Galles e Irlanda del Nord, e sono stati elencati in ordine alfabetico sotto il nome della città in cui si trovano, o vicino a cui si trovano. L'Indice delle Città a pagina 254 e le Mappe a colori nell'ultima parte della guida riportano tutte le città, i centri e i villaggi che hanno un campeggio elencato in questa guida. Usate questi riferimenti per trovare in un modo facile e veloce un alloggio adatto. Se sapete in quale campeggio volete stare, controllate l'Indice dei Campeggi a pagina 249.

Se il luogo dove volete stare è compreso nell'indice delle città, andate alla pagina indicata per trovarvi i campeggi disponibili. I nomi delle città appaiono in nero sulla mappa nell'ultima pagina della guida nel modo in cui sono stati indicati dal riferimento alla mappa nella voce relativa. Controllate anche le mappe a colori per trovarvi altri luoghi vicini che hanno anche dei campeggi elencati in questa guida.

Se il luogo che volete non si trova nell'indice delle città - o avete solo un'idea generale della zona in cui volete stare - usate le mappe a colori. Alcune zone appaiono in più di una mappa, ma i nomi delle città (stampati in nero sulle mappe) sono indicati soltanto una volta.

Le posizioni dei campeggi appaiono solo a titolo indicativo. Le indicazioni fornite dagli esercenti dei campeggi vengono riportate sotto alla relativa inserzione nell'elenco. In caso di difficoltà, si consiglia di rivolgersi per indicazioni a qualcuno nelle vicinanze del campeggio.

I segnali internazionali indicati qui sopra vengono usati in Gran Bretagna per aiutare i visitatori a trovare i campeggi. Non sono ancora stati installati per tutti i campeggi e non indicano il nome di nessun campeggio. Indicano però se il campeggio è per tende, roulottes o ambedue.

Cambiamenti dei confini

Nell'aprile del 1996 i confini e i nomi di molte contee e regioni della Gran Bretagna sono stati cambiati come conseguenza della riorganizzazione degli enti locali. I cambiamenti che sono stati annunciati al momento di compilare l'edizione del 1997 sono stati riportati sulle mappe e le descrizioni delle città di questa guida. Per l'aprile 1997 sono in programma degli altri cambiamenti che non sono stati ancora confermati.

Servizi di ricerca campeggi

I Tourist Information Centres di tutta la Gran Bretagna (v. pagine finali) possono fornire ai campeggiatori informazioni sui campeggi nelle loro zone di responsabilità.

Alcuni Tourist Information Centres offrono servizi di ricerca campeggi che forniscono informazioni sulla disponibilità di posteggi e spesso aiutano a effettuare le prenotazioni. I Tourist Information Centres che attualmente offrono questo servizio coprono le seguenti zone del paese: **Londra**, London Tourist Board, Victoria Station; **Peak District**, (01629) 814341; **New Forest**, (01703) 283771; **Cornovaglia**, (01872) 74057. Nel Galles, molti Tourist Information Centres possono fornire informazioni sulla disponibilità di posti dalla fine di maggio alla fine di agosto.

Come evitare i problemi dell'alta stagione

Nei mesi estivi, da giugno a settembre, i campeggi nelle zone più frequentate del paese: Galles settentrionale, Cumbria, Inghilterra sud-occidentale e la New Forest nel Hampshire, registrano molto presto il tutto esaurito. Si consiglia ai campeggiatori di arrivare presto o, se possibile, di prenotare in anticipo. Alcuni campeggi dispongono di zone di pernottamento temporaneo per i campeggiatori che arrivano tardi. Queste zone di pernottamento consentono di non disturbare gli altri campeggiatori durante la notte e di accogliere un maggior numero di nuovi arrivati, i quali vengono condotti a uno dei posti liberi la mattina seguente.

Altri luoghi di campeggio

A chi preferisce seguire il proprio itinerario attraverso la campagna britannica potrebbe interessare sapere che la Forestry Commission gestisce dei campeggi forestali nei sette parchi forestali del paese e nella New Forest. Alcuni offrono tariffe ridotte a gruppi organizzati di giovani in campeggio. Tutte le richieste d'informazioni vanno indirizzate direttamente alla Forestry Commission con qualche mese di anticipo sulla data di arrivo.

Granai da campeggio

Sono spesso degli edifici agricoli inutilizzati e trasformati in semplici alloggi per un massimo di 15 visitatori a prezzi ragionevoli. Le strutture sono le minime indispensabili: un posto per dormire, mangiare e cucinare, acqua corrente fredda e WC.

La Youth Hostel Association dispone di una rete di granai da campeggio che copre la zona tra Forest Bowland nel Lancashire, Durham e lo Yorkshire settentrionale. Per ulteriori informazioni, anche sulle modalità di prenotazione, rivolgersi a: YHA, Trevelyan House, 8 St. Stephen's Hill, St. Albans, Hertfordshire ALI 2DY. Tel: (01727) 855215.

I granai da campeggio esistono anche nel Peak National Park. Per ulteriori informazioni, scrivere al seguente indirizzo: Peak National Park, Losehill Hall, Castleton, Derbyshire S30 2WB.

Animali domestici

Molti campeggi sono lieti di accogliere i cani, ma si consiglia di verificare, al momento di effettuare la prenotazione, se sono in effetti ammessi e se vi sono tariffe supplementari per animali domestici.

L'importazione di animali in Gran Bretagna

La Rabbia

Dato l'obbligo della quarantena (di sei mesi per cani e gatti) non è né consigliabile né pratico portare animali con sé in vacanza in Gran Bretagna. Per importare gli animali è necessario ottenere una licenza d'importazione, richiedendola con almeno sei settimane di anticipo al Ministry of Agriculture, Fisheries and Food, Hook Rise South, Tolworth, Surbiton, Surrey KT6 7NF, Inghilterra. Tel: (0181) 330 4411. L'importazione di animali senza licenza è un reato. Qualunque animale importato illegalmente può essere soppresso per legge.

Avvertimento sugli stupefacenti per i turisti in arrivo

Le leggi britanniche sul contrabbando di stupefacenti prevedono delle sanzioni estremamente severe per i trasgressori. I trafficanti di droga tentano a volte di ingannare i viaggiatori. Si consiglia a chiunque abbia deciso di visitare il Regno Unito di evitare qualsiasi coinvolgimento con lo spaccio di stupefacenti e di non attraversare mai la dogana portando le valige o i pacchi di altri viaggiatori.

Aspetti giuridici

La migliore fonte d'informazioni per gli automobilisti che intendono visitare la Gran Bretagna è l'organizzazione automobilistica del paese di origine. Le regole che deve conoscere l'automobilista campeggiatore sono relativamente semplici.

Le automobili con roulotte o rimorchi al traino non devono superare i 96 chilometri orari (60 miglia all'ora) sulle strade a doppia carreggiata e sulle autostrade, e gli 80 chilometri orari (50 miglia all'ora) sulle strade normali. Sulle autostrade a tre carreggiate in ogni direzione, le roulotte ed i rimorchi non sono ammessi nella terza carreggiata (la più veloce). È vietato accendere fornelli nelle aree di servizio autostradali.

Nella maggior parte delle città, parcheggiare è reso difficile sia dai regolamenti che da difficoltà pratiche. Alle automobili con rimorchio è vietato l'uso di spazi con parchimetri e i posteggi di molti parcheggi cittadini sono intesi per automobili senza rimorchio, sebbene in alcuni di essi vi siano spazi anche per veicoli più lunghi.

Se parcheggiati sulla strada di notte, i rimorchi, o le automobili attaccate ai rimorchi, devono avere due luci anteriori e due luci posteriori accese, anche dove l'automobile senza rimorchio sarebbe esonerata da quest'obbligo.

I freni, le luci, il peso ecc. dei veicoli provenienti dall'estero non devono soddisfare i criteri tecnici delle norme britanniche. I rimorchi tuttavia non devono superare i limiti britannici, che sono: 7 metri di lunghezza e 2,3 metri di larghezza. I rimorchi devono recare il numero di targa del paese di provenienza. È vietato sostare di notte sui lati erbosi o nelle piazzole di sosta delle strade, dato che queste zone sono per legge considerate parti della strada.

Per concludere, è importante sapere l'ora entro la quale si è obbligati a liberare il posteggio nel giorno previsto per la partenza. Si consiglia di partire presto la mattina per evitare di dover pagare il prezzo di una giornata in più.

Consigli per i visitatori

La British Tourist Authority è sempre lieta di ricevere i commenti e le osservazioni dei turisti su qualsiasi aspetto del loro soggiorno in Gran Bretagna, che siano o meno favorevoli. Ci auguriamo che chiunque visiti il nostro paese non abbia mai occasione di lamentarsi. Se vi fosse ragione di lamentarsi, il consiglio è di rivolgersi in primo luogo alla gestione del campeggio, negozio o società di trasporti. Qualora la risposta non sia soddisfacente, consigliamo ai turisti di rivolgersi alla BTA che prenderà in esame la questione o suggerirà le misure da prendere.

Si possono portare in Gran Bretagna valute di qualsiasi denominazione senza limiti di quantità. Si può cambiare anche qualsiasi numero di traveller's cheque. Per cambiare le valute straniere durante le ore di chiusura delle banche ci si può rivolgere alle ricezioni di alcuni grandi alberghi, alle agenzie di viaggio, alle agenzie di cambiavalute indipendenti. Raccomandiamo di controllare il tasso e la commissione di cambio prima di cambiare i soldi.

Tutti i grandi negozi, i grandi magazzini la maggior parte degli alberghi e dei ristoranti accettano le carte di credito normalmente riconosciute nel mondo. A chi decida di fare spese nei mercati consigliamo di comprare solo in quelli grandi e riconosciuti e di esaminare accuratamente gli articoli prima di acquistarli.

Consigliamo di chiedere sempre il prezzo dei beni e dei servizi prima di impegnarsi all'acquisto e di fare attenzione ai borsaioli nei luoghi affollati.

Chiunque sia vittima di un furto, o coinvolto in un incidente o un incendio può telefonare al 999 (chiamata gratuita) e chiedere la polizia, il servizio ambulanze o i vigili del fuoco.

La British Tourist Authority si è adoperata per garantire l'esattezza delle informazioni contenute in questa pubblicazione al momento di andare in stampa. **Le informazioni vengono date in buona fede in base ai dati forniti alla British Tourist Authority dai promotori del campeggi elencati. La BTA non può tuttavia né garantire l'esattezza delle informazioni né assumersi la responsabilltà di qualsiasi errore o falsità. È esclusa tutta la responsabilità di perdite, delusioni, negligenza o di altri danni che risultino dall'aver fatto affidamento sulle informazioni contenute in questa guida o dal fallimento o dalla liquidazione di qualsiasi società, individuo o ditta, o dalla cessazione delle attività di qualsiasi società, individuo o ditta. Si consiglia di verificare** l'esattezza delle informazioni al momento di effettuare la prenotazione.

Tutti i campeggi elencati in questa guida rispettano le norme dell'ente per il turismo. A pagina 221 riportiamo un elenco di queste norme applicabili ai campeggi per tende e roulottes.

Tutti i campeggi elencati hanno pagato per la loro inserzione nella guida.

BRITISH HOLIDAY AND HOME PARKS ASSOCIATION

The Association (formerly known as the National Federation of Site Operators) represents commercial operators of all kinds throughout Britain. Its aim is to ensure a high standard of excellence in members' parks for the satisfaction of the visitor.

Parks listed in this Guide all conform to the standards set by the British Tourist Authority but BH&HPA Members' Parks, which are identified in the Guide by **(BH&HPA)**, must also abide by the BH&HPA Code of Conduct. This gives the visitor an assurance of a high standard of facilities and reliability.

The BH&HPA works with the British Tourist Authority and the national and regional tourist boards in England, Scotland and Wales, to safeguard tourist interests. It also works with Government and local government authorities to ensure that all aspects of legislation and control are applied and that proper safety measures are carried out for the comfort and protection of the visitor.

The BH&HPA will investigate problems encountered by visitors and can provide details of self-catering holidays and residential parks. Contact:

British Holiday and Home Parks Association Ltd, Chichester House, 6 Pullman Court, Great Western Road, Gloucester GL1 3ND. Telephone: (01452) 526911 and 413041 Fax: (01452) 307226.

THE NATIONAL CARAVAN COUNCIL

The National Caravan Council is the representative body of the British caravan industry in that it represents the manufacturers of caravans, caravan dealers, caravan park operators and those companies who provide the industry with its supplies and services.

The Council operates an approval system for caravans, certifying that they are manufactured in accordance with the British Standard. All Dealer members and Park Operator members, which are identified in the Guide by **(NCC)**, agree to comply with Conditions of Membership which require them to provide their customers with a high standard of service.

The Council works closely with the British Tourist Authority, the tourist boards of England, Scotland and Wales and regional tourist boards to promote tourism and particularly to promote the important role which all kinds of caravans play in providing tourists with the facilities they require.

Full information on its members and its activities together with assistance on any difficulties encountered can be obtained from:

The National Caravan Council, Catherine House, Victoria Road, Aldershot, Hampshire GU11 1SS. Telephone: (01252) 318251 Fax: (01252) 22596.

CARAVAN HOLIDAY HOME AWARD SCHEME

Rose Award, English Tourist Board, Thames Tower, Black's Road, Hammersmith, London W6 9EL.

The national tourist boards for England, Scotland and Wales run similar Award schemes for holiday caravan homes on highly graded caravan parks. They recognise high standards of caravan accommodation and enable you to step into a comfortable, fully furnished holiday home set amongst landscaped surroundings with all amenities you could wish for.

Thistle Award, Scottish Tourist Board, Thistle House, Beechwood Park North, Inverness IV2 3ED.

All the caravan parks included in the Award scheme have been inspected and meet the criteria demanded by the scheme. In addition to complying to joint tourist board standards for 'Holiday Caravan Parks and in Caravan Holiday Homes' all Award caravans must have a shower or bath, toilet, mains electricity and water heating (at no extra charge) and a refrigerator (many also have a colour television).

Dragon Award, Wales Tourist Board, Brunel House, 2 Fitzalan Road, Cardiff CF2 IUY.

A complete list of the parks in each country, plus further information about them, can be obtained free from the national tourist boards (see page 236). Look out for these plaques displayed by all Award winning parks, and by each caravan which meets the required standards. Many parks listed in this guide are participating in these schemes and are indicated accordingly.

COUNTRY CODE

Always follow the Country Code
🐾 Enjoy the countryside and respect its life and work 🐾 Guard against all risk of fire 🐾 Fasten all gates 🐾 Keep your dogs under close control 🐾 Keep to public paths across farmland 🐾 Use gates and stiles to cross fences, hedges and walls 🐾 Leave livestock, crops and machinery alone 🐾 Take your litter home 🐾 Help to keep all water clean 🐾 Protect wildlife, plants and trees 🐾 Take special care on country roads 🐾 Make no unnecessary noise

LONDON

No one can capture the atmosphere of London in words alone.
One of the eternally great cities, it remains true that 'if you're tired of
London, you're tired of life'.

Buckingham Palace, the Tower and
Madame Tussaud's are just the
beginning... London has more than
100 museums and galleries, the finest
theatres in the world and some of
the most exciting shops, restaurants
and markets.

Stroll through the many gracious
parks, discover Jack the Ripper's East
End, explore 'the City', follow in the
footsteps of Dickens. Or if you
prefer, hop on a red bus or
catch a black cab.
Whichever way you go,
seeing the sights of
London is an unforgettable
experience.

FOR MORE INFORMATION CONTACT:
London Tourist Board
26 Grosvenor Gardens, London SW1W 0DU

Where to Go in London - see pages 38-40
Where to Stay in London - see pages 43-44

LONDON

Where to Go and What to See

You will find hundreds of interesting places to visit during your stay in London, just some of which are listed in these pages. Contact any Tourist Information Centre in the region for more ideas on days out in London.

■ **Bankside Gallery**
48 Hopton Street,
London SE1 9JH
Tel: (0171) 928 7521
Home of The Royal Watercolour Society and The Royal Society of Painter-Printmakers. Changing exhibitions of watercolours and prints.

■ **British Museum**
Great Russell Street,
London WC1B 3DG
Tel: (0171) 636 1555
One of the great museums of the world, showing the works of man from all over the world from prehistoric times to the present day.

■ **Cabinet War Rooms**
Clive Steps,
King Charles Street,
London SW1A 2AQ
Tel: (0171) 930 6961
The underground headquarters used by Winston Churchill and the British Government during World War II. Includes Cabinet Room,

transatlantic telephone room and Map Room.

■ **Design Museum**
Shad Thames,
London SE1 2YD
Tel: (0171) 403 6933
A study collection showing the development of design in mass production. Review of new products, graphics gallery, and changing programme of exhibitions.

■ **Dickens House**
48 Doughty Street,
London WC1N 2LF
Tel: (0171) 405 2127
Charles Dickens' home from 1837-1839. Collection of letters, pictures, first editions, furniture, memorabilia, restored rooms.

■ **Fan Museum**
12 Crooms Hill,
London SE10 8ER
Tel: (0181) 305 1441
The only venue in the world devoted entirely to the art and craft

of the fan. Changing exhibitions. Beautifully restored 18thC houses. Gift shop.

■ **Guards Museum**
Wellington Barracks,
Birdcage Walk,
London SW1E 6HQ
Tel: (0171) 414 3428
Collection of uniforms, colours and artefacts spanning over 300 years of history of the Foot Guards.

■ **Hampton Court Palace**
Hampton Court,
Surrey KT8 9AU
Tel: (0181) 781 9500
Oldest Tudor palace in England. Tudor kitchens, tennis courts, maze, state apartments and King's apartments.

■ **HMS Belfast**
Morgan's Lane, Tooley Street,
London SE1 2JH
Tel: (0171) 407 6434
11,500 tonne World War II cruiser moored on the Thames. Now a

floating naval museum, with seven decks to explore. Many naval exhibits on show.

■ **Imperial War Museum**
Lambeth Road,
London SE1 6HZ
Tel: (0171) 416 5000
The story of 20thC war from Flanders to Bosnia. Features include the Blitz Experience, Operation Jericho and the Trench Experience.

■ **London Dungeon**
28-34 Tooley Street,
London SE1 2SZ
Tel: (0171) 403 0606
World's first medieval horror museum. Now featuring two major shows: "The Jack the Ripper Experience" and "The Theatre of the Guillotine".

■ **Madame Tussaud's**
Marylebone Road,
London NW1 5LR
Tel: (0171) 935 6861
Wax figures in themed settings, including The Garden Party, 200 Years, Superstars, The Grand Hall, The Chamber of Horrors and The Spirit of London.

■ **Museum of London**
150 London Wall,
London EC2Y 5HN

Tel: (0171) 600 3699
Galleries illustrate over 2000 years of the capital's social history, from prehistoric times to the 20thC. Regular temporary exhibitions, lunchtime lecture programmes.

■ **Museum of the Moving Image**
South Bank, Waterloo,
London SE1 8XT
Tel: (0171) 928 3535
A celebration of cinema and television. 44 exhibit areas offer plenty of hands-on participation, and a cast of actors to tell visitors more.

■ **National Gallery**
Trafalgar Square,
London WC2N 5DN
Tel: (0171) 839 3321
Western painting from 1260-1920, including work by Van Gogh, Rembrandt, Cezanne, Turner, Gainsborough, Leonardo da Vinci, Renoir and Botticelli.

■ **National Maritime Museum**
Romney Road, Greenwich,
London SE10 9NF
Tel: (0181) 858 4422
Britain's maritime heritage illustrated through actual and model ships, paintings, uniforms, navigation and astronomy

instruments, archives and photographs. Queen's House.

■ **National Portrait Gallery**
St Martin's Place,
London WC2H 0HE
Tel: (0171) 306 0055
Permanent collection of portraits of famous men and women from the Middle Ages to the present day.

■ **National Postal Museum**
King Edward Building,
King Edward Street,
London EC1A 1LP
Tel: (0171) 239 5420
One of the most important and extensive collections of postage stamps in the world, including the Phillips and Berne Collections. Temporary exhibitions.

■ **Natural History Museum**
Cromwell Road,
London SW7 5BD
Tel: (0171) 938 9123
Home of the wonders of the natural world, one of the most popular museums in the world, and one of London's finest landmarks.

■ **Old Royal Observatory**
(Flamsteed House),
Greenwich Park,
London SE10 9NF
Tel: (0181) 858 4422

Museum of time and space. Greenwich Meridian, working telescopes, planetarium and timeball. Wren's Octagon Room. Intricate clocks and computer simulations. Restored in 1993.

■ **Rock Circus**
London Pavilion, Piccadilly Circus, London W1V 9LA
Tel: (0171) 734 7203
The exhibition is an amazing combination of stereo sound through personal headsets, audio animatronic (moving) and Madame Tussauds (wax) figures of over 50 rock stars.

■ **Royal Air Force Museum**
Grahame Park Way,
London NW9 5LL
Tel: (0181) 205 2266
Britain's National Museum of aviation features over 70 full size aircraft, Flight Simulator, "Touch & Try" Jet Provost Trainer and Eurofighter 2000 Theatre.

■ **Science Museum**
Exhibition Road,
London SW7 2DD
Tel: (0171) 938 8000
National Museum of Science and Industry. Full size replica of Apollo 11 Lunar Lander, launch pad, Wellcome Museum of History of Medicine, flight lab, food for thought, optics.

■ **Sherlock Holmes Museum**
221B Baker Street,
London NW1 6XE
Tel: (0171) 935 8866
Grade 2 listed lodging house. 1st floor Holmes' apartment. Second floor Mrs Hudson's room and Doctor Watson's room. Third floor souvenir shop. Reading room and exhibition room.

■ **Thames Barrier Visitors' Centre**
Unity Way, London SE18 5NJ
Tel: (0181) 854 1373
Exhibition with 10-min video, a working scale model and a multi-media show. Also riverside walkways, children's play area and Thames Barrier Buffet.

■ **Tower Bridge**
London SE1 2UP
Tel: (0171) 403 3761
Exhibition explains the history of the bridge and how it operates. Original steam powered engines on view. Panoramic views from fully-glazed walkways. Gift shop.

■ **Tower of London**
Tower Hill,
London EC3N 4AB
Tel: (0171) 709 0765
Building spans 900 years of British history. The nation's Crown Jewels, regalia and armoury robes on display. Home of the "Beefeaters" and ravens.

■ **Victoria and Albert Museum**
Cromwell Road,
London SW7 2RL
Tel: (0171) 938 8500
The V & A is the world's finest museum of the decorative arts. Its collection, housed in magnificent Victorian buildings, span 2000 years including sculpture and furniture.

FIND OUT MORE

A free information pack about holidays and attractions in London is available on written request from:
London Tourist Board and Convention Bureau,
26 Grosvenor Gardens,
London SW1W 0DU.

TOURIST INFORMATION

Tourist and leisure information can be obtained from Tourist Information Centres throughout England. Details of centres and other information services in Greater London are given below. The symbol ⊨ means that an accommodation booking service is provided.

Points of arrival
Victoria Station, Forecourt, SW1 ⊨
Easter-October, daily 0800-1900.
November-Easter, reduced opening hours.
Liverpool Street Underground Station, EC2 ⊨
Monday-Friday 0800-1800.
Saturday-Sunday 0845-17.30.
Heathrow Terminals 1, 2, 3 Underground Station Concourse (Heathrow Airport) ⊨
Daily 0800-1800.
Heathrow Terminal 3 Arrivals Concourse ⊨
0600-2300.
Waterloo International Arrivals Hall ⊨
0830-2100
The above information centres provide a London and Britain tourist information service, offer a hotel accommodation booking service, stock free and saleable publications on Britain and London and sell theatre tickets, tourist tickets for bus and underground and tickets for sightseeing tours.

Inner London
British Travel Centre ⊨
12 Regent Street, Piccadilly Circus, SW1Y 4PQ
Monday-Friday 0900-1830.
Saturday-Sunday 1000-1600
(0900-1700 Saturdays May-September).

Tower Hamlets Tourist Information Centre
107a Commercial Street, E1 6BG
Tel: (0181) 375 2549
Monday-Friday 0930-1630.
Greenwich Tourist Information Centre ⊨
46 Greenwich Church Street, SE10 9BL
Tel: (0181) 858 6376
April-September, daily 1015-1645. October-March, reduced opening hours.
Hackney Museum and Tourist Information Centre
Central Hall, Mare Street, E8
Tel: (0181) 985 9055
Tuesday-Friday 1000-1700.
Saturday 1330-1700.
Islington Tourist Information Centre ⊨
44 Duncan Street, N1 8BW
Tel: (0171) 278 8787
Monday 1400-1600.
Tuesday-Saturday 1000-1700.
Lewisham Tourist Information Centre
Lewisham Library, Lewisham High Street, SE13 6LG
Tel: (0181) 297 8317
Monday 1000-1700.
Tuesday-Friday 0900-1700
Selfridges ⊨
Oxford Street, W1. Basement Services Arcade
Open during normal store hours.
Southwark Tourist Information Centre ⊨
Hay's Galleria,
Tooley Street, SE1 2HD
Tel: (0171) 403 8299

Monday-Friday 1030-1700.
Saturday-Sunday 1100-1700.
(Reduced winter opening).

Outer London
Bexley Tourist Information Centre
Central Library, Townley Road, Bexleyheath DA6 7HJ
Tel: (0181) 303 9052
Monday, Tuesday, Thursday 0930-2000.
Wednesday & Friday 0930-1730.
Saturday 0930-1700.
Also at Hall Place Visitor Centre
Bourne Road, Bexley
Tel: (01322) 558676
June-September, daily 1130-1630.
Croydon Tourist Information Centre ⊨
Katharine Street,
Croydon CR9 1ET
Tel: (0181) 253 1009
Monday-Wednesday & Friday 0900-1800. Thursday 0930-1800.
Saturday 0900-1700.
Sunday 1200-1700.
Foots Cray Tourist Information Centre ⊨
Tesco Store Car Park,
Edgington Way, Sidcup DA14 5AH
Summer only, Monday-Saturday 1000-1800.
Sunday 1000-1600.
Harrow Tourist Information Centre
Civic Centre, Station Road, Harrow HA1 2XF
Tel: (0181) 424 1103
Monday-Friday 0900-1700.

Hillingdon Tourist Information Centre
Central Library,
14 High Street,
Uxbridge UB8 1HD
Tel: Uxbridge (01895) 250706
Monday, Tuesday
& Thursday 0930-2000.
Friday & Wednesday 0930-1730.
Saturday 0930-1600.

Hounslow Tourist Information Centre
24 The Treaty Centre,
Hounslow High Street,
Hounslow TW3 1ES
Tel: (0181) 572 8279
Monday, Wednesday, Friday
& Saturday 0930-1730.
Tuesday, Thursday 0930-2000.

Kingston Tourist Information Centre
The Market House,
The Market Place,
Kingston upon Thames
KT1 1JS
Tel: (0181) 547 5592
Monday-Friday 1000-1700.
Saturday 0900-1600.

Redbridge Tourist Information Centre
Town Hall, High Road, Ilford,
Essex IG1 1DD
Tel: (0181) 478 3020
Monday-Friday 0830-1700.

Richmond Tourist Information Centre 🛏
Old Town Hall,
Whittaker Avenue,
Richmond upon Thames
TW9 1TP
Tel: (0181) 940 9125
Monday-Friday 1000-1800.
Saturday 1000-1700.
May-October,
also Sunday 1015-1615.

Twickenham Tourist Information Centre
The Altrium, Civic Centre,
York Street,
Twickenham TW1 3BZ
Tel: (0181) 891 7272
Monday-Friday 0900-1700.

Visitorcall

The London Tourist Board and Convention Bureau's 'Phone Guide to London' operates 24 hours a day. To access a full range of information call 0839 123456. To access specific lines dial 0839 123 followed by:

What's on this week - 400
What's on next 3 months - 401
Sunday in London - 407
Rock and pop concerts - 422
Popular attractions - 480
Where to take children - 424
Museums - 429
Palaces (including Buckingham Palace) - 481
Current exhibitions - 403
Changing the Guard - 411
Popular West End shows - 416
London dining - 485
Calls cost 45p per minute cheap rate, 50p per minute at all other times (as at October '96).
To order a Visitorcall card please call (0171) 971 0026.
Information for callers using push-button telephones:
(0171) 971 0027.

Artsline

London's information and advice service for disabled people on arts and entertainment.
Call (0171) 388 2227.

CHECK THE MAPS

The colour maps at the back of this guide show
all the cities, towns and villages for which you will
find accommodation entries.

Refer to the town index to find the page
on which it is listed.

WHERE TO STAY (LONDON)

Parks in the London area are listed in alphabetical order of place name, and then in alphabetical order of establishment. A contact address is given where it differs from the address of the establishment.

Map references refer to the colour location maps at the back of this guide. The first number indicates the map to use; the letter and number which follow refer to the grid reference on the map.

At-a-glance symbols can be found inside the back cover flap.

Keep this open for easy reference.

CHINGFORD

Map ref 3D2

Lee Valley Campsite ⚑
⊖✓✓✓✓✓
Sewardstone Road, Chingford
E4 7RA
☎ (0181) 529 5689
Jcn 26 of M25 follow signs to Waltham Abbey, turn left at traffic lights - two miles on right. Signposted.
5.20 hectares (13 acres). Level, sloping, grassy, hard.
200 touring pitches

200	🚐	£7.93—£11.16

Open April–October
Cards accepted: Access, Visa, Switch/Delta
⚓P🖭🚿👿🐾♨🅿🔌♨⚡📶🗑♨🚙
☺⚠♨☻
[Ad] See display advertisement on page 44

EDMONTON

Map ref 3D2

Lee Valley Regional Park Authority ⚑
⊖✓✓✓
Lee Valley Leisure Centre, Picketts Lock Lane, London N9 OAS
☎ (0181) 345 6666
Fax (0181) 884 4975
A406 - Montagu Road. Signposted.

2.40 hectares (6 acres). Level, grassy, hard.
200 touring pitches

62	🚐	£7.93—£11.16
63	🚍	£7.93—£11.16
75	⛺	£7.93—£11.16

Cards accepted: Access, Visa, Switch/Delta
⚓P🖭🚿👿🐾♨🅿🔌♨⚡✖📶🗑♨🗑
♨🚙☺⚠🔥♨🐾🅿♨
[Ad] See display advertisement on page 44

HACKNEY

Map ref 3D2

Tent City - Hackney ⚑
Millfields Road, Hackney, London
E5 OAR
☎ (0181) 985 7656
Fax (0181) 749 9074
London A11, A102 to Hackney, Millfields Rd over Cow Bridge. Signposted.
1.20 hectares (3 acres). Level, grassy, hard, sheltered.
200 touring pitches

20	🚐	£10.00—£10.00
20	🚍	£10.00—£10.00
160	⛺	£10.00—£10.00

Open June–August
⚓P🖭🚿👿🐾♨☺♨⚡📶🗑♨🚙☺
♨⚠Ｕ🅿♫

LEYTON

Map ref 3D2

Lee Valley Park, Eastway Cycle Circuit ⚑
⊖✓✓
Temple Mill Lane, Leyton, London
E15 2EN
☎ (0181) 534 6085
A106 North from Blackwall Tunnel to Leyton. West from M11 Leytonstone. Signposted.
0.80 hectares (2 acres). Level, grassy.
100 touring pitches

	🚐	£8.30—£13.50
	🚍	£8.30—£13.50
	⛺	£8.30—£13.50.

Open March–October
Cards accepted: Access, Visa
P🖭🐾♨✖♨📶🗑♨♨⊙Ｕ🐾♨
[Ad] See display advertisement on page 44

LOUGHTON

Map ref 3D1

The Elms Caravan Park
⊖✓✓✓
Member BH&HPA
Lippitts Hill, High Beech, Loughton, Essex IG10 4AW
☎ (0181) 508 3749 & 508 1000
Fax (0181) 508 9414
Continued ▶

LONDON – THE ELMS CARAVAN AND CAMPING PARK
LIPPITTS HILL, HIGH BEECH, LOUGHTON, ESSEX

Ideal base for visiting London. The Elms is situated in Epping Forest Conservation Area. A small, quiet family run park just 3 miles from the underground, 30 minutes journey time to London. Shopping basics on site. Pub with children's room within 200 yards. Our individual shower and toilet cubicles second to none. Bicycle hire on site. Riding, fishing, golf, boating, swimming, restaurants and shops all nearby. Booking advisable. Tel: 0181-508 3749/1000; Fax: 0181-508 9414.
Junction 26 off M25. Follow signs to Waltham Abbey (A121), turn left at traffic lights (A112) for 1.3 miles, third turning left beside Plough Pub, half a mile to Lippitts Hill. Or from Loughton Station, 'phone for pick-up. **FREE BUS TO AND FROM UNDERGROUND STATION**

LOUGHTON
Continued

Junction 26 off M25, follow signs to Waltham Abbey (A121). Turn left at traffic lights (A112) for 1.3 miles. Third turning left beside Plough pub, half-mile to Lippitts Hill.
1.20 hectares (3 acres). Level, grassy, hard, sheltered.
40 touring pitches

10	🚐	£8.00
40	🚎	£8.00
40	⛺	£8.00

Open March–October
🔋 👥 🛠 🚿 🐕 ⊙ 🛒 🗘 🖉 🕒 🍴 ⚲
Ad See display advertisement on page 43

STANSTED
Kent
Map ref 4B3

Thriftwood Caravan & Camping Park
⊖✓✓✓✓
Member BH&HPA
Plaxdale Green Road, Stansted, Sevenoaks, Kent TN15 7PB
☎ Fairseat (01732) 822261
Fax (01732) 822261

Exit 2A M26 follow A20 towards London and follow brown international camping signs. Signposted.
8 hectares (20 acres). Level, grassy, hard, sheltered.
150 touring pitches

150	🚐	£8.00—£10.75
150	🚎	£8.00—£10.75
150	⛺	£6.00—£10.75
4	🏠	£125.00—£280.00

6 units not for hire
Open January, March–December
Cards accepted: Access, Visa
🔋 P 🔌 🔋 🔦 🛠 🚿 💧 🐕 ⊙ 🛒 🖉 🖉 📦
🕒 ⚲ 🍴 ⚲ T

CUMBRIA

Cumbria is simply one of the most extraordinarily beautiful places on earth. Wordsworth lived here among its shimmering lakes and towering crags, and called it 'the loveliest spot that man hath ever found'; a 'spot' which attracts walkers, climbers and watersports enthusiasts, all year round.

But you don't have to be energetic! There are pretty villages, working farms, museums, visitors centres - plus the whole of the Lake District National Park to explore.

To the west of the Lakes lies Cumbria's unspoilt coastline. To the north you'll find the wild North Pennines and Borderlands. To the southeast, the peaceful Eden Valley. And between... paradise.

FOR MORE INFORMATION CONTACT:
Cumbria Tourist Board
Ashleigh, Holly Road, Windermere,
Cumbria LA23 2AQ
Tel: (015394) 44444 **Fax:** (015394) 44041

Where to Go in Cumbria – see pages 46-49
Where to Stay in Cumbria – see pages 50-55

CUMBRIA

Where to Go and What to See

You will find hundreds of interesting places to visit during your stay in Cumbria, just some of which are listed in these pages. The number against each name will help you locate it on the map (page 49). Contact any Tourist Information Centre in the region for more ideas on days out in Cumbria.

1 Linton Tweeds
Shaddon Mills, Shaddon Gate,
Carlisle, Cumbria CA2 5TZ
Tel: (01228) 27569
Shows history of weaving in Carlisle up to Lintons today. Available for visitors to have hands on weaving and other activities.

2 Tullie House Museum and Art Gallery
Castle Street, Carlisle,
Cumbria CA3 8TP
Tel: (01228) 34781
Major tourist complex housing: museum, art gallery, education facility, lecture theatre, shops, herb garden, restaurant and terrace bars.

3 Four Seasons Farm Experience
Sceugh Mire, Southwaite,
Carlisle CA4 0LS
Tel: (016974) 73753
An open farm where you can meet the animals, bottle feed the lambs, make your own butter and bread, plus other farming activities.

4 Senhouse Roman Museum
The Battery, Sea Brows,
Maryport, Cumbria CA15 6JD
Tel: (01900) 816168
Once the headquarters of Hadrian's Coastal Defence system. UK's largest group of Roman altars, stones and inscriptions from a single site. Roman military equipment, stunning sculpture.

5 Lakeland Sheep and Wool Centre
Egremont Road, Cockermouth,
Cumbria CA13 0QX
Tel: (01900) 822673
An all weather attraction with live sheep shows and working dog demonstrations. Includes large screen and other tourism exhibitions on the area, a wool shop and seafood restaurant.

6 The Printing House Museum
102 Main Street, Cockermouth,
Cumbria CA13 9LX
Tel: (01900) 824984
Printing machinery and equipment. Tour of the museum follows the development of printing from the 15thC to the present day.

7 Dalemain Historic House and Gardens
Dalemain Estate Office
Penrith,
Cumbria CA11 0HB
Tel: (017684) 86450
Historic house with Georgian furniture. Westmorland and Cumberland Yeomanry Museum, agricultural bygones, adventure playground, licensed restaurant, famous gardens.

8 Mirehouse
Underskiddaw,
Cumbria CA12 4QE
Tel: (017687) 72287
17thC house with wide ranging literary and artistic connections. Grounds to Bassenthwaite Lake include playgrounds, garden, tearoom.

46

9 Dove Cottage & Wordsworth Museum
Town End, Grasmere,
Ambleside, Cumbria LA22 9SH
Tel: (015394) 35544
Wordsworth's home 1799-1808. Poet's possessions, museum with manuscripts, farmhouse reconstruction, paintings and drawings. Special events throughout the year.

10 Rydal Mount
Ambleside, Cumbria LA22 9LU
Tel: (015394) 33002
William Wordsworth's home for 37 years. Family portraits, furniture, first editions and personal possessions. Garden landscaped by the poet. 9thC Norse Mound, magnificent views.

11 Sellafield Visitors Centre
Sellafield, Seascale,
Cumbria CA20 1PG
Tel: (019467) 27027
Exhibition of nuclear power and the nuclear industry.

12 Eskdale Corn Mill
Boot, Holmrook,
Cumbria CA19 1TG
Tel: (019467) 23335
A historic water-powered corn mill near Dalegarth Station, approached via packhorse bridge. Early wooden machinery, milling and farming. Exhibition and waterfalls.

13 Brockhole - Lake District National Park Visitor Centre
Windermere,
Cumbria LA23 1LJ
Tel: (015394) 46601
Exhibitions include National Park Story, slide shows, films, shop, gardens, grounds, adventure playground, drystone walling area, trails, events. Gaddums restaurant, tearoom, putting.

14 Muncaster Castle, Gardens and Owl Centre
Ravenglass,
Cumbria CA18 1RQ
Tel: (01229) 717614
14thC pele tower with 15th and 19thC additions. Gardens contain an exceptional collection of rhododendrons and azaleas. Extensive collection of owls.

15 Ravenglass and Eskdale Railway
Ravenglass, Cumbria CA18 1SW
Tel: (01229) 717171
England's oldest narrow-guage railway runs for 7 miles through glorious scenery to the foot of England's highest hills. Most trains steam hauled.

16 Steam Yacht Gondola
Pier Cottage, Coniston,
Cumbria LA21 8AJ
Tel: (015394) 41288
Victorian steam powered vessel now National Trust owned and completely renovated with opulently upholstered saloon.

17 Amazonia
Glebe Road, Bowness-on-Windermere, Windermere,
Cumbria LA23 3HE
Tel: (015394) 48002
Large display of exotic reptiles and insects from around the world including pythons, crocodiles and tarantula spiders! Visitors are able to handle certain animals.

18 The World of Beatrix Potter
The Old Laundry, Crag Brow,
Bowness-on-Windermere,
Windermere, Cumbria LA23 3BX
Tel: (015394) 88444
The life and works of Beatrix Potter presented on a 9 screen video wall, film on her life, and three-dimensional recreations of some of the scenes from her popular tales.

19 Levens Hall
Levens, Kendal, Cumbria LA8 0PD
Tel: (015395) 60321
Elizabethan mansion, incorporating a pele tower. Famous topiary

garden laid out in 1694, steam
collection, plant centre, shop, play
and picnic areas.

20 Sizergh Castle
Kendal, Cumbria LA8 8AE
Tel: (015395) 60070
*Strickland family home for 750
years, now National Trust owned.
With 14thC pele tower, 15thC
great hall, 16thC wings. Stuart
connections. Rock garden, rose
garden, daffodils.*

23 Lakeside & Haverthwaite Railway
Haverthwaite Station,
Ulverston,
Cumbria LA12 8AL
Tel: (015395) 31594
*Standard gauge steam railway
operating a daily seasonal service
through the beautiful Leven Valley.
Steam and diesel locomotives
on display.*

26 South Lakes Wild Animal Park
Crossgates,
Dalton-in-Furness,
Cumbria LA15 8JR
Tel: (01229) 466086
*Wild animal park in over 14 acres
with over 120 species of animals
from all over the world. Large
water-fowl ponds.
Miniature railway.*

**21 Heron Corn Mill
and Museum of Papermaking**
Waterhouse Mills,
Beetham, Milnthorpe,
Cumbria LA7 7AR
Tel: (015395) 63363
*Restored working corn mill featuring
14ft high waterwheel. The museum
shows paper-making both historic
and modern with artefacts, displays
and diagrams.*

22 Heron Glass
54 The Gill, Ulverston,
Cumbria LA12 7BL
Tel: (01229) 581121
*A combined visitor centre and
workshop. Traditional glassmaking
demonstrations daily.
Factory shop.*

**24 Phil Cotton's Classic Bikes
Working Museum**
Victoria Road,
Ulverston,
Cumbria LA12 0BY
Tel: (01229) 586099
*Classic motorcycle display, with
video, restoration areas and small
shop.*

25 Holker Hall and Gardens
Cark in Cartmel,
Cumbria LA11 7PL
Tel: (015395) 58328
*Victorian wing, formal and
woodland garden, deer park,
motor museum, adventure
playground and gift shop.
Exhibitions including Timeless Toys
and Teddies.*

27 The Dock Museum
North Road,
Barrow-in-Furness,
Cumbria LA14 2PW
Tel: (01229) 870871
*Presents the story of steel
shipbuilding for which
Barrow is famous.
Interactive displays, nautical
adventure playground.*

28 Furness Abbey
Barrow-in-Furness,
Cumbria LA13 0TJ
Tel: (01229) 823420
*Ruins of a 12C Cistercian abbey.
Extensive remains include
transepts, choir, west tower
of church, canopied seats
and arches.*

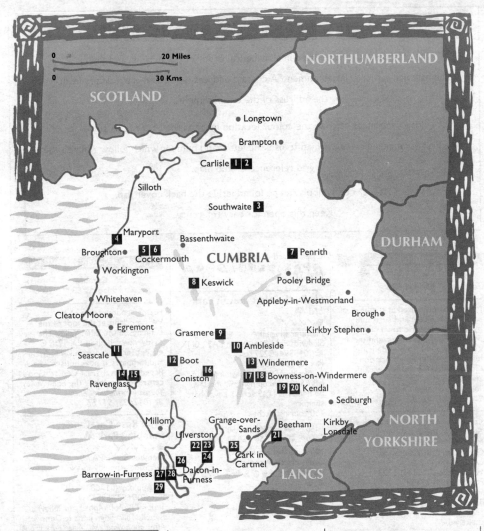

0 ——————————— 20 Miles
0 ——————————— 30 Kms

SCOTLAND

NORTHUMBERLAND

● Longtown

Brampton ●

Carlisle **1** **2**

Silloth

Southwaite **3**

Maryport

Bassenthwaite

DURHAM

Broughton ● **5** **6**
Cockermouth

CUMBRIA

7 ● Penrith

● Workington

8 ● Keswick

Pooley Bridge ●

Appleby-in-Westmorland

● Whitehaven

Brough ●

Cleator Moor ●

● Egremont

Grasmere **9**

Kirkby Stephen ●

10 ● Ambleside

Seascale **11**

12 ● Boot

13 ● Windermere

14 **15**
Ravenglass

16
Coniston

17 **18** ● Bowness-on-Windermere

19 **20** ● Kendal

● Sedburgh

Millom ●

Grange-over-Sands

Beetham

Kirkby
Lonsdale

NORTH

Ulverston ●

22 **23**
24

25

Cark in
Cartmel

21

YORKSHIRE

26

Barrow-in-Furness **27** **28** Dalton-in-Furness

29

LANCS

4

FIND OUT MORE

Further information about
holidays and attractions in
Cumbria is available from:
Cumbria Tourist Board,
Ashleigh,
Holly Road,
Windermere,
Cumbria LA23 2AQ.
Tel: (015394) 44444

These publications are
available from the
Cumbria Tourist Board:
■ **Cumbria The Lake District
Touring Map** - including tourist
information and touring caravan
and camping parks £3.45.
Laminated poster £2.95.
■ **Days Out in Cumbria** -
Over 200 ideas for a great day
out £1.25.

■ **Short Walks** - Good for
Families - route descriptions,
maps and information for
14 walks in lesser known areas
of Cumbria 95p.
■ **Wordsworth's
Lake District** - folded map
showing major Wordsworthian
sites plus biographical details
60p. Japanese language version
£1. Laminated poster £1.

WHERE TO STAY (CUMBRIA)

Parks in this region are listed in alphabetical order of place name, and then in alphabetical order of establishment. A contact address is given where it differs from the address of the establishment.

Map references refer to the colour location maps at the back of this guide.

The first number indicates the map to use; the letter and number which follow refer to the grid reference on the map.

At-a-glance symbols can be found inside the back cover flap.

Keep this open for easy reference.

AMBLESIDE

Cumbria
Map ref 6A3

Market town situated at the head of Lake Windermere and surrounded by fells. The historic town centre is now a conservation area and the country around Ambleside is rich in historic and literary associations. Good centre for touring, walking and climbing.
Tourist Information Centre
☎ *(015394) 32582*

Greenhowe Caravan Park ⋀⋀
⊖✓✓✓✓ Rose Award
Member BH&HPA
Great Langdale, Ambleside
LA22 9JU
☎ Langdale (015394) 37231
Fax (015394) 37464
From Ambleside take A593 then B5343. Site on right. Signposted.
1.2 hectares (3 acres). Sloping, stony, sheltered.

46	⊡	£150.00—£350.00

Open March–November
⚓ P 🅿 🅛 🔥 ♨ ⏱ 🛒 📶 📺 ⚡ ☇ ⚓ ⊙ ⚡ ⋀
🛇 🅐 🔳

Skelwith Fold Caravan Park Ltd ⋀⋀
⊖✓✓✓✓
Member BH&HPA
Skelwith Fold, Ambleside LA22 0HX
☎ (015394) 32277
Fax (015394) 32327
Ambleside A593 to Coniston for 1m left B5286 1m on right. Signposted.
50 hectares (125 acres). Level, hard, sheltered.
150 touring pitches

150	🚐	£8.50—£9.50
150	🚎	£7.50—£8.50

300 units not for hire
Open March–November
⚓ P 🔳 🅛 🔥 ♨ ⏱ 🛒 📶 📺 ⚡ ☇ ⚓ ⊙
⋀ 🅐

APPLEBY-IN-WESTMORLAND

Cumbria
Map ref 6B3

Former county town of Westmorland, at the foot of the Pennines in the Eden Valley. The castle was rebuilt in the 17th C, except for its Norman keep, ditches and ramparts. It now houses a Rare Breeds Survival Trust Centre. Good centre for exploring the Eden Valley.
Tourist Information Centre
☎ *(017683) 51177*

Wild Rose Caravan & Camping Park ⋀⋀
⊖✓✓✓✓✓
Member BH&HPA
Ormside, Appleby-in-Westmorland
CA16 6EJ
☎ Appleby (017683) 51077
Fax (017683) 52551
Turn off B6260 (Appleby to Tebay) at Burrells. Follow sign posts to Ormside. After approximately 2 miles park is on right hand side. Signposted.

16 hectares (40 acres). Level, sloping, grassy, hard.
240 touring pitches

240	🚐	£7.10—£11.10
80	🚏	£7.10—£11.10
80	⛺	£7.10—£11.10

240 units not for hire
Cards accepted: Access, Visa, Switch/Delta

🖵🏕🧺🛉🛢🚻🚲✕📺🔌🗑🧺♨🛒
☺🔍⚙🏔🚶🎯☉
Ad See display advertisement on page 50

BRAITHWAITE

Cumbria
Map ref 6A3

Braithwaite nestles at the foot of the Whinlatter Pass and has a magnificent backdrop of the mountains forming the Coledale Horseshoe.

Scotgate Holiday Park 🏔
⊖✓✓✓✓
Member BH&HPA
Scotgate Holiday Park, Braithwaite, Keswick CA12 5TF
☎ Keswick (017687) 78343
2 miles west of Keswick just off A66 on B5292. Signposted.
3.6 hectares (9 acres). Level, grassy.
165 touring pitches

15	🚐	£10.00—£14.00
165	🚏	£5.20—£6.20
165	⛺	£6.70—£7.70
27	🚉	£160.00—£315.00

Open March–October

🛢🏕🖵🧺🛉🛢🚻🚲✕🔌🗑🧺♨🛒
☺🔍
Ad See display advertisement on this page

> Map references apply to the colour maps at the back of this guide.

> All accommodation in this guide has been graded, or is awaiting a grading, by a trained Tourist Board inspector.

Cumbria
Map ref 6A2

Cumbria's only city is rich in history. Attractions include the small red sandstone cathedral and 900-year-old castle with magnificent view from the keep. Award-winning Tullie House Museum and Art Gallery brings 2,000 years of Border history dramatically to life. Excellent centre for shopping.
Tourist Information Centre ☎ (01228) 512444

Dalston Hall Caravan Park 🏔
⊖✓✓✓✓
Member BH&HPA
Dalston Hall, Dalston, Carlisle CA5 7JX
☎ (01228) 710165
M6 exit 42 take Dalston road 15m Take B5299 Site 1.00m on R Signposted.
1.6 hectares (4 acres). Level, grassy, hard.
60 touring pitches

40	🚏	£6.50—£7.00
20	⛺	£5.50—£6.00

17 units not for hire
Open March–October

🛢🏕🖵🧺🛉🛢🚻🚲✕🍽🔌🗑🧺♨🛒
☺🏔🚶🎯⛺

Dandy Dinmont Caravan & Camping Site 🏔
⊖✓✓✓✓
Blackford, Carlisle CA6 4EA
☎ Rockcliffe (01228) 74611
Exit M6 J44, A7 1.5 mile. After Blackford sign follow road directional signs to site. Signposted.
1.6 hectares (4 acres). Level, grassy, hard.
47 touring pitches

27	🚐	£6.75—£7.00
27	🚏	£6.75—£7.00
20	⛺	£5.50—£6.00

15 units not for hire
Open March–October
🛢P🏕🧺🛉🛢🚻🔌🗑🧺♨☺

> Please mention this guide when making your booking.

Orton Grange Caravan Park 🏔
⊖✓✓✓✓
Member BH&HPA
Wigton Road, Carlisle CA5 6LA
☎ (01228) 710252
Fax (01228) 710252
4 miles west Carlisle on A595 left side of road coming from Carlisle. Signposted.
2 hectares (5 acres). Level, grassy, sheltered.
50 touring pitches

30	🚐	£6.20—£8.50
30	🚏	£6.20—£8.50
20	⛺	£6.20—£8.50
4	🚉	£102.00—£180.00

18 units not for hire
Cards accepted: Access, Visa

🛢🖵🏕🧺🛉🛢🚻🛒📺🔌🗑♨🛒
☺🔍🏔🎯⛺

CROOK

Cumbria
Map ref 6A3

Delightful, unspoilt open farming parish with many attractive and gentle walks giving fine views of the high fells. The village is centred around the local pub and is a good base for touring, having easy access to the motorway link.

Pound Farm Caravan Site 🏔
⊖✓✓✓
Member BH&HPA
Crook, Kendal LA8 8JZ
☎ Staveley (01539) 821220
M6 J36, follow A591 for 9 miles to roundabout north west of Kendal. First left onto B5284 for 2 miles. Pound Farm is on the left before the Sun Inn. Signposted.
0.8 hectares (2 acres). Level, sloping, grassy, stony, hard, sheltered.
20 touring pitches

10	🚐	£6.50—£7.75
10	🚏	£6.50—£7.75
10	⛺	£5.25—£6.75
2	🚉	

14 units not for hire
Open March–October

🛢P🧺🛉🛢🔌🗑♨🛒☺🏔🚶🎯⛺

CROOK

Continued

Ratherheath Lane Camping and Caravan Park ⚑
⊖✓✓✓✓
Member BH&HPA
Chain House, Bonningate, Kendal
LA8 8JU
☎ (01539) 821154
M6 J36 follow signs for Windermere A591. Exit at roundabout onto B5284 signed Crook. Continue 1.5 miles, turn right at Ratherheath Lane. Signposted.
0.6 hectares (1.5 acres). Level, sloping, grassy, hard.
20 touring pitches

10	🚐	£6.00—£9.50
10	🚌	£6.00—£7.50
12	⛺	£3.00—£7.50
8	⬒	£99.00—£320.00

Open March—November
🚗P🏪🎣♨🔥⛽TV🔌☺🔍✂⚿

ESKDALE

Cumbria
Map ref 6A3

Several minor roads lead to the west end of this beautiful valley, or it can be approached via the east over the Hardknott Pass, the Lake District's steepest pass. Scafell Pike and Bow Fell lie to the north and a miniature railway links the Eskdale Valley with Ravenglass on the coast.

Fisherground Farm Campsite ⚑
⊖✓✓✓
Fisherground, Eskdale, Holmrook
CA19 1TF
☎ (019467) 23319
From George IV Inn turn towards Boot. First farm on the left, 400 metres. Signposted.
64 hectares (160 acres). Level, grassy, sheltered.
30 touring pitches

30	🚌	£7.00—£7.00
30	⛺	£7.00—£7.00

Open March—November
⚑P🎣♨🔥🔌🔌✳⬒☺⚿

Information on accommodation listed in this guide has been supplied by the proprietors. As changes may occur you are advised to check details at the time of booking.

FLOOKBURGH

Cumbria
Map ref 6A3

Village, once a market town, renowned for winkle and fluke fishing.

Lakeland Leisure Park ⚑
⊖✓✓✓✓ Rose Award
Member BH&HPA/NCC
Moor Lane, Flookburgh,
Grange-over-Sands LA11 7LT
☎ Reservations/Free brochure
(01442) 248668
Fax (01442) 232459
Take exit 36 from the M6 onto the A590. Turn left onto the A6/A590 for Barrow in Furness. Take B5277 through Grange-over-Sands to Flookburgh. at village square turn immediately left. Park is 1 mile down this road. Signposted.
42 hectares (105 acres). Level, grassy.
100 touring pitches

100	🚐	£7.15—£18.00
100	🚌	£7.15—£18.00
25	⛺	£7.15—£13.75
200	⬒	£109.00—£522.00

500 units not for hire
Open March—October
Cards accepted: Access, Visa, Switch/Delta

🚗🏪🎣♨🔥🔌☺🔍✕🍴TV🔌🔌✳
⬒☺🎢🔥🎵♫🔊🆃®
🆔 See display advertisement inside front cover

GRANGE-OVER-SANDS

Cumbria
Map ref 6A3

Set on the beautiful Cartmel Peninsula, this tranquil resort, known as Lakeland's Riviera, overlooks Morecambe Bay. Pleasant seafront walks and beautiful gardens. The bay attracts many species of wading birds.

Greaves Farm Caravan Park ⚑
⊖✓✓✓✓
Member BH&HPA
Field Broughton, Grange-over-Sands
LA11 6HR
☎ (015395) 36329
Leave A590, 1 mile south of Newby Bridge, signed 'Cartmel 4'. Proceed 2 miles to 3 bungalows on left. Approximately 200 yards before Field Broughton church. Signposted.
1.2 hectares (3 acres). Level, grassy, hard.
8 touring pitches

3	🚐	£6.00—£9.00
3	🚌	£6.00—£9.00
5	⛺	£6.00—£9.00
2	⬒	£160.00—£200.00

18 units not for hire
Open March—October
🚗P🏪🎣♨🔥🔌☺🔥☺♨®

Old Park Wood Caravan Park
⊖✓✓✓✓
Member BH&HPA
Holker, Grange-over-Sands
LA11 7PP
☎ Flookburgh (015395) 58266
Follow signs for Holker Hall Stately Home, 1.5 miles past main gate on B5278. Signposted.
14 hectares (35 acres). Hard.
32 touring pitches

32	🚐	£11.50—£12.00
32	🚌	£11.50—£12.00

325 units not for hire
Open March—October
🏪🎣♨🔥🔌☺🔌✳⬒☺🎢🔊
🔥♨

HAWKSHEAD

Cumbria
Map ref 6A3

Lying near Esthwaite Water, this village has great charm and character. Its small squares are linked by flagged or cobbled alleys and the main square is dominated by the market house, or Shambles, where the butchers had their stalls in days gone by.

The Croft Caravan and Camp Site ⚑
⊖✓✓✓
North Lonsdale Road, Hawkshead,
Ambleside LA22 0NX
☎ (015394) 36374
Fax (015394) 36544
From Ambleside take B5286 5 miles to Hawshead. Signposted.
2 hectares (5 acres). Level, grassy, sheltered.
100 touring pitches

15	🚐	£9.00—£9.00
85	⛺	£8.50—£8.50
18	⬒	£140.00—£245.00

Open March—November
🚗🏪🎣♨🔥TV🔌🔌✳⬒☺🔍♨

COLOUR MAPS

Colour maps at the back of this guide pinpoint all places in which you will find accommodation listed.

KENDAL

Cumbria
Map ref 6B3

The "Auld Grey Town" lies in the valley of the River Kent with a backcloth of limestone fells. Situated just outside the Lake District National Park, it is a good centre for touring the Lakes and surrounding country. Ruined castle, reputed birthplace of Catherine Parr.
Tourist Information Centre ☎ *(01539) 725758*

Waters Edge Caravan Park
⊖✓✓✓✓✓
Member BH&HPA
Crooklands, Milnthorpe LA7 7NN
☎ Crooklands (015395) 67708
Fax (015395) 67610
Located at Crooklands 3/4 mile along A65 N M6 junction 36. Signposted.
1.2 hectares (3 acres). Level, grassy, hard, sheltered.
40 touring pitches

30	🚐	£7.95—£13.50
30	🚛	£7.95—£13.50
10	⛺	£4.50—£12.50
2	🏠	£150.00—£230.00

Open March–November
Cards accepted: Access, Visa
⚡P📶🅿🔥♨🚿♿🛒🍴📺🛁📻⌀
🔌☉🛍🏍♫ⓉＴ

KESWICK

Cumbria
Map ref 6A3

Beautifully positioned town beside Derwentwater and below the mountains of Skiddaw and Blencathra. Excellent base for walking, climbing, watersports and touring. Motor-launches operate on Derwentwater and motor boats, rowing boats and canoes can be hired.
Tourist Information Centre
☎ *(017687) 72645*

Castlerigg Hall Caravan & Camping Park **M**
⊖✓✓✓✓
Castlerigg Hall, Keswick CA12 4TE
☎ (017687) 72437
Fax (017687) 72437
1.5m. SE of Keswick off A591. Signposted.

6 hectares (15 acres). Level, sloping, grassy, stony, hard, sheltered.
174 touring pitches

54	🚐	£8.75
54	🚛	£7.00
120	⛺	£6.00—£7.00
5	🏠	£120.00—£260.00

24 units not for hire
Open March–November
P📶🅿🔥♨🚿♿🛒🍴📺🛁⌀📻🔌☉
🏔♿
Ad See display advertisement on this page

Lakeside Holiday Park Norman Garner Ltd **M**
⊖✓✓✓✓
Member BH&HPA/NCC
Crow Park Road, Keswick
CA12 5EW
☎ (017687) 72878
J40 from M6 Penrith. Ignore first exit off A66 and continue to roundabout and follow signs to Keswick town centre. Follow camping and caravan signs. Signposted.
1.8 hectares (4.5 acres). Level, grassy, hard, sheltered.
18 touring pitches

18	🚐	£7.00—£12.25
18	🚛	£7.00—£12.25
12	🏠	£142.00—£367.00

20 units not for hire
Open March–November
⚡P📶🅿🔥♨🚿♿🛒🛁📻⌀📻🔌☉🏔
⚓⛺🏍🎣♿◉

LAMPLUGH

Cumbria
Map ref 6A3

Near the A5086 between Cockermouth and Cleator Moor, Lamplugh is a scattered village famous for its "Lamplugh Pudding". Ideal touring base for the western Lake District.

Inglenook Caravan Park **M**
⊖✓✓✓
Member BH&HPA
Lamplugh, Workington CA14 4SH
☎ (01946) 861240
Leave A66 at Egremont sign, 5086 for 7 miles, turn left just past Lamplugh Tip public house, 0.5 miles on right. Signposted.
1.44 hectares (3.6 acres). Level, grassy, hard.

36 touring pitches

30	🚐	£7.50—£8.50
30	🚛	£7.50—£8.50
6	⛺	£6.50—£8.50
5	🏠	£130.00—£250.00

14 units not for hire
⚡P📶🅿🔥♨🚿♿🛒🛁✖💈📻☉🏔
🏍♿

MILNTHORPE

Cumbria
Map ref 6B3

Attractive limestone village with popular market. Good base for touring southern Cumbria and Morecambe Bay.

Fell End Caravan Park **M**
⊖✓✓✓✓✓
Slack Head Road, Hale, Milnthorpe
LA7 7BS
☎ (015395) 62122
Fax (015395) 63810
Exit M6 J35, A601 to J35A. Take A6 north (Milnthorpe) for 3.5 miles to Cumbria county border, then take first turn left signposted Arnside and 'sites'. The park is 0.75 mile. Look for Fell End signs. Signposted.
11.2 hectares (28 acres). Level, grassy, hard, sheltered.
106 touring pitches

94	🚐	£9.00—£12.00
94	🚛	£9.00—£12.00
12	⛺	£6.50—£11.00

218 units not for hire
Cards accepted: Access, Visa, Switch/Delta
⚡🔥📶🅿🔥♨🚿♿🛒🛁✖🍴📻⌀
🔌☉🏔⛵🎣♿

A key to symbols can be found inside the back cover flap.

The **M** symbol after an establishment name indicates that it is a Regional Tourist Board member.

PENRITH

Cumbria
Map ref 6B2

Ancient and historic market town, the northern gateway to the Lake District. Penrith Castle was built as a defence against the Scots. Its ruins, open to the public, stand in the public park. High above the town is the Penrith Beacon, made famous by William Wordsworth.
Tourist Information Centre ☎ *(01768) 867466*

Lowther Caravan Park
❸✓✓✓✓
Member BH&HPA
Elysian Fields, Eamont Bridge, Penrith CA10 2JB
☎ (01768) 63631
Fax (01768) 68126
From M6 J40 take A66 to Scotch Corner. At next roundabout take A6 south entrance to park 1 mile on right. Signposted.
20 hectares (50 acres). Level, sloping, grassy, hard, sheltered.
225 touring pitches

225	🚐	£9.00—£10.00
225	🚛	£9.00—£10.00
225	▲	£9.00—£10.00

397 units not for hire
Open March–November
Cards accepted: Access, Visa, Switch/Delta

POOLEY BRIDGE

Cumbria
Map ref 6A3

The bridge is on the northern tip of Lake Ullswater and spans the River Eamont where it emerges from the lake. Good centre for exploring, walking and sailing.

Waterside House Campsite ∧
❸✓✓✓✓
Waterside House, Howtown Road, Pooley Bridge, Penrith CA10 2NA
☎ (017684) 86332
M6 - Junction 40 - A66 follow signs for Ullwater - A592 to Pooley Bridge. 1 mile along Howtown Road on right. Signposted.

111.6 hectares (279 acres). Grassy.
90 touring pitches

| 90 | 🚛 | £6.00—£8.00 |
| 90 | ▲ | £6.50—£7.50 |

Open March–October

SILLOTH

Cumbria
Map ref 6A2

Small port and coastal resort on the Solway Firth with wide cobbled roads and an attractive green leading to the promenade and seashore known for its magnificent sunsets.
Tourist Information Centre ☎ *(016973) 31944*

Stanwix Park Holiday Centre ∧
❸✓✓✓✓ Rose Award
Member BH&HPA/NCC
Greenrow, West Silloth, Silloth, Carlisle CA5 4HH
☎ (016973) 31671
Fax (016973) 32555
From Silloth take B5300 west 0.5 miles. Site on right. Signposted.
7 hectares (17.5 acres). Level, grassy, sheltered.
121 touring pitches

121	🚐	£9.60—£12.60
121	🚛	£9.60—£12.60
121	▲	£9.60—£12.60
77	🏠	£135.00—£370.00

135 units not for hire
Open March–October
Cards accepted: Access, Visa, Switch/Delta

Tanglewood Caravan Park ∧
❸✓✓✓✓
Member BH&HPA
Causewayhead, Silloth CA5 4PE
☎ (016973) 31253
From Wigton B5302 W. for 13miles. Left onto Blackdyke Rd - 0.25yds. Signposted.
2.8 hectares (7 acres). Level, grassy, hard, sheltered.
31 touring pitches

21	🚐	£6.00—£6.00
21	🚛	£6.00—£6.00
10	▲	£6.00—£6.00
5	🏠	£120.00—£240.00

55 units not for hire
Open March–October

WATERMILLOCK

Cumbria
Map ref 6A3

Hamlet 2 miles along the lakeside of Ullswater from Pooley Bridge, with splendid elevated views of this most beautiful stretch of water.

Cove Caravan and Camping Park ∧
❸✓✓✓✓✓
Member BH&HPA
Ullswater, Watermillock, Penrith CA11 0LS
☎ Pooley Bridge (017684) 86549
M6 junction 40. Take A66 Keswick. A592 Ullswater, right at T junction. 1 mile turn right Brackenrigg Hotel. 1.50 miles on left. Signposted.
2 hectares (5 acres). Level, sloping, grassy, sheltered.
50 touring pitches

3	🚐	£8.00—£8.50
3	🚛	£6.40—£6.80
50	▲	£6.40—£6.80
1	🏠	£185.00—£220.00

38 units not for hire
Open March–October

WESTWARD

Cumbria
Map ref 6A2

Clea Hall Holiday Park ∧
❸✓✓✓✓✓
Member BH&HPA
Westward, Wigton CA7 8NQ
☎ Wigton (016973) 42880
M6 Junction 41 Wigton. Left at Goose Green Estates, right at second crossroads. Site is 2.5 miles on right. Signposted.
4 hectares (10 acres). Sloping.
16 touring pitches

16	⊿	£8.00—£12.00
16	⊞	£8.00—£12.00
16	Å	£8.00—£12.00
2	⊞	£80.00—£160.00

79 units not for hire
Open March–November

⚡P▣⊿⊡♠△♀⊙⚑♀TV◨◻
⚡⊙⚑⚑⟲♫♠
[Ad] See display advertisement on
page 54

WINDERMERE

Cumbria
Map ref 6A3

Once a tiny hamlet before the
introduction of the railway in 1847,
now adjoins Bowness which is on
the lakeside. Centre for sailing and
boating. A good way to see the lake
is a trip on a passenger steamer.
Steamboat Museum has a fine
collection of old boats.
Tourist Information Centre
☎ *(015394) 46499*

Park Cliffe Caravan & Camping Estate ⋀

⊖✓✓✓✓✓
Member BH&HPA
Birks Road, Windermere LA23 3PG
☎ Newby Bridge (015395) 31344
Fax (015395) 31971
Exit M6 J36, A590 towards Barrow. At
Newby Bridge turn right onto A592
towards Windermere, after 4 miles
turn right into Birks Road, 0.3 mile on
right. Signposted.
10 hectares (25 acres). Level, sloping,
grassy, hard, sheltered.
300 touring pitches

45	⊿	£10.00—£12.00
50	⊞	£8.50—£12.00
200	Å	£8.40—£11.20

50 units not for hire
Open March–October
Cards accepted: Access, Visa,
Switch/Delta

⚡⚡▣⊿♠△♀⊙⚑♀×♀◨◻⚡
⚑⊙⚑▶♠

White Cross Bay Caravan Park ⋀

⊖✓✓✓✓
Member BH&HPA/NCC
Ambleside Road, Troutbeck Bridge,
Windermere LA23 1LF
☎ (015394) 43937
Fax (015394) 88704
Situated on A591 between
Windermere and Ambleside.
Signposted.
28 hectares (70 acres). Level, sloping,
hard.
125 touring pitches

125	⊿	£12.00—£13.50
25	⊞	£12.00—£13.50
137	⊞	£140.00—£500.00

100 units not for hire
Open March–November
Cards accepted: Access, Visa, Diners,
Switch/Delta

⚡⚡P⊿⚑♠△♀⊙⚑♀×♀TV◨
◻⚡⚑⊙⚑⚑⟲⚸♠T

COUNTRY CODE

Always follow the Country Code 🌿 Enjoy the countryside and
respect its life and work 🌿 Guard against all risk of fire
🌿 Fasten all gates 🌿 Keep your dogs under close control
🌿 Keep to public paths across farmland 🌿 Use gates and
stiles to cross fences, hedges and walls 🌿 Leave livestock, crops
and machinery alone 🌿 Take your litter home 🌿 Help to keep
all water clean 🌿 Protect wildlife, plants and trees 🌿 Take
special care on country roads 🌿 Make no unnecessary noise

USE YOUR *i*'s

There are more than 550 Tourist Information Centres throughout England offering friendly help with accommodation and holiday ideas as well as suggestions of places to visit and things to do. There may well be a centre in your home town which can help you before you set out. You'll find the address of your nearest Tourist Information Centre in your local Phone Book.

AT-A-GLANCE SYMBOLS

Symbols at the end of each accommodation entry give useful information about services and facilities. A key to symbols can be found inside the back cover flap.

Keep this open for easy reference.

CHECK THE MAPS

The colour maps at the back of this guide show all the cities, towns and villages for which you will find accommodation entries.

Refer to the town index to find the page on which it is listed.

NORTHUMBRIA

Spectacular countryside awaits the visitor to Northumbria. The high Cheviots and the rugged Pennines leave an indelible impression while the majestic coastline offers sandy beaches, quaint fishing villages and surprisingly lively seaside resorts!

In contrast, Northumbria is also a region with vibrant industrial heritage, cosmopolitan cities and a long tradition of excellence in both the sporting and cultural arenas.

Soak up the history - don't miss Durham Cathedral - explore Catherine Cookson country and visit a traditional Northern pub. Or why not the Metro Centre, Europe's largest shopping city! Wherever you go, you'll be sure of a warm, northern welcome.

FOR MORE INFORMATION CONTACT:
Northumbria Tourist Board
Aykley Heads, Durham DH1 5UX
Tel: (0191) 375 3000 **Fax:** (0191) 386 0899

Where to Go in Northumbria - see pages 58-61
Where to Stay in Northumbria - see pages 62-63

NORTHUMBRIA

Where to Go and What to See

You will find hundreds of interesting places to visit during your stay in Northumbria, just some of which are listed in these pages. The number against each name will help you locate it on the map (page 61). Contact any Tourist Information Centre in the region for more ideas on days out in Northumbria.

1 Lindisfarne Castle
Holy Island,
Berwick-upon-Tweed
Northumberland TD15 2SH
Tel: (01289) 89244
Fort converted into a private home in 1903 for Edward Hudson by the architect Edwin Lutyens.

2 Farne Islands
Seahouses off Northumberland coast,
Northumberland
Tel: (01665) 720651
Bird reserve holding around 55,000 pairs of breeding birds of 21 species. Also home to a large colony of grey seals.

3 Bamburgh Castle
Bamburgh, Northumberland,
NE69 7DF
Tel: (01668) 214208
Magnificent coastal castle completely restored in 1900. Collections of china, porcelain, furniture, paintings, arms and armour.

4 Alnwick Castle
Alnwick,
Northumberland NE66 1NQ
Tel: (01665) 510777
Largest inhabited castle in England after Windsor Castle. Home of the Percys, Dukes of Northumberland since 1309.

5 Cragside House, Gardens and Grounds
Cragside, Rothbury,
Northumberland NE65 7PX
Tel: (01669) 620333
House built 1864-84 for the first Lord Armstrong, Tyneside Industrialist. The first house to be lit by electricity generated by water power.

6 Kielder Water Leaplish Waterside Park
Kielder,
Northumberland NE48 1BX
Tel: (01434) 240395
Largest man made lake in Western Europe. Water sports, fishing, log cabins and caravan site. Cycle hire, crazy golf and restaurant.

7 Wallington House Walled Garden and Grounds
Wallington, Cambo,
Northumberland NE61 4AR
Tel: (01670) 74283
Built 1688 on site of earlier medieval castle. Altered in 1740s. Interior has plasterwork, porcelain, furniture, pictures and needlework.

8 Morpeth Chantry Bagpipe Museum
The Chantry, Bridge Street,
Morpeth,
Northumberland NE61 1PJ
Tel: (01670) 519466
Set in a 13thC church building, this unusual museum specialises in the history and development of Northumbrian small pipes and their music.

9 Sea Life Centre
Grand Parade, Long Sands,
Tynemouth,
Tyne & Wear NE30 4JF
Tel: (0191) 257 6100
Journey beneath the North Sea and

discover thousands of amazing creatures. Over 30 hi-tech displays.

10 Wet 'N Wild
Rotary Way,
North Shields,
Tyne & Wear NE29 6DA
Tel: (0191) 296 1333
Tropical indoor waterpark. A fun water playground providing the UK's wildest and wettest indoor rapid experience.

11 Castle Keep
Saint Nicholas Street,
Castle Garth,
Newcastle upon Tyne NE1 1RQ
Tel: (0191) 232 7938
Built 1168-1178. One of the finest surviving examples of a Norman keep in the country. Panoramic views of the city from the roof. Small museum within keep.

12 Bede's World
Church Bank,
Jarrow,
Tyne & Wear NE32 3DY
Tel: (0191) 489 2106
New museum opened May 1995. Late 18thC hall, excavated finds from Anglo-Saxon and medieval monastery of St Pauls Jarrow nearby. Anglo-Saxon farm with rare breeds.

13 Metroland
Gateshead,
Tyne & Wear NE11 9YZ
Tel: (0191) 493 2048
Europe's only indooor theme park within a large shopping complex. Rollercoaster, dodgems, swinging chairs, pirate ship plus live entertainment.

14 Housesteads Roman Fort
Hadrian's Wall,
Northumberland NE47 6NN
Tel: (01434) 344363
Best preserved and most impressive of the Roman forts. Vercovicium was a 5-acre fort for extensive civil settlement. Only example of a Roman hospital.

15 Wildfowl & Wetlands Trust
Washington,
Tyne & Wear NE38 8LE
Tel: (0191) 416 5454
Collection of 1,250 wildfowl of 108 varieties. Viewing gallery, picnic areas, hides and winter wild bird feeding station. Flamingos, wild grey heron. Food available.

16 Beamish – The North of England Open Air Museum
Beamish, Co Durham DH9 0RG
Tel: (01207) 231811
Visit a town, colliery village, farm

and railway station recreated to show life in the North of England early this century. Pockerley Manor illustrates life in the early 1800s.

17 Durham Castle
Palace Green,
Durham DH1 3RW
Tel: (0191) 374 3863
Fine Bailey castle founded in 1072, Norman chapel dating from 1080. Kitchens and great hall dated 1499 and 1284 respectively.

18 Durham Cathedral
Durham DH1 3EH
Tel: (0191) 386 4266
Widely considered to be the finest example of Norman church architecture in England. Has the tombs of St Cuthbert and The Venerable Bede.

19 Killhope Leadmining Centre
Cowshill,
St John's Chapel,
Co Durham DL13 1AR
Tel: (01388) 537505
Most complete lead mining site in Great Britain. Includes crushing mill with 34ft water wheel, reconstruction of Victorian machinery and miners accommodation.

20 High Force Waterfall
Forest-in-Teesdale,
Middleton-in-Teesdale,
Co Durham DL12
Tel: (01833) 640209
High Force is the most majestic of the waterfalls on the River Tees. The falls are only a short walk from a bus stop, car park and picnic area.

21 Raby Castle
Staindrop,
Co Durham DL2 3AH
Tel: (01833) 660202
Medieval castle in 200-acre park. 600-year-old kitchen and carriage collection. Walled gardens and deer park. Home of Lord Barnard's family for over 350 years.

22 Butterfly World
Preston Park, Yarm Road,
Stockton-on-Tees,
Tees Valley TS18 3RH
Tel: (01642) 791414
An indoor tropical garden populated by exotic free-flying butterflies and complemented by a display of fascinating insects and reptiles.

23 Preston Hall Museum
Yarm Road, Stockton-on-Tees,
Tees Valley TS18 3RH
Tel: (01642) 781184
A Georgian country house set in a park which is a museum of Victoriana. Return to a bygone age, stroll along a high street, explore 100 acres of parkland overlooking the Tees.

24 Captain Cook Birthplace Museum
Stewart Park,
Marton,
Middlesbrough,
Tees Valley TS7 6AS
Tel: (01642) 311211
Early life and voyages of Captain Cook and the countries he visited. Temporary exhibitions.

25 Ormesby Hall
Church Lane,
Ormesby,
Middlesbrough,
Tees Valley TS7 9AS
Tel: (01642) 324188
18thC Palladian mansion with impressive contemporary plasterwork. Magnificent stableblock attributed to Carr of York. Model railway exhibition and children's play area.

26 Hartlepool Historic Quay
Maritime Avenue,
Hartlepool,
Tees Valley TS24 0XZ
Tel: (01429) 860006
An exciting reconstruction of a seaport of the 1800s with buildings and lively quayside.

27 Saltburn Smugglers Heritage Centre
Ship Inn, Saltburn-by-the-Sea,
Tees Valley TS12 1HF
Tel: (01287) 625252
Experience the authentic sights, sounds and smells of Saltburn's smuggling heritage. Listen to tales of John Andrew, "King of the Smugglers".

FIND OUT MORE
Further information about holidays and attractions in Northumbria is available from:
Northumbria Tourist Board,
Aykley Heads,
Durham DH1 5UX.
Tel: (0191) 375 3000

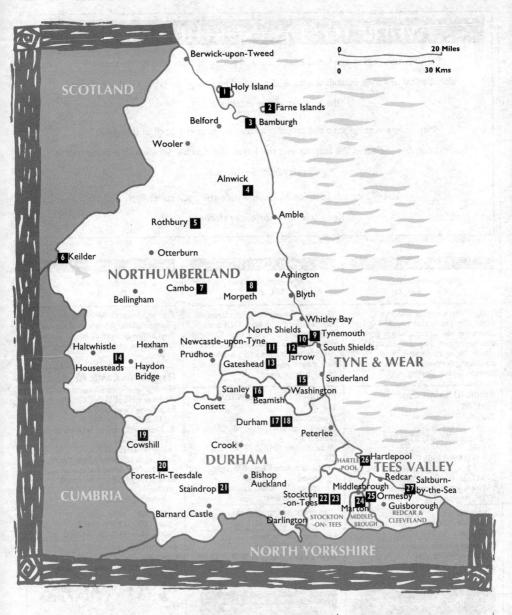

Berwick-upon-Tweed

SCOTLAND

Holy Island
1

2 Farne Islands

Belford

3 Bamburgh

Wooler

Alnwick
4

Amble

Rothbury **5**

Otterburn

6 Keilder

NORTHUMBERLAND

Cambo **7**

Bellingham

8

Morpeth

Ashington

Blyth

Whitley Bay

North Shields

Newcastle-upon-Tyne

Tynemouth **9**

10

11 **12**

South Shields

Haltwhistle

Hexham

Prudhoe

14

Housesteads

Haydon Bridge

Gateshead **13**

Jarrow

TYNE & WEAR

Sunderland

Stanley **16**

Washington **15**

Consett

Beamish

Durham **17** **18**

Peterlee

19

Cowshill

Crook

DURHAM

HARTLE-
POOL **26** Hartlepool

TEES VALLEY

20

Forest-in-Teesdale

Bishop Auckland

Redcar

Saltburn-
by-the-Sea

Staindrop **21**

Middlesbrough

27 Ormesby

Stockton
-on-Tees **22** **23**

Guisborough

CUMBRIA

24 **25**

Marton

REDCAR & CLEEVELAND

Barnard Castle

Darlington

STOCKTON
-ON- TEES

MIDDLES
BROUGH

NORTH YORKSHIRE

0   20 Miles

0   30 Kms

These publications are available free from the Northumbria Tourist Board:
■ **Northumbria Breaks 1997**
■ **Bed & Breakfast Map - Northumbria and Cumbria**
■ **Great Days Out - regional attraction guide**

■ **Freedom Caravan and Camping Guide - Northumbria, Yorkshire, East Riding, Cumbria and North West**
■ **Schools Out - educational brochure**

Also available are (prices include postage and packaging):
■ **Northumbria Touring Map and Guide** £4.75
■ **Leisure Guide to Northumbria** £10.99
■ **Walk Northumbria** £6.

61

WHERE TO STAY (NORTHUMBRIA)

Parks in this region are listed in alphabetical order of place name, and then in alphabetical order of establishment. A contact address is given where it differs from the address of the establishment.

Map references refer to the colour location maps at the back of this guide.

The first number indicates the map to use; the letter and number which follow refer to the grid reference on the map.

At-a-glance symbols can be found inside the back cover flap.

Keep this open for easy reference.

BAMBURGH

Northumberland
Map ref 6C1

Village with a spectacular red sandstone castle standing 150 ft above the sea. On the village green the magnificent Norman church stands opposite a museum containing mementoes of the heroine Grace Darling.

Bradford Kaims Caravan Park ⚠
⊖✓✓✓
Bamburgh NE70 7JT
☎ Belford (01668) 213432 & 213595
Fax (01668) 213891
Take A1 N. Turn right to Lucker & take B1341 for 1m. Signposted.
16 hectares (40 acres). Sheltered.
80 touring pitches

80	🚐	£6.50—£7.50
80	🚚	£6.50—£7.50
80	⛺	£6.50—£7.50

270 units not for hire
Open April–October

BEADNELL

Northumberland
Map ref 6C1

Charming fishing village on Beadnell Bay. Seashore lime kilns (National Trust), dating from the 18th C, recall busier days as a coal and lime port and a pub is built on to a medieval pele tower which survives from days of the border wars.

Beadnell Links Caravan Park
⊖✓✓✓
Member BH&HPA
Beadnell Harbour, Beadnell, Chathill NE67 5BN
☎ Seahouses (01665) 720993 & 720526
B1340 to Beadnell signed thereon. Signposted.
4 hectares (10 acres). Level, grassy.
16 touring pitches

16	🚐	£7.50—£10.50
16	🚚	£7.50—£10.50

150 units not for hire
Open April–October

BEAL

Northumberland
Map ref 6B1

Tiny hamlet with an inn at the junction of the A1 which leads on to the causeway to Holy Island. Some farmhouses and buildings are dated 1674.

Haggerston Castle ⚠
⊖✓✓✓✓✓ Rose Award
Member BH&HPA/NCC
Beal, Berwick-upon-Tweed TD15 2PA
☎ Reservations/free brochure (01442) 248668
Fax (01442) 232459
The park is signposted from the A1, 7 miles south of Berwick-upon-Tweed.
88 hectares (220 acres). Level, grassy.
159 touring pitches

159	🚐	£7.20—£19.50
159	🚚	£7.20—£19.50
400	⛺	£120.00—£499.00

540 units not for hire
Open March–October
Cards accepted: Access, Visa, Switch/Delta

🆂 See display advertisement inside front cover

BERWICK-UPON-TWEED

Northumberland
Map ref 6B1

Guarding the mouth of the Tweed, England's northernmost town with the best 16th C city walls in Europe. The handsome Guildhall and barracks date from the 18th C. Three bridges cross to Tweedmouth, the oldest built in 1634.
Tourist Information Centre ☎ (01289) 330733

Beachcomber House Camping Site
❸✓✓✓✓
Beachcomber House, Goswick Sands, Berwick-upon-Tweed TD15 2RW
☎ (01289) 381217
Turn off A1 at Cat Inn site signposted from A1 north and south. Follow signs over railway line through golf club to end of track. Approx 3 miles off A1. Signposted.
1.6 hectares (4 acres). Level, sloping, grassy.
50 touring pitches

5	🚐	£8.50—£8.50
45	🚛	£8.50—£8.50
45	⛺	£8.50—£8.50

Open April–September
🚗🅿️🏕️🔔♨️🔌☕🔋✕🍴🍳📱🛢️❌☺️🔍
🏔️∪🔍📶♿

Berwick Holiday Centre ♈
❸✓✓✓
Member BH&HPA/NCC
Magdalene Fields,
Berwick-upon-Tweed TD15 1NE
☎ Reservations/free brochure
(01442) 248668
Fax (01442) 232459
Berwick is signposted from the A1 both north and south and you will find signs directing you to Berwick Holiday Centre in the town.
20 hectares (50 acres). Level, grassy.
35 touring pitches

35	🚐	£8.00—£18.00
35	🚛	£8.00—£18.00
350	🏠	£100.00—£425.00

446 units not for hire
Open March–November
Cards accepted: Access, Visa, Switch/Delta
🚗🅿️🏕️🔔♨️🔌☕🔋✕🍴📺📱🛢️
🔌☺️🔍🏔️🚲🎣📶♿🅣🔌
Ad See display advertisement inside front cover

Ord House Caravan Park ♈
❸✓✓✓✓✓
Member NCC
East Ord, Berwick-upon-Tweed TD15 2NS
☎ (01289) 305288
Fax (01289) 330832
Turn off A1 Berwick by-pass signed East Ord. Follow caravan sign. Signposted.
16.4 hectares (41 acres). Level, sloping, grassy, sheltered.
70 touring pitches

70	🚐	£7.00—£11.50
36	🚛	£7.00—£11.50

200 units not for hire
Open March–December
Cards accepted: Access, Visa
🏕️🔔🏕️🔔♨️🔌☕✕🍴📱🛢️🔌🛢️☺️
🔍🏔️🍳📶♿☺️

CASTLESIDE

Durham
Map ref 6B2

Village on the edge of the North Pennines on the A68, one of the main routes from England to Scotland.

Manor Park Caravan Park ♈
❸✓✓✓✓
Broadmeadows, Rippon Burn, Castleside, Consett, County Durham DH8 9HD
☎ Consett (01207) 501000
Fax (01207) 582947
Signposted from A68, 2.5 m. S. Castleside.
2.8 hectares (7 acres). Sloping, grassy, sheltered.
30 touring pitches

30	🚐	£5.50—£6.50
7	🚛	£5.50—£6.50
5	⛺	£5.50—£6.50

10 units not for hire
Open April–October
🚗🚐🏕️🔔♨️🔌☕🔋📱🔌🛢️☺️∪🔍
♿

For ideas on places to visit refer to the introduction at the beginning of this section.

The ♈ symbol after an establishment name indicates that it is a Regional Tourist Board member.

GREENHEAD

Northumberland
map ref 6B2

Small hamlet, overlooked by the ruins of Thirlwall Castle, at the junction of the A69 and the B6318 which runs alongside Hadrian's Wall. Some of the finest sections of the wall and the Carvoran Roman Military Museum are nearby.

Roam-n-Rest Caravan Park ♈
❸✓✓✓✓
Raylton House, Greenhead CA6 7HA
☎ Gilsland (016977) 47213
Leave A69 at Greenhead junction and follow short link road, turn direct left up short hill 250 metres park on right. Signposted.
0.4 hectares (1 acres). Level, grassy, sheltered.
15 touring pitches

15	🚐	£7.00—£7.50
15	🚛	£7.00—£7.50
15	⛺	£7.00—£7.50
1	🏠	

3 units not for hire
Open March–October
🚗🅿️🏕️🏕️🔔♨️🔌☕🔋☺️🏔️▶️♿

HEXHAM

Northumberland
Map ref 6B2

Old coaching and market town near Hadrian's Wall. Since pre-Norman times a weekly market has been held in the centre with its market-place and abbey park, and the richly-furnished 12th C abbey church has a superb Anglo-Saxon crypt.
Tourist Information Centre ☎ (01434) 605225

Causey Hill Caravan Park ♈
❸✓✓✓
Member BH&HPA
Causey Hill, Hexham NE46 2JN
☎ (01434) 602834 & 604647
Hexham B430 N to Blanchland 1.5m turn R onto Racecourse Rd at Causey Hill. Signposted.
2.8 hectares (7 acres). Sloping, grassy, hard, sheltered.
38 touring pitches

30	🚐	£7.50—£10.00
30	🚛	
8	⛺	£6.00—£8.00

68 units not for hire
Open April–October
🏕️🔔🏕️🔔♨️🔌☕📱🛢️🔌🛢️❌🔍♿

HEXHAM

Continued

Riverside Leisure ♠
☻✓✓✓✓✓ Rose Award
Tyne Green, Hexham NE46 3RY
☎ (01434) 604705
Take A6079 off A69 to Hexham. Follow road to "Haugh Lane" park clearly signposted at crossroads.
2.2 hectares (5.5 acres). Level, grassy, hard, sheltered.
30 touring pitches

30	⛟	£11.00—£12.00
30	🚐	£11.00—£12.00
30	⛺	£10.00—£11.00
6	🏠	£135.00—£300.00

100 units not for hire
Open January, March–December

KIELDER

Northumberland
Map ref 6B1

Wide area of forest established earlier this century on moors edging the North Tyne. Kielder village is overlooked by Kielder Castle, a former hunting lodge now a visitor centre. Forest and lake provide a wide variety of recreations which include boating, fishing and camping.

Kielder Camp Site
☻✓✓✓✓
Member BH&HPA
Kielder, Hexham NE48 2AJ
☎ Hexham (01434) 250291
Follow C200 from Bellingham, past Kielder Water. Campsite lies to north of Kielder village. Signposted.
Level, grassy, hard, sheltered.
70 touring pitches

50	⛟	£7.00—£10.00
50	🚐	£7.00—£10.00
20	⛺	£3.50—£10.00

Open April–September
Cards accepted: Access, Visa

ROWLANDS GILL

Tyne and Wear
Map ref 6C2

Adjacent to the Derwent Walk Country Park on the side of the River Derwent, opposite the National Trust Gibside Chapel.

Derwent Park Camping & Caravan Site ♠
☻✓✓✓✓
Rowlands Gill NE39 1LG
☎ (01207) 543383
Fax (01207) 543383
Leave A1 either carriageway at exit A694 Consett. Follow A694 for 3.5 miles site junction A694/B6314 in Rowlands Gill Signposted.
1.6 hectares (4 acres). Level, grassy.
47 touring pitches

35	⛟	£8.00—£9.25
35	🚐	£6.75—£8.00
12	⛺	£5.50—£7.50

25 units not for hire
Open April–September

SEAHOUSES

Northumberland
Map ref 6C1

Small modern resort developed around a 19th C herring port. Just offshore, and reached by boat from here, are the rocky Farne Islands (National Trust) where there is an important bird reserve. The bird observatory occupies a medieval pele tower.

Seafield Caravan Park
☻✓✓✓✓ Rose Award
Seafield Road, Seahouses NE68 7SP
☎ Alnwick (01665) 720628
Fax (01665) 720088
B1340 from Alnwick 14m. East to coast. Signposted.
8 hectares (20 acres). Level, grassy.
22 touring pitches

22	⛟	£7.00—£13.00
22	🚐	£7.00—£13.00
5	🏠	£95.00—£440.00

202 units not for hire
Open March–December

WAREN MILL

Northumberland
Map ref 6C1

On Budle Bay just north of Bamburgh, in a designated area of outstanding natural beauty. This area is a favourite place for bird-watchers.

Waren Caravan Park ♠
☻✓✓✓✓✓ Rose Award
Member BH&HPA/NCC
Waren Mill, Belford NE70 7EE
☎ Bamburgh (01668) 214366
Fax (01668) 214224
From A1, turn off at Belford onto B1342 for 3 miles (sign- posted). Signposted.
12 hectares (30 acres). Level, sloping, grassy, sheltered.
180 touring pitches

180	⛟	£7.50—£11.00
180	🚐	£7.50—£11.00
180	⛺	£7.50—£11.00
15	🏠	£110.00—£380.00

285 units not for hire
Open April–October
Cards accepted: Access, Visa, Switch/Delta

[Ad] See display advertisement on this page

NORTH WEST

The legacy of the Industrial Revolution can be seen in the North West's fine Victorian architecture, magnificent mill buildings and miles of canals - once used for transportation but today, navigated for pleasure.

Manchester and Liverpool are vibrant centres of popular and 'high' culture while stylish Lytham St Anne's, Southport or glittering Blackpool are among Britain's most famous coastal resorts.

Explore elegant Chester, the historic city of Lancaster or, in total contrast, the pretty villages of the Wirral and the unspoilt border country of Cheshire. From birdlife to nightlife, markets to music festivals, the North West has it all.

FOR MORE INFORMATION CONTACT:
North West Tourist Board
Swan House, Swan Meadow Road,
Wigan Pier, Wigan WN3 5BB
Tel: (01942) 821222 **Fax:** (01942) 820002

Where to Go in the North West -
see pages 66-69
Where to Stay in the North West -
see pages 70-72

NORTH WEST

Where to Go and What to See

You will find hundreds of interesting places to visit during your stay in the North West, just some of which are listed in these pages. The number against each name will help you locate it on the map (page 69). Contact any Tourist Information Centre in the region for more ideas on days out in the North West.

1 Frontierland Western Theme Park
Marine Road, Morecambe,
Lancashire LA4 4DG
Tel: (01524) 410024
Over 40 thrill rides and attractions including the Texas Tornado, the Polo Tower Perculator and Stampede Roller Coaster.

2 Lancaster Castle
Shire Hall, Castle Parade,
Lancaster, Lancashire
Tel: (01524) 64998
Collection of coats of arms, dungeons, crown court, Jane Scott's chair. Grand Jury Room. External tour of castle walls.

3 Blackpool Pleasure Beach
Ocean Boulevard,
Blackpool, Lancashire FY4 1EZ
Tel: (01253) 341033
Amusement park with rides including Space Invader, Big Dipper and Revolution. Funshineland for children. Summer season ice show, Mystique illusion show in Horseshoe Bar.

4 Blackpool Sea Life Centre
The Promenade,
Blackpool,
Lancashire FY1 5AA
Tel: (01253) 22445
Tropical sharks up to 8 feet in length housed in a 100,000 gallon display with underwater walk-through.

5 Blackpool Tower
Promenade,
Blackpool,
Lancashire FY1 4BJ
Tel: (01253) 22242
Tower Ballroom, Bug World, Jungle Jim's playground. Out of this World. Children's entertainment in Hornpipe Galley, Undersea World. Tower Circus, Laser fantasy and Lift Ride.

6 Ribchester Museum of Childhood
Church Street,
Ribchester,
Lancashire PR3 3YE
Tel: (01254) 878520
Large 10-room building contaning childhood toys, dolls and dolls' houses, 20-piece model fairground, Tom Thumb replica, collectors' toy shop.

7 Pleasureland Amusement Park
Marine Drive,
The Fun Coast,
Southport,
Merseyside PR8 1RX
Tel: (01704) 532717
Traditional amusement park with wide variety of thrilling and family rides.

8 Astley Hall
Astley Park,
Chorley,
Lancashire PR7 1NP
Tel: (01257) 262166
Hall dates from 1580 with subsequent additions. Unique collection of furniture including a fine Elizabethan bed and the famous shovel board table in the Long Gallery.

9 Camelot Theme Park and Rare Breeds Farm
Park Hall Road, Charnock Richard,
Lancashire PR7 5LP
Tel: (01257) 453044
Magical kingdom offering over 100 thrilling rides, attractions and medieval entertainment.

10 Wildfowl and Wetland Centre
Martin Mere, Burscough,
Lancashire L40 0TA
Tel: (01704) 895181
45 acres of gardens with over 1600 ducks geese and swans of 120 different kinds. Two flocks of flamingos. 300-acre wild area with 20-acre lake.

11 East Lancashire Railway
Bolton Street Station,
Bury, Lancashire BL9 0EY
Tel: (0161) 764 7790
Eight-mile-long preserved railway operated principally by steam traction, transport museum nearby.

12 Rufford Old Hall
Rufford, Ormskirk,
Lancashire L40 1SG
Tel: (01704) 821254
Fine 15thC building with a magnificent Great Hall, particularly noted for its immense moveable screen.

13 Wigan Pier
Wallgate, Wigan,
Lancashire WN3 4EU
Tel: (01942) 323666
The Way We Were – life in Wigan in 1900. World's largest steam mill engine, cotton machinery hall, shops, picnic gardens, cafeteria, waterbuses and Victorian classroom.

14 Granada Studios Tour
Water Street, Manchester,
Greater Manchester M60 9EA
Tel: (0161) 832 9090
Major television theme park providing an insight into the fascinating world behind the TV screen. Visit three of the most famous streets in Britain.

15 Museum of Science and Industry in Manchester
Liverpool Road, Castlefield,
Manchester,
Greater Manchester M3 4JP
Tel: (0161) 832 2244
The Museum of Science and Industry in Manchester based in the world's oldest passenger railway station, with 15 galleries that amaze, amuse and entertain.

16 Knowsley Safari Park
Prescot,
Merseyside L34 4AN
Tel: (0151) 430 9009
Five-mile drive through game reserves, set in 400 acres of parkland containing lions, tigers, elephants, rhinos, etc. Large picnic areas and children's amusement park.

17 Albert Dock
The Colonnades,
Albert Dock,
Liverpool, L3 4AA
Tel: (0151) 708 8854
Britain's largest Grade I listed historic building. Restored 4-sided dock, including shops, bars, restaurants, entertainment, marina and maritime museum.

18 Croxteth Hall and Country Park
Off Muirhead Avenue East,
Liverpool,
Merseyside L12 0HB
Tel: (0151) 228 5311
500 acre country park and hall with displays, furnished rooms and walled garden. Farm with rare breeds, miniature railway, gift shop, picnic area, riding centre, adventure playground.

19 Tate Gallery Liverpool
Albert Dock, Liverpool L3 4BB
Tel: (0151) 709 3223
The national collection of modern art in the North of England.

20 **Dunham Massey Hall and Park**
Altrincham, Cheshire WA14 4SJ
Tel: (0161) 941 1025
Historic house, garden and park with restaurant and shop.

21 **Lyme Park**
Disley, Cheshire SK12 2NX
Tel: (01663) 762023
Country estate within 1377 acres of moorland, woodland and park. Magnificent house with 17 acres of historic gardens.

22 **Quarry Bank Mill**
Styal, Cheshire SK9 4LA
Tel: (01625) 527468
Georgian water-powered cotton-spinning mill. Four floors of displays and demonstrations, 284 acres of parkland.

23 **Norton Priory Museum and Gardens**
Tudor Road, Runcorn,
Cheshire WA7 1SX
Tel: (01928) 569895
Excavated Augustinian priory, remains of church, cloister and chapter house. Later site of Tudor

mansion and Georgian house. Walled garden and woodland.

24 **Boat Museum**
Dock Yard Road, Ellesmere Port,
Cheshire L65 4FW
Tel: (0151) 355 5017
Over 50 historic craft, largest floating collection in the world with restored buildings, traditional cottages, workshops, steam engines, boat trips, shop and cafe.

25 **Arley Hall and Gardens**
Arley, Northwich,
Cheshire CW9 6NA
Tel: (01565) 777353
Early Victorian building set in 12 acres of magnificent gardens. 15thC Tythe barn. Unique collection of water colours of the area.

26 **Macclesfield Silk Museum**
The Heritage Centre,
Roe Street, Macclesfield,
Cheshire SK11 6UT
Tel: (01625) 613210
Information centre, town history exhibition, silk museum, Sunday school, history exhibition, guided trails.

27 **Jodrell Bank Science Centre and Arboretum**
Lower Withington,
Macclesfield, Cheshire SK11 9DL
Tel: (01477) 571339
Exhibition and interactive exhibits on astronomy, space, satellites, energy and the environment. Planetarium and the world-famous Lovell telescope and 35 acre arboretum.

28 **Cheshire Oaks Designer Outlet Village**
Ellesmere Port,
The Wirral L65 9JJ
Over 60 individual stores selling famous branded goods.

29 **Chester Zoo**
Upton-by-Chester,
Chester, Cheshire CH2 1LH
Tel: (01244) 380280
Penguin pool with underwater views, tropical house, spectacular displays of spring and summer bedding plants. Chimpanzee house and new monorail.

FIND OUT MORE

Further information about holidays and attractions in the North West is available from:
North West Tourist Board,
Swan House,
Swan Meadow Road,
Wigan Pier,
Wigan WN3 5BB.
Tel: (01942) 821222

These publications are available free from the North West Tourist Board:
■ **North West Welcome Guide**
■ **Discover England's North West**
■ **Attraction Map**
■ **Group Travel Guide**
■ **Bed & Breakfast Map**
■ **Caravan and Camping Parks Guide**

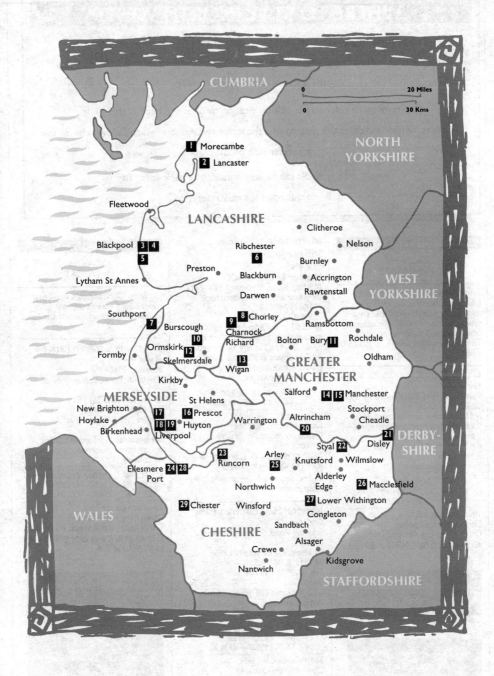

CUMBRIA

20 Miles
30 Kms

NORTH YORKSHIRE

1 Morecambe
2 Lancaster

Fleetwood

LANCASHIRE

Clitheroe
Nelson

Blackpool **3** **4**
5

Ribchester
6

Burnley
Accrington
Rawtenstall

WEST YORKSHIRE

Lytham St Annes

Preston
Blackburn
Darwen

Southport

8 Chorley
9
Charnock Richard

Ramsbottom

Burscough
10
Ormskirk **12**
Skelmersdale

Bolton   Bury **11**   Rochdale

7

Formby

13
Wigan

GREATER MANCHESTER

Oldham

Kirkby

MERSEYSIDE

Salford **14** **15** Manchester

New Brighton
Hoylake
Birkenhead

St Helens
17 **16** Prescot
18 **19** Huyton
Liverpool

Warrington

Altrincham
20

Stockport
Cheadle

21
Disley

DERBY-SHIRE

23
Runcorn

Styal **22**

Wilmslow

Ellesmere Port **24** **28**

Arley
25

Knutsford

WALES

29 Chester

Northwich

Winsford

Alderley Edge
26 Macclesfield

27 Lower Withington
Congleton

CHESHIRE

Sandbach
Alsager

Crewe

Kidsgrove

Nantwich

STAFFORDSHIRE

WHERE TO STAY (NORTH WEST)

Parks in this region are listed in alphabetical order of place name, and then in
alphabetical order of establishment. A contact address is given where it differs from
the address of the establishment.

Map references refer to the colour location maps at the back of this guide.

The first number indicates the map to use; the letter and number which follow refer to the
grid reference on the map.

At-a-glance symbols can be found inside the back cover flap.

Keep this open for easy reference.

BLACKPOOL

Lancashire
Map ref 5A1

Britain's largest fun resort, with
Blackpool Pleasure Beach, 3 piers
and the famous Tower. Host to the
spectacular autumn illuminations -
"the greatest free show on earth".
Tourist Information Centre ☎ *(01253)
21623*

Gillett Farm Caravan Park Ltd
☻✓✓✓✓
Peel Road, Peel, Blackpool FY4 5JU
☎ (01253) 761676
*M55 Junction 4 turn left onto A583.
0.25 mile turn right and immediate left
into Peel Road. Signposted.*
4.4 hectares (11 acres). Sloping,
grassy, hard.
76 touring pitches

46	🚐	£8.00—£11.50
6	🚎	£8.00—£11.50
30	⛺	£5.00—£12.00

100 units not for hire
Open March–October
Cards accepted: Access, Visa

Please check prices and other
details at the time of booking.

A key to symbols can be
found inside the back
cover flap.

Marton Mere Holiday Village ⚠
☻✓✓✓
Member BH&HPA/NCC
Mythop Road, Blackpool FY4 4XN
☎ Reservations/free brochure
(01442) 248668
Fax (01442) 232459
*J4 A583 to Blackpool. turn right at
second set of traffic lights. Park is 150
yards down on the left. Signposted.*
37.2 hectares (93 acres). Level,
grassy, stony, hard.
422 touring pitches

422	🚐	£7.15—£18.00
150	🚐	£153.00—£555.00

912 units not for hire
Open March–October
Cards accepted: Access, Visa,
Switch/Delta

[Ad] See display advertisement inside
front cover

Newton Hall Caravan Park
☻✓✓✓✓
Staining Road, Staining, Blackpool
FY3 0AX
☎ Poulton-Le-Fylde (01253)
882512 & 885465
Fax (01253) 893101
Signposted.
11.2 hectares (28 acres). Level,
sloping, grassy.
33 touring pitches

33	🚐	£8.00—£13.00
33	🚎	£8.00—£12.00
64	🚐	£105.00—£330.00

361 units not for hire
Open March–October

CABUS

Lancashire
Map ref 5A1

Close to Garstang, this small market
town offers easy access to
Lancaster, Morecambe and the Lake
District.

Claylands Caravan Park ⚠
☻✓✓✓✓
Member BH&HPA
Claylands Farm, Cabus, Preston
PR3 1AJ
☎ Forton (01524) 791242
Fax (01524) 792406
*2 miles North Garstang off A6
Signposted.*
5.4 hectares (13.5 acres). Level,
grassy, hard, sheltered.
64 touring pitches

64	🚐	£10.00—£12.00
32	🚎	£10.00—£12.00
32	⛺	£10.00—£12.00

22 units not for hire
Open March–December
Cards accepted: Access, Visa

The map references refer
to the colour maps towards
the end of the guide.
The first figure is the
map number; the letter and
figure which follow indicate
the grid reference
on the map.

CLEVELEYS

Lancashire
Map ref 5A1

Popular holiday resort on the Fylde coast close to Blackpool, with pleasant promenade, sandy beaches and shopping area. Close by, at Thornton, is a historic Marsh Windmill.
Tourist Information Centre ☎ (01253) 853378

Kneps Farm Holiday Park ⚐
☺✓✓✓✓✓
Member NCC
River Road, Cleveleys, Blackpool FY5 5LR
☎ (01253) 823632
Fax (01253) 863967
Leave A585 at roundabout (B5412) Little Thornton. Turn right at St John's Church into Stanah Road leading to River Road. Signposted.
4 hectares (10 acres). Level, grassy, stony, hard, sheltered.
72 touring pitches

62	🚐	£7.75—£10.25
58	🚏	£7.75—£10.25
10	▲	£7.75—£10.25

93 units not for hire
Open March–October
Cards accepted: Access, Visa, Diners, Amex, Switch/Delta

FLEETWOOD

Lancashire
Map ref 5A1

Major fishing port and resort bounded by the sea on 3 sides. Fine sands, bathing and large model-yacht pond. Good views across Morecambe Bay and peaks of Lake District.
Tourist Information Centre ☎ (01253) 773953

Cala Gran ⚐
☺✓✓✓✓
Member BH&HPA/NCC
Fleetwood Road, Fleetwood FY7 8JY
☎ Reservations/free brochure (01442) 248668
Fax (01442) 232459
J3 M55. Follow A585 to Fleetwood. At fourth roundabout take third turning. Park is 500yds down on the left. Signposted.
17.6 hectares (44 acres). Level, grassy.

240	🛏	£120.00—£450.00

600 units not for hire
Open March–October, December

Cards accepted: Access, Visa, Switch/Delta

Ad See display advertisement inside front cover

LITTLEBOROUGH

Greater Manchester
Map ref 5B1

Attractive small town on the edge of the South Pennine Moors, with many historic buildings and industrial heritage features. Attractions include Hollingworth Lake, the Rochdale Canal and access to the Pennine Way.

Hollingworth Lake Caravan Park ⚐
☺✓✓✓
Member BH&HPA
Round House Farm, Rakewood, Littleborough, Lancashire OL15 0AT
☎ Rochdale (01706) 378661
M62 exit 21, Milnrow/Rochdale A640, turn left onto B6225 then left into Kiln Lane. Follow Hollingworth Lake Country Park signs. Signposted.
2 hectares (5 acres). Level, sloping, grassy, hard, sheltered.
45 touring pitches

25	🚐	£6.00—£7.00
10	🚏	£5.00—£7.00
10	▲	£4.50—£7.00

25 units not for hire
Cards accepted: Visa

LYTHAM ST ANNES

Lancashire
Map ref 5A1

Pleasant resort famous for its championship golf-courses, notably the Royal Lytham and St Annes. Fine sands and attractive gardens. Some half-timbered buildings and an old windmill recently restored.
Tourist Information Centre ☎ (01253) 725610

Eastham Hall Caravan Park ⚐
☺✓✓✓
Member BH&HPA
Saltcoates Road, Lytham St Annes FY8 4LS
☎ St Annes (01253) 737907
From Preston on A584 turn right onto B5259, site 0.75 miles right. Signposted.
10 hectares (25 acres). Level, grassy, hard.
250 touring pitches

250	🚏	£8.50—£9.50

180 units not for hire
Open March–October

MORECAMBE

Lancashire
Map ref 6A3

Famous for its shrimps, Morecambe is a traditional resort on a wide bay with spacious beaches, entertainments and seafront illuminations. Bubbles Leisure Park, Frontierland and various attractions nearby. Stunning views across the bay.
Tourist Information Centre ☎ (01524) 582808 or 582809

Regent Leisure Park ⚐
☺✓✓✓✓✓ Rose Award
Member NCC
Westgate, Morecambe LA3 3DF
☎ (01524) 413940
Fax (01524) 832247
Leave M6 junction 34. A683 for 1.5 miles, take A589 to Morecambe, turn left at third roundabout, park 1.5 miles on left. Signposted.
6 hectares (15 acres). Level, grassy, stony, hard, sheltered.
23 touring pitches

23	🚐	£9.00—£14.00
23	🚏	£9.00—£14.00
51	🛏	£100.00—£365.00

200 units not for hire
Open January, March–December

RIMINGTON

Lancashire
Map ref 5B1

Rimington Caravan Park ⚐
☺✓✓✓✓
Hardcacre Lane, Rimington, Clitheroe BB7 4DS
☎ Clitheroe (01200) 445355
From Gisburn take A682 S, Rt. after .75m at 1st junction. Signposted.
4.8 hectares (12 acres). Level, grassy, hard.
20 touring pitches

20	🚏	£7.00—£8.50

150 units not for hire
Open March–October

Please mention this guide when making your booking.

71

ROCHDALE

Greater Manchester
Map ref 5B1

Pennine mill town made prosperous by wool and later cotton-spinning, famous for the Co-operative Movement started in 1844 by a group of Rochdale working men. Birthplace of John Bright (Corn Law opponent) and more recently Gracie Fields. Fine Victorian Gothic town hall.
Tourist Information Centre ☎ (01706) 356592

Gelder Wood Country Park
⊖✓✓✓
Member BH&HPA
Oak Leigh Cottage, Ashworth Road, Rochdale, Lancashire OL11 5UP
☎ (01706) 364858 & 620300
Off B6222 Bury to Rochdale road Signposted.
19.2 hectares (48 acres). Sloping, grassy.
34 touring pitches

24	🚐	£7.00—£9.00
5	🚐	£7.00—£9.00
5	▲	£7.00—£9.00

🚗⊙📻🔥🔱🚰⊙∪⚘

SOUTHPORT

Merseyside
Map ref 5A1

Delightful Victorian resort noted for gardens, sandy beaches and 6 golf-courses, particularly Royal Birkdale. Attractions include the Atkinson Art Gallery, Southport Railway Centre, Pleasureland and the annual Southport Flower Show. Excellent shopping, particularly in Lord Street's elegant boulevard.
Tourist Information Centre ☎ (01704) 533333

Shaw Hall Caravan Park
⊖✓✓✓✓
Member NCC
Smithy Lane, Scarisbrick, Ormskirk, Lancashire L40 8HJ
☎ Halsall (01704) 840298
Fax (01704) 840539
A570 Ormskirk - Southport. First turn right after Little Chef. Signposted.
8 hectares (20 acres). Level, grassy, hard, sheltered.
40 touring pitches

20	🚐	£10.00—£10.00
20	▲	£10.00—£10.00

297 units not for hire
Open March–December
Cards accepted: Access, Visa, Switch/Delta

🏧📻🔥🔱🚰⊙⚡🅿️📺🏪🔆⚡📞⊙
🔍⚠️🎵🅿️⚘

WARRINGTON

Cheshire
Map ref 5A2

Has prehistoric and Roman origins. Once the "beer capital of Britain" because so much beer was brewed here. Developed in the 18th and 19th C as a commercial and industrial town. The cast-iron gates in front of the town hall were originally destined for Sandringham.
Tourist Information Centre ☎ (01925) 442180

Holly Bank Caravan Park 𝐌
⊖✓✓✓✓
Warburton Bridge Road, Rixton, Warrington WA3 6HU
☎ (0161) 775 2842
Two miles east of junction 21 M6 onto A57 (Irlam). Turn right at lights onto Warburton Bridge Road. Entry to site is on left. Signposted.
3.2 hectares (8 acres). Level, grassy, hard, sheltered.
75 touring pitches

50	🚐	£8.00—£10.50
10	🚐	£8.00—£10.50
15	▲	£7.00—£10.50

🅿️🏧📻🔥🔱🚰⊙⚡🏪🔆⚡📞⊙
🔍⚠️🅿️⚘

COUNTRY CODE

Always follow the Country Code
🍂 Enjoy the countryside and respect its life and work 🍂 Guard against all risk of fire 🍂 Fasten all gates 🍂 Keep your dogs under close control 🍂 Keep to public paths across farmland 🍂 Use gates and stiles to cross fences, hedges and walls 🍂 Leave livestock, crops and machinery alone 🍂 Take your litter home 🍂 Help to keep all water clean 🍂 Protect wildlife, plants and trees 🍂 Take special care on country roads 🍂 Make no unnecessary noise

YORKSHIRE

Yorkshire encompass an area of vastly differing landscapes and moods. The wildness of the Yorkshire Moors and 'Brontë Country' soften into the mellow valleys of the Yorkshire Dales, contrasted by the coastline of towering cliffs, lively resorts and pleasant fishing ports.

Many of the grandest gardens in Britain are here. It's also where you can taste fish and chips at their best, sample ale straight from the brewery or go down a coalmine!

Don't miss historic York with its world-famous Minster. You'll also find some of the best museums and industrial heritage sites in England.

FOR MORE INFORMATION CONTACT:
Yorkshire Tourist Board
312 Tadcaster Road, York YO2 2HF
Tel: (01904) 707961 or 707070 (24 hour brochure line)
Fax: (01904) 701414

Where to Go in Yorkshire - see pages 74-77
Where to Stay in Yorkshire - see pages 78-85

YORKSHIRE

Where to Go and What to See

You will find hundreds of interesting places to visit during your stay in Yorkshire, just some of which are listed in these pages. The number against each name will help you locate it on the map (page 77). Contact any Tourist Information Centre in the region for more ideas on days out in Yorkshire.

1 Sea Life Centre
Scalby Mills,
Scarborough,
North Yorkshire YO12 6RP
Tel: (01723) 376125
At the Sea Life Centre you have the opportunity to meet creatures that live in and around the oceans of the British Isles, ranging from starfish and crabs to rays and seals.

2 North Yorkshire Moors Railway
Pickering Station,
Pickering,
North Yorkshire YO18 7AJ
Tel: (01751) 472508
Operates the route between Grosmont and Pickering, through some of the most magnificent scenery of the North York Moors National Park.

3 Flamingo Land Theme Park, Zoo and Holiday Village
Kirby Misperton,
North Yorkshire YO17 0UX
Tel: (01653) 668287
One price family funpark with over 100 attractions, nine shows and Europe's largest privately owned zoo. Large lake, children's and thrill rides.

4 Fountains Abbey and Studley Royal
Ripon,
North Yorkshire HG4 3DZ
Tel: (01765) 608888
Largest monastic ruin in Britain, founded by Cistercian monks in 1132. Landscaped garden laid out 1720-40 with lake, formal watergarden, temples and deer park.

5 Lightwater Valley Theme Park
North Stainley, Ripon,
North Yorkshire HG4 3HT
Tel: (01765) 635321
175 acres of country park featuring range of white-knuckle rides (including the world's biggest rollercoaster), skill testing activities, leisurely pursuits, live entertainment.

6 Castle Howard
Malton,
North Yorkshire YO6 7DA
Tel: (01653) 648444
Set in 1,000 acres of magnificent parkland with nature walks, scenic lake and stunning rose gardens. Attractions include important furniture and works of art.

7 Sewerby Hall and Gardens
Sewerby, Bridlington,
East Riding of Yorkshire
YO15 1EA
Tel: (01262) 673769
Children's zoo, aviary, old English walled garden, bowls, putting, golf, children's corner, museum, art gallery, Amy Johnson collection, novel train from park to North Beach.

8 Yorkshire Dales Falconry & Conservation Centre
Crows Nest, Giggleswick,
North Yorkshire LA2 8AS
Tel: (01729) 825164
Falconry centre with many species

of birds of prey from around the world including vultures, eagles, hawks, falcons and owls. Free flying displays, lecture room and aviaries.

9 Ripley Castle
Ripley,
North Yorkshire HG3 3AY
Tel: (01423) 770152
Ingilby family home since 1345, fine armour, furniture, chandeliers, panelling, priests hiding hole. Langley Castle in Barbara Taylor Bradford's book "Voice from the Heart".

10 Beningbrough Hall
Shipton-by-Beningbrough,
York YO6 1DD
Tel: (01904) 470666
Handsome Baroque house built 1716, nearly 100 pictures from the National Portrait Gallery. Victorian laundry, potting shed, garden, adventure playground, National Trust shop.

11 Skipton Castle
Skipton,
North Yorkshire BD23 1AQ
Tel: (01756) 792442
One of the most complete and well-preserved medieval castles in England. Beautiful Conduit Court with famous yew.

12 Archaeological Resource Centre
St Saviourgate, York YO1 2NN
Tel: (01904) 654324
Visitors can "touch the past", handling ancient finds of pottery and bone, stitching Roman sandals and picking a Viking padlock. A/V display and exploration of dig by computer.

13 Jorvik Viking Centre
Coppergate, York YO1 1NT
Tel: (01904) 643211
Visitors travel back in time in a timecar to a recreation of Viking York. They will see excavated remains of Viking houses and a display of objects found.

14 National Railway Museum
Leeman Road, York YO2 4XJ
Tel: (01904) 621261
Experience nearly 200 years of technical and social history on the railways and see the way they shaped the world.

15 York Castle Museum
The Eye of York, York YO1 1RY
Tel: (01904) 653611
England's most popular museum of everyday life including reconstructed streets and period rooms, Edwardian park, costume and jewellery, arms and armour, craft workshops.

16 York Minster
Deangate, York YO1 2JA
Tel: (01904) 624426
The largest Gothic cathedral in England. Museum of Saxon and Norman remains, chapter house and crypt. Unrivalled views from Norman tower.

17 Hornsea Freeport
Hornsea,
East Riding of Yorkshire
HU18 1UT
Tel: (01964) 534211
Brand names such as Laura Ashley and Alexon all at discount prices. Birds of prey, Butterfly World, Neptunes Kingdom and more.

18 Harewood House
Harewood, Leeds LS17 9LQ
Tel: (0113) 288 6225
18thC Carr/Adam house, Capability Brown landscape, fine Sevres and Chinese porcelain, English and Italian paintings, Chippendale furniture. Exotic bird garden.

19 National Museum of Photography, Film and Television
Pictureville, Bradford,
West Yorkshire BD1 1NQ
Tel: (01274) 727488
This free museum houses the largest cinema screen (Imax) in

Britain. Fly on a magic carpet, operate a TV camera, become a newsreader for a day.

20 Transperience
Transperience Way,
Low Moor,
Bradford,
West Yorkshire BD12 7HQ
Tel: (01274) 690909
With historic vehicle rides and state of the art interactive technology. Travel on a unique journey through the past, present and future of public transport.

21 Royal Armouries Museum
Leeds LS10 1LT
Tel: (0113) 220 1999
History in action at Britain's newest museum. The thrill of jousting tournaments and terror of battlefield recaptured. See one of the world's finest collections of arms and armour.

22 Tetley's Brewery Wharf
The Waterfront,
Leeds LS1 1QG
Tel: (0113) 242 0666
A unique new development which

brings to life the story through the ages of one of the greatest British traditions – the pub.

23 Museum of Army Transport
Beverley,
East Riding of Yorkshire
HU17 0NG
Tel: (01482) 860445
Army road, rail, sea and air exhibits excitingly displayed in two huge indoor exhibition halls, plus the last remaining Blackburn Beverly aircraft. D-Day exhibition.

24 Eureka! The Museum for Children
Discovery Road, Halifax,
West Yorkshire HX1 2NE
Tel: (01422) 330069
Eureka! is the first museum of its kind designed especially for children up to the age of 12. Wherever you go in Eureka! you can touch, listen, feel and smell, as well as look.

25 Piece Hall
Halifax, West Yorkshire HX1 1RE
Tel: (01422) 358087
Historic, colonnaded cloth hall, surrounding open-air courtyard and

comprising 40 speciality shops, art gallery, Tourist Information Centre, three weekly markets and Calderdale Kaleidoscope display.

26 National Coal Mining Museum for England
Caphouse Colliery,
New Road, Overton,
Wakefield,
West Yorkshire WF4 4RH
Tel: (01924) 848806
Exciting, award-winning museum of the Yorkshire coalfield including guided underground tour in authentic old workings, surface displays, working steam winder.

27 Yorkshire Sculpture Park
Bretton, Wakefield,
West Yorkshire WF4 4LG
Tel: (01924) 830302
Beautiful parkland containing regular exhibitions of contemporary sculpture. Permanent collection includes sculpture by Barbara Hepworth and Henry Moore.

28 National Fishing Heritage Centre
Alexandra Dock, Grimsby,
North East Lincolnshire
DN31 1UZ
Tel: (01472) 344867
Spectacular 1950's steam trawler experience. See, hear, smell and touch a series of recreated environments. Museum displays, shop, aquarium and historic fishing vessels.

29 Pleasure Island Theme Park
Kings Road, Cleethorpes,
North East Lincolnshire
DN35 0PL
Tel: (01472) 211511
The East Coast's newest outdoor theme park with great rides, slides and attractions including the Big Splash, Boomerang, Giant Wheel, Mini Mine Train, Terror Rack and Octopus rides.

FIND OUT MORE

Further information about holidays and attractions in Yorkshire, East Riding and Northern Lincolnshire is available from **Yorkshire Tourist Board**, 312 Tadcaster Road, York YO2 2HF. Tel: (01904) 707961 or 707070 (24 hour brochure line)

These publications are available free from the Yorkshire Tourist Board:

■ **Main Holidays and Shortbreaks guide -** information on the region, including hotels, self-catering and caravan and camping parks

■ **Days Out in Yorkshire** (available Easter '97) - information on attractions, major events, getting around the region, etc.

■ **Bed & Breakfast Touring Map**

■ **What's On -** 3 issues per year
■ **Overseas Brochure -** French, Dutch, German
■ **'Freedom' -** caravan and camping guide
■ **Getting Around Yorkshire -** guide to public transport

WHERE TO STAY (YORKSHIRE)

Parks in this region are listed in alphabetical order of place name, and then in alphabetical order of establishment. A contact address is given where it differs from the address of the establishment.

Map references refer to the colour location maps at the back of this guide.

The first number indicates the map to use; the letter and number which follow refer to the grid reference on the map.

At-a-glance symbols can be found inside the back cover flap.

Keep this open for easy reference.

ALLERTON PARK

North Yorkshire
Map ref 5B1

Allerton Park Caravan Park ⚠

⊖✓✓✓✓✓
Member BH&HPA
Allerton Park, Knaresborough
HG5 0SE
☎ Boroughbridge (01423) 330569
Fax (01423) 330569
Site is 0.25m east of A1 leading from A59 York-Harrogate Road. Signposted.
4.8 hectares (12 acres). Level, grassy, hard, sheltered.
90 touring pitches

70	🚐	£7.75—£8.75
20	⛺	£7.75—£8.75
4	🏠	£180.00—£295.00

100 units not for hire
Open February–December
🏕🅿🗄🍴👜🥤🔌🚿⚡🛁🏳🚻🍴 💧📶
☺⛰🅥🛒🅣

ALNE

North Yorkshire
Map ref 6C3

Alders Caravan Park ⚠

⊖✓✓✓✓✓
Home Farm, Alne, York YO6 2LB
☎ Easingwold (01347) 838722
Fax (01347) 838722
Situated 2 miles west of the A19 and 9 miles north of York. In the centre of the village.
152 hectares (380 acres). Level, grassy.
40 touring pitches

40	🚐	£5.50—£8.00
40	⛺	£5.50—£8.00

Open March–October
🅿🗄🍴👜🥤🔌🚿☺🏳🚻💧◉

BEDALE

North Yorkshire
Map ref 6C3

Ancient church of St Gregory and Georgian Bedale Hall occupy commanding positions over this market town situated in good hunting country. The hall, which contains interesting architectural features including great ballroom and flying-type staircase, now houses a library and museum.

Pembroke Park ⚠

⊖✓✓✓✓
19 Low Street, Leeming Bar,
Northallerton DL7 9BW
☎ (01677) 422608 & 422652
One mile from the A1 and half a mile from the A684. Signposted.
0.4 hectares (1 acre). Grassy, sheltered.
25 touring pitches

25	🚐	£5.00—£6.00
25	⛺	£5.00—£6.00
25	⛺	£4.00—£6.00

Open March–October
🏕🅿🗄🍴👜🥤🔌🚿🏳🚻💧⛰🍴

All accommodation in this guide has been graded, or is awaiting a grading, by a trained Tourist Board inspector.

BENTHAM

North Yorkshire
Map ref 6B3

Bentham is said to mean "Home on the Common". A weekly market has been held here since the 14th C. Good walking country.

Riverside Caravan Park

⊖✓✓✓✓✓
Member BH&HPA
Wenning Avenue, Bentham,
Lancaster LA2 7LW
☎ (015242) 61272
Fax (015242) 62163
South off B6480 at Black Bull Hotel in Bentham follow signs. Signposted.
4.8 hectares (12 acres). Level, grassy, sheltered.
30 touring pitches

30	🚐	£7.30—£7.80
30	⛺	£7.30—£7.80
30	⛺	£5.00

170 units not for hire
Open March–October
🏕🗄🍴👜🥤🔌🚿📺🍴🗄💧🚐☺
🥤⛰🅥🛒🍴🏳🍴🛁

Please check prices and other details at the time of booking.

The ⚠ symbol after an establishment name indicates that it is a Regional Tourist Board member.

BRANDESBURTON

East Riding of Yorkshire
Map ref 5D1

The village church retains work from the Norman period through to the 15th C, and the shaft of a medieval cross stands on the village green.

Dacre Lakeside Park ⚠

⊖✓✓✓✓✓
New Road, Brandesburton, Driffield, North Humberside Y025 8SA
☎ Hornsea (01964) 543704
Fax (01964) 543851
From M62 head for Beverley and on to Bridlington on the A1035 and A165 for eleven miles to Brandesburton. Signposted.
5.6 hectares (14 acres). Level, grassy, hard, sheltered.
90 touring pitches

90	🚐	£6.50—£9.75
90	🚎	£6.50—£9.75
90	⛺	£6.50—£9.75

Open March—October
⚓🅿🏕🔌🏍🍴🐟🔥⊙🔆💈🎱🍽🎬🖊 ⊘🔥⊙🔍⛰🎣🎵🔥

CROPTON

North Yorkshire
Map ref 6C3

Moorland village at the top of a high ridge with stone houses, some of cruck construction, a Victorian church and the remains of a 12th C moated castle. Cropton Forest nearby.

Spiers House Campsite ⚠

⊖✓✓✓✓
Member BH&HPA
Forestry Commission, Cropton, Pickering YO18 8ES
☎ Lastingham (01751) 417591
Off A170 at Wrelton, between Pickering and Kirkbymoorside. Signposted.
4 hectares (10 acres). Sloping, sheltered.
150 touring pitches

100	🚎	£6.00—£7.00
50	⛺	£6.00—£7.00

Open March—September
⚓🚐🔌🍴🔥🔆💈🎱🎬🖊⊘🔥🔥⊙ ⛰🔥

FILEY

North Yorkshire
Map ref 6D3

Resort with elegant Regency buildings along the front and 6 miles of sandy beaches bounded by natural breakwater, Filey Brigg. Starting point of the Cleveland Way.

Crows Nest Caravan Park ⚠

⊖✓✓✓ Rose Award
Gristhorpe, Filey YO14 9PS
☎ Scarborough (01723) 582206
On A165 five miles south of Scarborough, two miles north of Filey. Signposted.
8 hectares (20 acres). Level, grassy, hard.
150 touring pitches

50	🚐	£7.00—£14.00
50	🚎	£7.00—£10.00
100	⛺	£7.00—£10.00
50	🚲	£110.00—£330.00

150 units not for hire
Open March—October
⚓🚐📻🔌🏍🍴🐟⊙🔆💈🎱🍽🎬🖊🖊🖊 ⊙🔍⛰🎣🎵🔥

Orchard Farm Holiday Village ⚠

⊖✓✓✓✓✓
Stonegate, Hunmanby, Filey YO14 OPU
☎ Scarborough (01723) 891582
Turn off the A165 Scarborough - Bridlington road, signposted Hunmanby. Near Filey. Signposted.
5.6 hectares (14 acres). Level, grassy, hard, sheltered.
85 touring pitches

60	🚐	£5.50—£8.00
60	🚎	£5.50—£8.00
25	⛺	£5.00—£6.50

6 units not for hire
⚓🅿📻🔌🏍🍴🐟🔥🔆💈🎱🍽🎬🖊 🖊🚐⊙⛰🎣🔥⊘🔍🎵🔥
Ad See display advertisement on this page

A key to symbols can be found inside the back cover flap.

HARROGATE

North Yorkshire
Map ref 5B1

A major conference, exhibition and shopping centre, renowned for its spa heritage and award winning floral displays, spacious parks and gardens. Famous for antiques, toffee, fine shopping and excellent tea shops, also its Royal Pump Rooms and Baths.
Tourist Information Centre ☎ (01423) 525666

High Moor Farm Park ⚠

⊖✓✓✓✓✓ Rose Award
Member BH&HPA
Skipton Road, Harrogate HG3 2LT
☎ (01423) 563637 & 564955
From Harrogate take A59 west for four miles. Site on left on private road. Signposted.
34.4 hectares (86 acres). Level, grassy, hard, sheltered.
160 touring pitches

150	🚐	£8.75—£8.75
10	🚎	£8.75—£8.75
160	⛺	£8.75—£8.75
5	🚲	£175.00—£200.00

180 units not for hire
Open April—October
Cards accepted: Access, Visa, Switch/Delta
⚓🚐📻⊙🔍🏍🔌🐟🔥🎱✖🍽🖊🖊 ⊙🔍⛰🎣🎵🔥

Rudding Holiday Park ⚠

⊖✓✓✓✓✓ Rose Award
Member BH&HPA/NCC
Rudding Park, Follifoot, Harrogate HG3 1JH
☎ (01423) 870439
Fax (01423) 872286
Three miles south of Harrogate to the north of A658 between its junction with the A61 to Leeds and the A661 to Wetherby. Signposted.
12 hectares (30 acres). Level, sloping, grassy, sheltered.
141 touring pitches

141	🚐	£8.30—£19.00
141	⛺	£6.00—£13.50

90 units not for hire
Open March—December
Cards accepted: Access, Visa
⚓🅿📻🔌🏍🍴🐟🔥🔆💈🎱🍽🖊🖊🚐 ⊙🔍⛰🎣🔥🔆⊙🔥

HATFIELD

South Yorkshire
Map ref 5C1

Hatfield Water Park
⊖✓✓✓✓
Hatfield, Doncaster DN7 6EQ
☎ Doncaster (01302) 841572
Leave M18 at Junction 5, take A18 into Hatfield. The site is signposted at the entrance to the village. Signposted.
4 hectares (10 acres). Level, grassy, sheltered.
75 touring pitches

75	🚐	£6.00
75	🚙	£6.00
75	▲	£3.20—£6.00

🚗🖥🔌🏠👜🔥✕💷⚡☉⛺🚼⚓
🔺🚣♨

HAWES

North Yorkshire
Map ref 6B3

The capital of Upper Wensleydale on the famous Pennine Way, renowned for great cheeses. Popular with walkers. Dales National Park Information Centre and Folk Museum. Nearby is spectacular Hardraw Force waterfall.

Bainbridge Ings Caravan and Camping Site 🅰
⊖✓✓✓
Hawes DL8 3NU
☎ (01969) 667354
A684 Bainbridge, Hawes left at Gayle before Hawes. Signposted.
2 hectares (5 acres).
55 touring pitches

4	🚐	£6.00
1	🚙	£5.50
40	▲	£5.50
3	🛖	£90.00—£130.00

11 units not for hire
Open April–October
🚗🏠👜🔥☉🚼✓☉♨

HELMSLEY

North Yorkshire
Map ref 6C3

Pretty town on the River Rye at the entrance to Ryedale and the North York Moors, with large square and remains of 12th C castle, several inns and All Saints' Church.

Foxholme Touring Caravan Park 🅰
⊖✓✓✓✓✓
Member BH&HPA
Harome, York YO6 5JG
☎ (01439) 770416 & 771696
Leave Helmsley on the A170 in the direction of Scarborough. After 0.5 mile turn right for Harome. Turn left at the church, through the village and then follow the caravan signs. Signposted.
2.4 hectares (6 acres). Level, grassy, sheltered.
60 touring pitches

60	🚐	£6.00—£6.50
60	🚙	£6.00—£6.50
60	▲	£6.00—£6.50

Open April–October
P🖥🔌🏠👜🔥☉💷⚡🚗☉🚼♨

Golden Square Caravan and Camping Park 🅰
⊖✓✓✓✓✓
Member BH&HPA
Oswaldkirk, York YO6 5YQ
☎ Ampleforth (01439) 788269
From Helmsley A170 to Thirsk take the first left onto the B1257 to York. Take the first right to Ampleforth and the turning 0.5 mile on the right. Signposted.
4 hectares (10 acres). Level, grassy, hard, sheltered.
129 touring pitches

129	🚙	£6.00—£8.50
129	▲	£6.00—£8.50

Open March–October
🚗🖥🔌🏠👜🔥☉🚼⚡💷⚡🚗☉
⚓⛺♨🔌🚼Ⓣ
Ad See display advertisement on this page

HORNSEA

East Riding of Yorkshire
Map ref 5D1

Small holiday town situated on strip of land between beach bordering North Sea and Hornsea Mere, a large natural freshwater lake. Some sailing and fishing permitted on protected nature reserve. Hornsea Pottery and retail "freeport" attract many visitors.

Longbeach Leisure Park 🅰
⊖✓✓✓✓
Member BH&HPA
South Cliff, Hornsea, North Humberside HU18 1TL
☎ (01964) 532506
Fax (01964) 536846
A165 Beverley - Bridlington, turn right in Leven to Hornsea.
34 hectares (85 acres). Level, grassy, sheltered.
50 touring pitches

40	🚐	£9.00—£11.00
10	▲	£8.00—£10.00

350 units not for hire
Open March–December
🚗P🖥🔌🏠👜🔥☉💷⚡💷⚡🚗☉🚗
☉⚓⛺Ⓤ🚼✓♨

HORSFORTH

West Yorkshire
Map ref 5B1

St. Helenas Caravan Site 🅰
⊖✓✓✓
None-Go-Bye Farm, Otley Old Road, Horsforth, Leeds LS18 5HZ
☎ Leeds (0113) 284 1142
Follow A65 to the A658 past the airport to Carlton crossroads, then turn right at sign for Cookridge, Horsforth down Otley Old Road for three quarters of a mile. Signposted.
4.8 hectares (12 acres). Level, grassy, hard, sheltered.
60 touring pitches

50	🚐	£5.00—£6.00
6	🚙	£5.00—£6.00
4	▲	£5.00—£5.00

40 units not for hire
🚗🏠👜🔥💷⚡⚡🚗☉♨

HUMBERSTON

North East Lincolnshire
Map ref 5D1

Thorpe Park Holiday Centre ⚠

⊖✓✓✓
Member BH&HPA/NCC
Humberston, Grimsby, South
Humberside DN36 4NG
☎ Reservations/free brochure
(01442) 248668
Fax (01442) 232459
A18 to Cleethorpes, with coast on the left follow signs for caravan parks. Signposted.
80 hectares (200 acres). Level, grassy.
70 touring pitches

70	🚐	£7.00—£16.50
70	🚏	£7.00—£16.50
80	🏠	£120.00—£379.00

2260 units not for hire
Open March–October
Cards accepted: Access, Visa, Switch/Delta

🏕🅿⚓🛆🏃🛉🍴♿🛒✕🍽🎠📺🖥🔲 ✳
📻⊙⚡🎣⚓🎵
Ad See display advertisement inside front cover

LOTHERSDALE

North Yorkshire
Map ref 5B1

Village on the Pennine Way with Bronte connections, and a church built in 1838.

Springs Caravan Park ⚠

⊖✓✓
Springs Farm, Lothersdale, Skipton
BD20 8HH
☎ Crosshills (01535) 632533
From A629 take A6068 signed Crosshills and Colne. Turn right to Lothersdale then left after two miles at cross roads. Take first left through village then first left again past lakes. Signposted.
1.6 hectares (4 acres). Sloping, grassy, hard.
37 touring pitches

37	🚐	£6.50—£7.00
1	🚏	£6.50—£7.00

Open April–October
🅿⚓🏃🛆🛉✳⊙✕🎠✳

A key to symbols can be found inside the back cover flap.

MASHAM

North Yorkshire
Map ref 6C3

Famous market town on the River Ure, with a large market square. St Mary's Church has Norman tower and 13th C spire. Theakston's "Old Peculier" ale is brewed here.

Fearby Caravan & Camping Site ⚠

⊖✓✓✓✓
Member BH&HPA
Black Swan Hotel, Fearby, Ripon
HG4 4NF
☎ Ripon (01765) 689477
Turn off the A6108, 0.25 miles north west of Masham. The site is two miles on, at the rear of the Black Swan, Fearby. Signposted.
1.2 hectares (3 acres). Level, sheltered.
50 touring pitches

50	🚏	£7.00—£7.00
50	⛺	£7.00—£7.00
1	🏠	£100.00—£200.00

Open March–October
🏕🅿⚓⚓🏃🛆🛉♿🛒✕🍽📺🖥 🔲✳📻⊙⚡🏕⊙∪🍴✖🎵♿

PATRINGTON

East Riding of Yorkshire
Map ref 5D1

Patrington Haven Leisure Park Ltd ⚠

⊖✓✓✓✓✓ Rose Award
Member BH&HPA/NCC
Patrington, Hull HU12 0PT
☎ Withernsea (01964) 630071
Fax (01964) 631060
Take A1033 Hull to Withernsea road and turn right upon entering Patrington village. Signposted.
16 hectares (40 acres). Level, grassy, sheltered.
12 touring pitches

12	🚏	£10.00—£15.00
30	🏠	£105.00—£405.00

454 units not for hire
Open April–October
Cards accepted: Access, Visa
🏕🅿⚓🏃🛆🛉♿🛒✕🍽📺🖥🔲 ✳📻⊙⚡🏕🔀∪🎣🎵♪🎵♿

COLOUR MAPS

Colour maps at the back of this guide pinpoint all places in which you will find accommodation listed.

PICKERING

North Yorkshire
Map ref 6D3

Market town and tourist centre on edge of North York Moors. Parish church has complete set of 15th C wall paintings depicting lives of saints. Part of 12th C castle still stands. Beck Isle Museum. The North York Moors Railway begins here.
Tourist Information Centre ☎ (01751) 473791

Wayside Caravan Park ⚠

⊖✓✓✓✓✓
Member BH&HPA
Wrelton, Pickering YO18 8PG
☎ (01751) 472608
Situated 2.5 miles west Pickering, 250 yards off A170 by the village of Wrelton. For correct turning watch for signs. Signposted.
4 hectares (10 acres). Level, grassy, sheltered.
72 touring pitches

40	🚐	£7.50
5	🚏	£6.50
32	⛺	£6.50

80 units not for hire
Open April–October
🏕🅿⚓⚓🏃🛆🛉♿🛒🍽🔲✳🏕 ⊙∪🍴✳

RICHMOND

North Yorkshire
Map ref 6C3

Market town on edge of Swaledale with 11th C castle, Georgian and Victorian buildings surrounding cobbled market-place. Green Howards' Museum is in the former Holy Trinity Church. Attractions include the Georgian Theatre, Richmondshire Museum and Easby Abbey.
Tourist Information Centre ☎ (01748) 850252 or 825994

Brompton-on-Swale Caravan Park ⚠

⊖✓✓✓✓
Member BH&HPA
Brompton-on-Swale, Richmond
DL10 7EZ
☎ (01748) 824629
On B6271 halfway between Brompton-on-Swale and Richmond on left. Signposted.
4 hectares (10 acres). Level, grassy.
150 touring pitches

150	🚐	£6.75
150	🚏	£6.75
150	⛺	£4.95

Continued ▶

RICHMOND
Continued

22 units not for hire
Open April–October

🏕🅿️🔌🔥🚿🛁🔋🔌🛒📺🛒🗑️
🛖☀️⛰️🎣🚶🐾🅣

RIPON
North Yorkshire
Map ref 6C3

Small, ancient city with impressive cathedral containing Saxon crypt which houses church treasures from all over Yorkshire. "Setting the Watch" tradition kept nightly by horn-blower in Market Square. Fountains Abbey nearby.

River Laver Holiday Park ⚠
⊖✓✓✓✓✓ Rose Award
Member BH&HPA
Studley Road, Ripon HG4 2QR
☎ (01765) 690508
Fax (01748) 811393
From the A1 take A61 or B6265 to Ripon, following signs for Fountains Abbey. Establishment is off the B6265 one mile from Ripon town centre. Signposted.
2 hectares (5 acres). Level, grassy, sheltered.
50 touring pitches

50	🚐	£8.50—£10.00
10	🚗	£8.50—£10.00
8	🏠	£120.00—£400.00

42 units not for hire
Open March–November
Cards accepted: Access, Visa

🏕🅿️🔌🔥🔋🚿🛁🔌🛒🗑️🛖
☀️⛰️🎣🐾🅣

Sleningford Watermill ⚠
⊖✓✓✓✓
Member BH&HPA
North Stainley, Ripon HG4 3HQ
☎ (01765) 635201
Travel five miles north from Ripon on the A6108 turn right at park sign

follow sign to reception. Signposted.
5.6 hectares (14 acres). Level, grassy, sheltered.
80 touring pitches

50	🚐	£7.00—£10.50
20	🚗	£7.00—£10.50
30	🏠	£7.00—£10.50

Open April–October

🔌🏕🚐🔌🔥🛁🔋🛒🗑️🛖
☀️🍴⛰️🎣🐾🅣

ROBIN HOOD'S BAY
North Yorkshire
Map ref 6D3

Picturesque village of red-roofed cottages with main street running from clifftop down ravine to seashore. Scene of much smuggling and shipwrecks in 18th C. Robin Hood reputed to have escaped to continent by boat from here.

Middlewood Farm Holiday Park ⚠
⊖✓✓✓✓✓ Rose Award
Member BH&HPA
Robin Hood's Bay, Whitby
YO22 4UF
☎ Whitby (01947) 880414
Fax (01947) 880414
From Scarborough take the A171, turn right for Fylingthorpe and right after the 30mph sign. From Whitby take A171 then the B1447 through Fylingthorpe. Signposted.
1.6 hectares (4 acres). Level, grassy, hard, sheltered.
50 touring pitches

50	🚐	£6.50—£7.50
50	🏠	£6.50—£7.50
25	🏠	£99.00—£295.00

5 units not for hire
Open April–October

🏕🔌🔥🛁🔌🛒🗑️🛖☀️⛰️

SCARBOROUGH
North Yorkshire
Map ref 6D3

Large, popular East Coast seaside resort, formerly a spa town. Beautiful gardens and two splendid sandy beaches. Castle ruins date from 1100; fine Georgian and Victorian houses. Scarborough Millennium depicts 1,000 years of town's history. Sea Life Centre. *Tourist Information Centre* ☎ *(01723) 373333*

Flower of May Holiday Park ⚠
⊖✓✓✓✓✓
Member BH&HPA/NCC
Lebberston Cliff, Scarborough
YO11 3NU
☎ (01723) 582324 & 584311
Fax (01723) 584311
Situated 4 miles from Scarborough on the A165, 2 miles from Filey, signposted from roundabout. Signposted.
8 hectares (20 acres). Level, grassy, hard.
300 touring pitches

270	🚐	£6.50—£10.00
270	🚗	£6.50—£10.00
30	🏠	£6.50—£10.00
45	🏠	£75.00—£335.00

130 units not for hire
Open March–October

🏕🅿️🔌🔥🔋🚿🛁🔌🛒✕🎣📺🛒
🗑️🛖☀️⛰️🎣🐾🐾🅣
Ad See display advertisement on this page

Jacob's Mount Caravan Park & Camping Site ⚠
⊖✓✓✓✓✓ Rose Award
Member BH&HPA
Stepney Road, Scarborough
YO12 5NL
☎ (01723) 361178
Fax (01723) 361178
Two miles west of Scarborough on A170 Thirsk Rd. Signposted.

2 hectares (5 acres). Level, sloping, grassy, sheltered.
56 touring pitches

44	🚐	£6.00—£9.00
44	🚍	£6.00—£9.00
12	⛺	£6.00—£9.00
10	🏚	£120.00—£310.00

34 units not for hire
Open March—October

🔌🅿️🚰♨️🧺💧🛒🔧✕🍴📺🍴📺🗑 ⚡
🔒☺️🍴⚠️♿

[Ad] See display advertisement on this page

SOUTH CAVE

East Riding of Yorkshire
Map ref 5C1

Lying on the famous Ermine Street, the Roman road stretching from Lincoln to York. Located only 3 miles from the River Humber, it is an ideal centre for touring the county of Humberside.

Waudby's Caravan and Camping Park ⚠
☺✓✓✓✓✓
Member BH&HPA
Brough Road, South Cave, Brough, North Humberside HU15 2DB
☎ Howden (01430) 422523 &
Mobile (0585) 494861
Fax (01430) 424777
M62 to A63 signposted South Cave turn right over bridge. Opposite petrol station. Signposted.
0.4 hectares (1 acre). Level, grassy, sheltered.
25 touring pitches

25	🚐	£4.50—£7.70
25	🚍	£4.50—£7.70
25	⛺	£4.00—£6.00

Open April—December
Cards accepted: Access, Visa, Amex, Switch/Delta

🔌🅿️🚰🔧♨️💧🛒☺️⚡☺️♿

STAINFORTH

North Yorkshire
Map ref 6B3

On the River Ribble. The waterfall known as Stainforth Force cascades down a series of limestone ledges just below the old packhorse bridge in this village. Good walking country.

Knight Stainforth Hall Caravan and Camping Park ⚠
☺✓✓✓✓
Member BH&HPA
Stainforth, Settle BD24 0DP
☎ Settle (01729) 822200
Take the A65 Skipton to Kendal road and turn right opposite Settle High School, along Stackhouse Lane for two miles. Signposted.
2.4 hectares (6 acres). Level, sloping.
100 touring pitches

50	🚐	£7.75
50	🚍	£7.75
50	⛺	£7.75

60 units not for hire
Open March—October
Cards accepted: Access, Visa

🔌🅿️🚰♨️💧🛒🔧🧺📺🍴🗑⚡🛒
☺️🍴⚠️♿🚬🏴

STRENSALL

North Yorkshire
Map ref 5C1

Moorside Caravan Park ⚠
☺✓✓✓✓✓
Moorside Park, Lords Moor Lane, Strensall, York YO3 5XF
☎ York (01904) 491208
Take the Strensall turning from A1237 Signposted.
2.4 hectares (6 acres). Level, grassy.
50 touring pitches

50	🚍	£6.50—£8.50
50	⛺	

Open April—October

🔌🅿️🚰🔧♨️💧🛒🍴🗑⚡🛒☺️🏴♿

THIRSK

North Yorkshire
Map ref 6C3

Thriving market town with cobbled square surrounded by old shops and inns and also with a local museum. St Mary's Church is probably the best example of Perpendicular work in Yorkshire.

Nursery Caravan Park ⚠
☺✓✓✓✓✓
Member BH&HPA
Rainton, Thirsk YO7 3PG
☎ (01845) 577277
1.5 miles east of A1 Rainton, to Topcliffe road. Signposted.
2 hectares (5 acres). Level, grassy, sheltered.
20 touring pitches

20	🚐	£7.00—£7.00
20	🚍	£7.00—£7.00
2	🏚	£130.00—£185.00

54 units not for hire
Open March—October and Christmas

🔌🅿️🚰🔧♨️💧🛒☺️📺🍴⚡🛒☺️
☺️⚠️🏴♿

Quernhow Caravan & Campsite
☺✓✓✓
Member BH&HPA
Great North Rd, Sinderby, Thirsk YO7 4LG
☎ (01845) 567221
Adjacent to A1 (north bound). Three miles north junction A1 and A61. Signposted.
1.6 hectares (4 acres). Grassy.
40 touring pitches

30	🚐	£6.50—£8.00
5	🚍	
5	⛺	

🚬🔌🅿️🚰🔧♨️💧🛒☺️✕🍴🛒☺️🍴
⚠️🔍♿

THORNE

South Yorkshire
Map ref 5C1

Market and mining town near Doncaster with a church of Norman origin.

Elder House Touring Park
⊖✓✓✓✓✓
Elder House Farm, Sandtoft Road, Thorne, Doncaster DN8 5TD
☎ (01405) 813173
Leave M180 at junction 1 onto A18 (Scunthorpe). 2 miles past roundabout turn right at Black Bull Inn. After 1/2 a mile turn left into farm and follow through to site. Signposted.
44 hectares (110 acres). Level, grassy, hard, sheltered.
10 touring pitches

10	🚐	£6.00—£7.00
10	�car	

P🔲🔯🏕☖♀☉✕

THRESHFIELD

North Yorkshire
Map ref 6B3

Wharfedale village, once an Anglian settlement which, according to moormen, probably gave it its name, being derived from "open land where threshing is done". In the Yorkshire Dales National Park.

Long Ashes Park ⋀
⊖✓✓✓
Member BH&HPA/NCC
Warfield Park Homes Ltd, Long Ashes Park, Threshfield, Skipton BD23 5PN
☎ Skipton (01756) 752261
Fax (01756) 752876
Take the B6265 from Skipton towards Grassington. At the village of Threshfield take the B6160 to Kettlewell. The park is on the left after 0.75 mile. Signposted.
Sloping, grassy, stony, sheltered.
19 touring pitches

19	🚐	£8.00—£12.00
19	�car	£8.00—£12.00

147 units not for hire
Open March—October

P🔯🏕☖♀☉✕🔲🔳⊘🚐☉🎵♪⚙

Wood Nook Caravan Park ⋀
⊖✓✓✓✓✓ Rose Award
Member BH&HPA
Skirethorns, Threshfield, Skipton BD23 5NU
☎ Grassington (01756) 752412
Fax (01756) 752412
From Skipton take the B6265 to Threshfield. In Threshfield turn left off B6160 (Burnsall, Kettlewell road) into unclassified road for Skirethorns. In 0.5 mile turn right at crossroads then take the 1st left. Signposted.
0.8 hectares (2 acres). Level, sloping, grassy, hard, sheltered.
40 touring pitches

40	🚐	£7.00—£9.50
40	�car	£7.00—£9.00
40	⛺	£7.00—£8.50
11	🏠	£170.00—£220.00

Open March—October
Cards accepted: Access, Visa

🚐🔲🔯🏕☖♀☉⚡🔳⊘🚐☉
⋀♠
[Ad] See display advertisement on this page

WAKEFIELD

West Yorkshire
Map ref 5B1

Thriving city with cathedral church of All Saints boasting 247-ft spire. Old Bridge, a 9-arched structure, has fine medieval chantry chapels of St Mary's. Fine Georgian architecture and good shopping centre (The Ridings). National Coal Mining Museum for England nearby. *Tourist Information Centre* ☎ *(01924) 305000 or 305001*

Nostell Priory Holiday Home Park ⋀
⊖✓✓✓✓✓ Rose Award
Member BH&HPA
Top Park Wood, Nostell, Wakefield WF4 1QD
☎ (01924) 863938
Wakefield A638 five miles left in Foulby. Signposted.
12.4 hectares (31 acres). Level, grassy, hard, sheltered.
60 touring pitches

60	🚐	£8.00—£9.00
7	�car	£8.00—£9.00
60	⛺	£8.00—£9.00
5	🏠	£115.00—£195.00

75 units not for hire
Open March—October
🚐P🔲🔯🏕☖♀☉⚡🔳🔳⊘🚐☉⋀
♪♠⚙

WHITBY

North Yorkshire
Map ref 6D3

Quaint holiday town with narrow streets and steep alleys at the mouth of the River Esk. Captain James Cook, the famous navigator, lived in Grape Lane. 199 steps lead to St Mary's Church and St Hilda's Abbey overlooking harbour. Dracula connections. Sandy beach.
Tourist Information Centre ☎ *(01947) 602674*

Northcliffe Holiday Park ⋀
⊖✓✓✓✓✓ Rose Award
Member BH&HPA
High Hawsker, Whitby YO22 4LL
☎ (01947) 880477
Fax (01947) 880972
South from Whitby 3 miles. Turn left B1447 to Robin Hood's Bay. Through Hawsker village. Go left at the top of the hill and turn left at the Park sign. Follow the private road for 0.5 mile. Signposted.
10.4 hectares (26 acres). Level, grassy, hard.
30 touring pitches

30	🚐	£4.50—£13.00
30	�car	£4.50—£13.00
30	⛺	£4.50—£9.00
11	🏠	£140.00—£320.00

150 units not for hire
Open March—October
Cards accepted: Access, Visa, Switch/Delta
🚐🔲🔯🏕☖♀☉⚡✕🔳⊘🚐☉
🔍⋀✕♠

> The map references refer to the colour maps towards the end of the guide.
> The first figure is the map number; the letter and figure which follow indicate the grid reference on the map.

YORK

North Yorkshire
Map ref 5C1

Ancient walled city nearly 2000 years old containing many well-preserved medieval buildings. Its Minster has over 100 stained glass windows. Attractions include Castle Museum, National Railway Museum, Jorvik Viking Centre and York Dungeon.
Tourist Information Centre ☎ (01904) 621756 or 621756 or 620557

Castle Howard Caravan and Camping Site ⚠

❸✓✓✓✓✓
Member BH&HPA
Coneysthorpe, York Y06 7DD
☎ Coneysthorpe (01653) 648366 & 648316
Fifteen miles north of York on A64, follow Castle Howard signs from main roads. Signposted.
5.2 hectares (13 acres). Grassy, sheltered.
70 touring pitches

70	🚐	£6.80
70	🚚	£6.80
70	⛺	£3.40

122 units not for hire
Open March–October

Cawood Holiday Park ⚠

❸✓✓✓✓✓
Member BH&HPA
Ryther Road, Cawood, Selby Y08 0TT
☎ Selby (01757) 268450
Fax (01757) 268537
Take the B1222 from the A1 or York and turn at Cawood traffic lights on the B1223, signposted Tadcaster. Site is one mile further on. Signposted.
3.6 hectares (9 acres). Level, grassy, hard, sheltered.
57 touring pitches

57	🚐	£8.00—£10.00
57	🚚	£8.00—£10.00
57	⛺	£8.00—£10.00
4	🏠	£165.00—£385.00

5 units not for hire
Open January, March–December

Goosewood Caravan Park ⚠

❸✓✓✓✓✓
Member BH&HPA
Sutton-on-the-Forest, York YO6 1ET
☎ Easingwold (01347) 810829
From the A64 take the A1237 then the B1363 north past the Haxby, Wiggington junction and take the next turning on the right. Signposted.
8 hectares (20 acres). Level, grassy, sheltered.
75 touring pitches

75	🚐	£7.50—£9.00
75	🚚	£7.50—£9.00

Open March–October

Naburn Lock Caravan & Camping Park ⚠

❸✓✓✓✓
Member BH&HPA
Naburn, York YO1 4RU
☎ (01904) 728697
Fax (01904) 728697
Four miles south of York on B1222. Signposted.
1.6 hectares (4 acres). Level, grassy, sheltered.
50 touring pitches

36	🚐	£9.00
14	⛺	£8.00

Open March–October

Rawcliffe Manor Caravan Park ⚠

❸✓✓✓✓✓
Member BH&HPA
Manor Lane, Shipton Road, York YO3 6TZ
☎ (01904) 624422
Two miles from York on the York side of the A19 York to Thirsk road, at junction with A1237 (York Northern By Pass). Signposted.
2 hectares (5 acres). Level, grassy, hard.
120 touring pitches

110	🚚	£7.00—£11.00
10	⛺	£4.30—£7.40

Cards accepted: Access, Visa

[Ad] See display advertisement on this page

Weir Caravan Park ⚠

❸✓✓✓✓✓ Rose Award
Member BH&HPA
Stamford Bridge, York YO4 1AN
☎ Stamford Bridge (01759) 371377
From York on A166 keep left on entering village. Signposted.
3.2 hectares (8 acres).
67 touring pitches

67	🚐	£7.75—£8.75
67	🚚	£7.75—£8.75
67	⛺	£7.75—£8.75
8	🏠	£180.00—£295.00

102 units not for hire
Open March–October

USE YOUR *i*'s

There are more than 550 Tourist Information Centres throughout England offering friendly help with accommodation and holiday ideas as well as suggestions of places to visit and things to do. There may well be a centre in your home town which can help you before you set out. You'll find the address of your nearest Tourist Information Centre in your local Phone Book.

AT-A-GLANCE SYMBOLS

Symbols at the end of each accommodation entry give useful information about services and facilities. A key to symbols can be found inside the back cover flap.

Keep this open for easy reference.

COUNTRY CODE

Always follow the Country Code ✿ Enjoy the countryside and respect its life and work ✿ Guard against all risk of fire ✿ Fasten all gates ✿ Keep your dogs under close control ✿ Keep to public paths across farmland ✿ Use gates and stiles to cross fences, hedges and walls ✿ Leave livestock, crops and machinery alone ✿ Take your litter home ✿ Help to keep all water clean ✿ Protect wildlife, plants and trees ✿ Take special care on country roads ✿ Make no unnecessary noise

HEART OF ENGLAND

The heart of England is a pot pourri of rural charm and urban vitality. From the spa town of Cheltenham to the busy streets of Birmingham, from the remote grandeur of the Western Marches to the gentle beauty of tiny Cotswold villages, the area will appeal to culture buffs and country lovers alike.

Visit Shakespeare country and Stratford with its world-famous theatre. Discover the craftsmanship of the Potteries and explore the rich industrial heritage of the Black Country. Or simply escape to the Staffordshire peaks, the Malvern Hills, or the gently meandering byways of the Severn Valley.

FOR MORE INFORMATION CONTACT:
Heart of England Tourist Board
Lark Hill Road, Worcester WR5 2EZ
Tel: (01905) 763436 or 763439
Fax: (01905) 763450

Where to Go in the Heart of England -
see pages 88-91
Where to Stay in the Heart of England -
see pages 92-95

HEART OF ENGLAND

Where to Go and What to See

You will find hundreds of interesting places to visit during your stay in the Heart of England, just some of which are listed in these pages. The number against each name will help you locate it on the map (page 91). Contact any Tourist Information Centre in the region for more ideas on days out in the Heart of England.

1 Spode
Spode Works, Church Street,
Stoke-on-Trent,
Staffordshire ST4 1BX
Tel: (01782) 744220
Visitors are shown the various processes in the making of Bone China. Samples can be bought at the Spode Shop.

2 Wedgwood Visitor Centre
Barlaston, Stoke-on-Trent,
Staffordshire ST12 9ES
Tel: (01782) 204141
Located in the Wedgwood Factory which lies within a 500 acre country estate. See potters and decorators at work. Museum and shop.

3 Alton Towers Theme Park
Alton, Staffordshire ST10 4DB
Tel: (0990) 204060
Theme Park with over 125 rides and attractions including Nemesis, Haunted House, Runaway Mine Train, Congo River Rapids, Log Flume, Thunderlooper and Toyland tours.

4 Shugborough Estate
Shugborough, Milford, Stafford,
Staffordshire ST17 0XB
Tel: (01889) 881388
18thC mansion house with fine collection of furniture. Gardens and park contain beautiful neo-classical monuments.

5 The Shrewsbury Quest
193 Abbey Foregate,
Shrewsbury,
Shropshire SY2 6AH
Tel: (01743) 243324
12thC Shrewsbury historical site. Visitors are invited to solve three mysteries, creating manuscripts and playing medieval garden games.

6 Ironbridge Gorge Museum
Ironbridge, Telford,
Shropshire TF8 7AW
Tel: (01952) 433522
Worlds first cast iron bridge, Museum of the River Visitor Centre, Tar Tunnel, Jackfield Tile Museum, Coalport China Museum, Rosehill House, Blists Hill Museum and Museum of Iron.

7 Walsall Arboretum
Lichfield Street,
Walsall, West Midlands
Tel: (01922) 653141
Picturesque Victorian park with over 79 acres of gardens, lakes and parkland, just 5 minutes walk from Walsall town centre. The arboretum is home to the Walsall illuminations.

8 Black Country Museum
Tipton Road, Dudley,
West Midlands DY1 4SQ
Tel: (0121) 557 9643
Midlands open air museum with shops, chapel, canal trip into limestone cavern houses, underground mining display and electric tramway.

9 Birmingham Botanical Gardens and Glasshouses
Westbourne Road,
Edgbaston, Birmingham,

West Midlands B15 3TR
Tel: (0121) 454 1860
Fifteen acres of ornamental gardens and glasshouses. Tropical plants of botanical interest. Aviaries with exotic birds and children's play area.

10 National Sea Life Centre
The Water's Edge, Brindleyplace,
Birmingham B1 2HL
Tel: (0121) 633 4700
Over 55 fascinating displays. The opportunity to come face-to-face with literally 100's of fascinating sea creatures from sharks to shrimps.

11 Cadbury World
Linden Road, Bournville,
Birmingham,
West Midlands B30 2LD
Tel: (0121) 451 4180
Story of Chocolate from Aztec times to present day includes chocolate-making demonstration and children's fantasy factory.

12 National Motorcycle Museum
Coventry Road, Bickenhill,
Solihull, West Midlands B92 0EJ
Tel: (01675) 443311
Museum with a collection of 650 British machines from 1898-1993, housed in a new high architectural standard building.

13 Museum of British Road Transport
St Agnes Lane,
Hales Street, Coventry,
West Midlands CV1 1NN
Tel: (01203) 832425
Museum with a collection of over 400 cars, commercial vehicles, cycles and motorcycles from 1818 to present day.

14 Rugby School Museum
10 Little Church Street,
Rugby, Warwickshire CV21 3AW
Tel: (01788) 574117
Tells the story of the School, scene of Tom Brown's Schooldays, and contains early memorabilia of the game of rugby invented on the School Close.

15 Severn Valley Railway
The Railway Station, Bewdley,
Worcestershire DY12 1BG
Tel: (01299) 403816
Preserved standard gauge steam railway running 16 miles between Kidderminster, Bewdley and Bridgnorth. Collection of locomotives and passenger coaches.

16 Warwick Castle
Warwick,
Warwickshire CV34 4QU
Tel: (01926) 406600
Set in 60 acres of grounds with state rooms, armoury, dungeon, torture chamber, clock tower. Exhibits include a Royal Weekend Party 1898, a preparation for battle scene and Kingmaker Feasts.

17 Ragley Hall
Alcester,
Warwickshire B49 5NJ
Tel: (01789) 762090
17thC Palladian House, home of the Earl and Countess of Yarmouth, restored with French furnishing. Also 3D maze, woodland walk and lakeside picnic area.

18 Heritage Motor Centre
Banbury Road,
Gaydon,
Warwick,
Warwickshire CV35 0BJ
Tel: (01926) 641188
Purpose-built transport museum containing collection of historic British cars. 63 acre site including 4 wheel drive circuit, playground, picnic area and nature reserve.

19 Elgar's Birthplace Museum
Crown East Lane,
Lower Broadheath,
Worcester,
Worcestershire WR2 6RH
Tel: (01905) 333224
The cottage in which Edward Elgar was born, now houses a museum of photographs, musical scores, letters and records.

20 Shakespeare's Birthplace
Henley Street,
Stratford-upon-Avon
Warwickshire CV37 6QW
Tel: (01789) 204016
Evoking the busy market town into which he was born, the exhibition covers Shakespeare's home background, schooling, marriage and theatre career in London.

21 Worcester Cathedral
10A College Green
Worcester, WR1 2LH
Tel: (01905) 611002
Norman crypt and chapter house. King John's Tomb. Prince Arthur's Chantry, medieval cloisters and buildings.

22 Malvern Hills
Children's Zoo
Solitaire, Danemoor Cross,
Welland, Malvern,
Worcestershire WR13 6NJ
Tel: (01684) 310016
Tropical animals, pets corner and creepy-crawly house. Visitors can handle the animals, reptiles and see snake demonstrations daily.

23 The New Mappa Mundi &
Chained Library Museum
Hereford Cathedral,
5 The Cloister, Hereford,
Herefordshire HR1 2NG
Tel: (01432) 359880
The New Library of Hereford Cathedral is open to visitors. See also the unique Mappa Mundi, the largest and most complete map in the world, drawn in 1289.

24 The National Birds
of Prey Centre
Newent, Gloucestershire GL18 1JJ
Tel: (01531) 820286
Large collection of birds of prey. Flying demonstrations daily, weather permitting, with eagles, falcons, hawks, owls and vultures. Also breeding aviaries.

25 Three Choirs Vineyards
Baldwins Farm, Newent,
Gloucestershire GL18 1LS
Tel: (01531) 890555
Home of internationally awarded Three Choirs wine. Visitors are welcome to look round the vineyards and taste the wines at no charge.

26 National Waterways
Museum
Llanthony Warehouse,
Gloucester Docks,
Gloucester GL1 2EH
Tel: (01452) 318054
Three floors of dockside warehouse with lively displays telling the story of Britain's canals. Outside craft area with demonstrations. Cafe and shop.

27 Soldiers of Gloucestershire
Museum
Custom House,
Gloucester Docks,
Gloucester GL1 2HE
Tel: (01452) 522682
Listed Victorian building in historic docks. The story of Gloucestershire's foot and horse soldiers in the last 300 years.

FIND OUT MORE

Further information about holidays and attractions in the Heart of England is available from: **Heart of England Tourist Board,** Lark Hill Road, Worcester WR5 2EZ.
Tel: (01905) 763436 (24 hours)

These publications are available free from the Heart of England Tourist Board:
■ **Bed & Breakfast Touring Map**
■ **Great Escapes - short breaks and leisure holidays for all seasons**
■ **Events list**

Also available are:
Places to Visit in the Heart of England - a comprehensive guide to over 750 varied attractions and things to see, also great ideas for where to go in winter, (over £40 in discount vouchers included). £3.99
■ **Cotswolds Map** £2.95
■ **Cotswold/Wyndean Map** £3.25
■ **Shropshire/Staffordshire Map** £3.25
Please add 60p postage for up to 3 items, plus 25p for each additional 3 items.

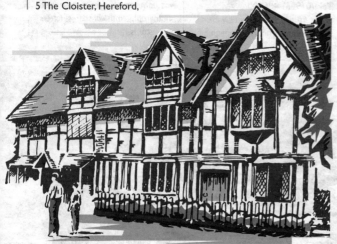

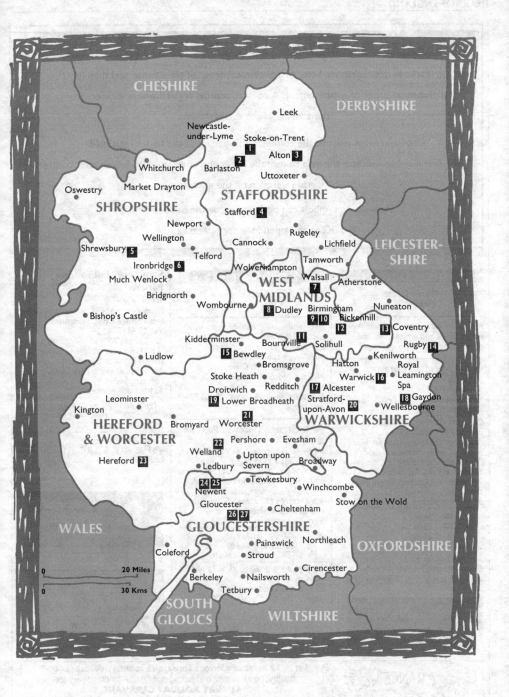

CHESHIRE

DERBYSHIRE

Leek

Newcastle-
under-Lyme
Stoke-on-Trent

1

Alton **3**

Whitchurch   Barlaston **2**

Uttoxeter

Oswestry   Market Drayton

STAFFORDSHIRE

SHROPSHIRE

Stafford **4**

Newport

Rugeley

LEICESTER-
SHIRE

Wellington

Cannock

Lichfield

Shrewsbury **5**

Telford

Wolverhampton

Tamworth

Ironbridge **6**

Walsall

Much Wenlock

WEST

Atherstone

7

Bridgnorth

MIDLANDS

Wombourne

Birmingham   Nuneaton

Bishop's Castle

8 Dudley

9 10

Bickenhill

12

13 Coventry

Kidderminster

Bournville **11**   Solihull

Rugby **14**

15 Bewdley

Hatton

Kenilworth
Royal

Ludlow

Bromsgrove

Warwick **16**

Leamington
Spa

Stoke Heath

Redditch   **17** Alcester

Droitwich

Stratford-   **18** Gaydon

Leominster

19 Lower Broadheath

upon-Avon **20**   Wellesbourne

Kington

21

WARWICKSHIRE

HEREFORD   Bromyard   Worcester

& WORCESTER

22   Pershore   Evesham

Welland

Upton upon

Hereford **23**

Ledbury   Severn   Broadway

24 25   Tewkesbury

Newent   Winchcombe

Gloucester   Cheltenham   Stow on the Wold

26 27

GLOUCESTERSHIRE

WALES

Painswick   Northleach

Coleford   Stroud

OXFORDSHIRE

Berkeley   Nailsworth   Cirencester

0   20 Miles

0   30 Kms

Tetbury

**SOUTH
GLOUCS**

WILTSHIRE

91

WHERE TO STAY (HEART OF ENGLAND)

Parks in this region are listed in alphabetical order of place name, and then in alphabetical order of establishment. A contact address is given where it differs from the address of the establishment.

Map references refer to the colour location maps at the back of this guide.

The first number indicates the map to use; the letter and number which follow refer to the grid reference on the map.

At-a-glance symbols can be found inside the back cover flap.

Keep this open for easy reference.

ASTON CANTLOW

Warwickshire
Map ref 3B1

Attractive village on the River Alne, with a black and white timbered guild house and a fine old inn.

Island Meadow Caravan Park ⚤
⊖✓✓✓✓
The Mill House, Aston Cantlow B95 6JP
☎ Great Alne (01789) 488273
Fax (01789) 488273
From Stratford take A46 w. for 3m., turn right on to unclassified road for 2.5m., take 2nd turning left, site 400yds, on right. Signposted.
2.8 hectares (7 acres). Level, grassy, sheltered.
34 touring pitches

24	🚐	£8.00
24	🚍	£8.00
10	⛺	£6.00
6	🏠	£155.00—£260.00

50 units not for hire
Open March–October
🚗🔌🏕🌳💧🔵🕐🔒🍴🏛📺☺⛰🅹🔥

BRIDGNORTH

Shropshire
Map ref 5A3

Red sandstone riverside town in 2 parts - High and Low - linked by a cliff railway. Much of interest including a ruined Norman keep, half-timbered 16th C houses, Midland Motor Museum and Severn Valley Railway.
Tourist Information Centre ☎ (01746) 763358

Park Grange Caravan Park ⚤
⊖✓✓✓✓
Morville, Bridgnorth WV16 4RN
☎ (01746) 714285
One and a half miles west of Morville on A458, on right hand side towards Much Wenlock. Signposted.
4.8 hectares (12 acres). Sloping, grassy, hard, sheltered.
5 touring pitches

5	🚐	£4.00—£5.00
5	🚍	£4.00—£5.00
4	🏠	£115.00—£260.00

🚗🅿🖥🌳💧🔥🔒🏛☺⛰🌙⚤🔵🎵➤🦌🍴🅹
[Ad] See display advertisement on this page

Stanmore Hall Touring Park ⚤
⊖✓✓✓✓✓
Member BH&HPA
Stourbridge Road, Bridgnorth WV15 6DT
☎ (01746) 761761
On A458 to Stourbridge two miles from Bridgnorth. Signposted.
4.8 hectares (12 acres). Level, grassy, hard, sheltered.
131 touring pitches

121	🚐	£10.00—£11.60
10	🚍	£10.00—£11.60
121	⛺	£8.80—£8.80

Cards accepted: Access, Visa
🚗🅿🖥🔌🏕🌳💧🔵🕐🔒🍴🏛📺☺⛰🅹

OPEN ALL YEAR

BROADWAY

Hereford and Worcester
Map ref 3B1

Beautiful Cotswold village called the
"Show village of England", with 16th
C stone houses and cottages. Near
the village is Broadway Tower with
magnificent views over 12 counties
and a country park with nature
trails and adventure playground.

Leedons Park ⚏
⊖✓✓✓✓✓ Rose Award
Member NCC
Childswickham Road, Broadway,
Worcestershire WR12 7HB
☎ (01386) 852423
*On leaving Broadway on A44 turn left
to Cheltenham then first right to
Childswickham. Signposted.*
22.4 hectares (56 acres). Level,
grassy.
450 touring pitches

225	⛃	£7.00—£9.00
225	⛺	£7.00—£9.00
225	▲	£7.00—£9.00
13	⚎	£127.00—£302.00

87 units not for hire
Cards accepted: Access, Visa,
Switch/Delta

⚓⛊⚙↰⚠△🚰⚗❍✕📺《📞🖳⚡
🗑⊙⚲⚑⚠⚡♖⚘

BROMYARD

Hereford and Worcester
Map ref 3B1

Market town on the River Frome
surrounded by orchards, with black
and white houses and a Norman
church. Nearby at Lower
Brockhampton is a 14th C
half-timbered moated manor house
owned by the National Trust.
Heritage Centre.
*Tourist Information Centre ☎ (01885)
482038*

Boyce Caravan Park ⚏
⊖✓✓✓✓✓
Stanford Bishop, Bringsty, Worcester
WR6 5UB
☎ (01885) 483439
*3 miles from Bromyard off B4220
Bromyard to Malvern. At Herefordshire
House Public House sharp left then
first right. Signposted.*
6.8 hectares (17 acres). Level,
sloping, grassy, sheltered.
24 touring pitches

24	⛃	£7.50
24	⛺	£7.50
12	▲	£7.50

80 units not for hire
Open March–December
⚓⛊P⚙↰⚠△🚰⚗❍《📞🖳⚡⚲❍⚠
⛵🎣⚘

CHELTENHAM

Gloucestershire
Map ref 3B1

Cheltenham was developed as a spa
town in the 18th C and has some
beautiful Regency architecture, in
particular the Pittville Pump Room.
It holds international music and
literature festivals and is also famous
for its race meetings and cricket.
*Tourist Information Centre ☎ (01242)
522878*

Longwillows Caravan &
Camping Park ⚏
⊖✓✓✓
Station Road, Woodmancote,
Cheltenham GL52 4HN
☎ (01242) 674113
Fax (01242) 678731
*Take A435 from Cheltenham turn off
at Bishops Cleeve, or B4632 turn off at
Southam. Signposted.*
1.6 hectares (4 acres). Grassy,
sheltered.
80 touring pitches

35	⛃	£5.50—£6.00
10	⛺	£5.50—£6.00
35	▲	£5.50—£6.00

Open March–October
⚓⚙↰⚠△🚰⚗❍✕⚲📞🖳⚡⚲⊙
⚠⚘

CIRENCESTER

Gloucestershire
Map ref 3B1

"Capital of the Cotswolds",
Cirencester was Britain's second
most important Roman town with
many finds housed in the Corinium
Museum. It has a very fine
Perpendicular church and old
houses around the market place.
*Tourist Information Centre ☎ (01285)
654180*

Mayfield Touring Park ⚏
⊖✓✓✓✓
Member BH&HPA
Cheltenham Road, Perrotts Brook,
Cirencester GL7 7BH
☎ (01285) 831301
*On A435 2m Cirencester, 13m
Cheltenham Signposted.*
4.8 hectares (12 acres). Level,
sloping, grassy, hard, sheltered.
36 touring pitches

36	⛃	£6.50—£8.75
16	⛺	£5.45—£8.75
36	▲	£5.05—£8.75
2	⚎	

⚓⛊P🖳⚙↰⚠△🚰⚗❍⚲《📞🖳⚡⚲
⊙⚠∪🎣✕⚘

ELLESMERE

Shropshire
Map ref 5A2

Small market town with old streets
and houses and situated close to 9
lakes. The largest, the Mere, has
many waterfowl and recreational
facilities and some of the other
meres have sailing and fishing.

Fernwood Caravan Park ⚏
⊖✓✓✓✓✓
Member BH&HPA/NCC
Lyneal, Ellesmere SY12 0QF
☎ Bettisfield (01948) 710221
Fax (01948) 710324
*Ellesmere A495 road at Welshampton
B5063, after canal follow signs.
Signposted.*
20 hectares (50 acre
60 touring pitches

60	⛃	£5.25—£9.50
60	⛺	£5.25—£9.50
1	⚎	£170.00—£290.00

165 units not for hire
Open March–November
⚓⛊⚙↰⚠△🚰⚗❍⚲《📞🖳⚡⚲❍⊙
⚠🎣✕⚘

EVESHAM

Hereford and Worcester
Map ref 3B1

Market town in the centre of a
fruit-growing area. There are
pleasant walks along the River Avon
and many old houses and inns. A
fine 16th C bell tower stands
between 2 churches near the
medieval Almonry Museum.
*Tourist Information Centre ☎ (01386)
446944*

The Ranch Caravan Park ⚏
⊖✓✓✓✓✓
Member BH&HPA/NCC
Station Road, Honeybourne,
Evesham, Worcestershire
WR11 5QG
☎ (01386) 830744
Fax (01386) 833503
*From Evesham take B4035 to Badsey
& Bretforton Signposted.*
19.2 hectares (48 acres). Level,
grassy.
120 touring pitches

Continued ▶

93

EVESHAM

Continued

120	🚐	£5.50—£18.50
120	🚏	£5.50—£18.50
4	🏕	£180.00—£350.00

176 units not for hire
Open March–November
Cards accepted: Access, Visa,
Switch/Delta

🚗🚲🔌👜🔥❄☕☎⚡✕☂📺📶🖥
⚡🛒☺🍴⛰⟋♪♨

KINNERLEY

Shropshire
Map ref 5A3

Village near the Welsh border has a
bright orange sandstone church
with Georgian nave.

Cranberry Moss Camping & Caravan Park 𝖠𝖠

☎✓✓✓✓
Kinnerley, Oswestry SY10 8DY
☎ Nesscliffe (01743) 741444 &
Knockin (01691) 682296
*From Shrewsbury take A5, 10M NW
turn left onto B4396, site 300 yds on
left. Signposted.*
1.6 hectares (4 acres). Level, sloping,
grassy, hard.
60 touring pitches

60	🚐	£5.20—£6.50
60	🚏	£5.20—£6.50
60	⛺	£1.50—£2.00

Open April–October

🚗🚲🔌👜🔥❄☕☎⚡🛒⚡✓🚗☺
⛰♨

RUGELEY

Staffordshire
Map ref 5B3

Town close to Cannock Chase
which has over 2000 acres of heath
and woodlands with forest trails and
picnic sites. Nearby is Shugborough
Hall (National Trust) with a fine
collection of 18th C furniture and
interesting monuments in the
grounds.

Silvertrees Caravan Park 𝖠𝖠

☎✓✓✓✓ Rose Award
Member BH&HPA
Stafford Brook Road, Penkridge
Bank, Rugeley WS15 2TX
☎ (01889) 582185
Fax (01889) 582185
*From Rugeley Western Springs Rd., W
at traffic lights for Penkridge after two
miles right into Stafford Brook Road.
(Unclassified road). Signposted.*
12 hectares (30 acres). Level, sloping,
grassy, hard, sheltered.

50 touring pitches

50	🚐	£7.00—£8.00
50	🚏	£7.00—£8.00
7	🏕	£150.00—£350.00

43 units not for hire
Open April–October
Cards accepted: Access, Visa

🚗🚲🔌👜🔥❄☕☺📺📶⚡⚡🚗☺🍴
⛰⟋♨♨

STOKE-ON-TRENT

Staffordshire
Map ref 5B2

Famous for its pottery. Factories of
several famous makers, including
Josiah Wedgwood, can be visited.
The City Museum has one of the
finest pottery and porcelain
collections in the world.
*Tourist Information Centre ☎ (01782)
284600*

The Star Caravan and Camping Park 𝖠𝖠

☎✓✓✓
Star Road, Cotton, Oakamoor,
Stoke-on-Trent ST10 3BN
☎ Oakamoor (01538) 702256 &
702564
Fax (01538) 702564
*Within 100 yards of Star crossroads at
Cotton on B5417, three quarters of a
mile from Alton Towers. Signposted.*
20 hectares (50 acres). Sloping,
grassy, hard, sheltered.
120 touring pitches

60	🚐	£6.00
30	🚏	£6.00
30	⛺	£6.00
6	🏕	£220.00

58 units not for hire
Open February–December

🚗🚲🔌👜🔥❄☕☺🛒📶🖥⚡🚗☺
⛰⚓🏍🚩♨

The 𝖠𝖠 symbol after an
establishment name indicates
that it is a Regional
Tourist Board member.

Information on
accommodation listed in this
guide has been supplied by the
proprietors. As changes may
occur you are advised to check
details at the time of booking.

STRATFORD-UPON-AVON

Warwickshire
Map ref 3B1

Famous as Shakespeare's home
town, Stratford's many attractions
include his birthplace, New Place
where he died, the Royal
Shakespeare Theatre and Gallery,
"The World of Shakespeare" 30
minute theatre and Hall's Croft (his
daughter's house).
*Tourist Information Centre ☎ (01789)
293127*

Dodwell Park 𝖠𝖠

☎✓✓✓✓
Member BH&HPA
Evesham Rd., (B439),
Stratford-upon-Avon CV37 9ST
☎ (01789) 204957
Fax (01789) 336476
*Two miles south west of Stratford-upon-
Avon on B439 (formerly A439). Not
the racecourse site. Signposted.*
0.8 hectares (2 acres). Level, sloping,
grassy, hard.
50 touring pitches

50	🚐	£7.00—£8.50
50	🚏	£7.00—£8.50
50	⛺	£4.00—£8.50

Cards accepted: Access, Visa

🚗🚲👜🔥❄☕☺🛒📶🖥⚡🚗☺♨

SYMONDS YAT WEST

Hereford and Worcester
Map ref 3A1

Jubilee Maze and Exhibition was
created here in 1977 to
commemorate Queen Elizabeth II's
Jubilee, and there are other
attractions beside the river. The
area of Symonds Yat is a
world-renowned beauty spot.

Sterretts Caravan Park

☎✓✓✓✓
Symonds Yat West, Ross-on-Wye,
Herefordshire HR9 6BY
☎ Dean (01594) 832888
*Half a mile off A40 at Whitchurch
follow Leisure Park Signs.*
2.6 hectares (6.5 acres). Level,
grassy.
8 touring pitches

8	🚐	£6.00—£8.00
8	🚏	£6.00—£8.00
8	⛺	£6.00—£8.00
5	🏕	£148.05—£197.40

77 units not for hire
Open March–October

🚗P🚲🔌👜🔥❄☕☺🛒✕📶🖥⚡🚗
☺⛰⚓🚩🏍🚩

TELFORD

Shropshire
Map ref 5A3

New Town named after Thomas Telford, the famous engineer who designed many of the country's canals, bridges and viaducts. It is close to Ironbridge with its monuments and museums to the Industrial Revolution, including restored 18th C buildings. *Tourist Information Centre* ☎ *(01952) 291370*

Severn Gorge Caravan Park ⚑

⊖✓✓✓✓
Bridgnorth Road, Tweedale, Telford TF7 4JB
☎ (01952) 684789
Short drive from junction 5 or 6 of M54 to Tweedale. Signposted.
4 hectares (10 acres). Level, grassy, hard, sheltered.
79 touring pitches

39	🚐	£7.30—£9.50
40	⚊	£5.50—£6.00

🚗🔌🔧🛁🚿🚽🛗🗑/🛒⚊☺🅰
♨⊗

WEM

Shropshire
Map ref 5A3

Small town connected with Judge Jeffreys who lived in Lowe Hall. Well known for its ales.

Lower Lacon Caravan Park ⚑

⊖✓✓✓
Member BH&HPA
Wem, Shrewsbury SY4 5RP
☎ (01939) 232376 & 232856
Fax (01939) 233606
From Wem over railway crossing L. on the B5065 site on L 0.5m Signposted.
14.4 hectares (36 acres). Level, grassy, hard, sheltered.
270 touring pitches

250	🚐	£7.00—£9.50
20	⚊	£7.00—£9.50
5	🏠	£75.00—£260.00

50 units not for hire
Cards accepted: Access, Visa, Amex, Switch/Delta

🚗🔌🔧🛁🚿🚽🛗🗑/🛒⚊☺🅰🔥🅿

COUNTRY CODE

Always follow the Country Code
🍂 Enjoy the countryside and respect its life and work 🍂 Guard against all risk of fire 🍂 Fasten all gates 🍂 Keep your dogs under close control 🍂 Keep to public paths across farmland 🍂 Use gates and stiles to cross fences, hedges and walls 🍂 Leave livestock, crops and machinery alone 🍂 Take your litter home 🍂 Help to keep all water clean 🍂 Protect wildlife, plants and trees 🍂 Take special care on country roads 🍂 Make no unnecessary noise

USE YOUR *i*'s

There are more than 550 Tourist Information Centres throughout England offering friendly help with accommodation and holiday ideas as well as suggestions of places to visit and things to do. There may well be a centre in your home town which can help you before you set out. You'll find the address of your nearest Tourist Information Centre in your local Phone Book.

AT-A-GLANCE SYMBOLS

Symbols at the end of each accommodation entry give useful information about services and facilities. A key to symbols can be found inside the back cover flap.

Keep this open for easy reference.

CHECK THE MAPS

The colour maps at the back of this guide show all the cities, towns and villages for which you will find accommodation entries.

Refer to the town index to find the page on which it is listed.

MIDDLE ENGLAND

Middle England can be enjoyed on foot, by car - and in some places, by canal boat.

From the heights of the High Peaks to the tranquil shire countryside, this region is as rich in history as it is in colour and contrast.

The English Civil War began in Middle England; the tapestry of history is closely woven - with historic houses, heritage centres and museums bearing witness.

Don't miss Lincoln or the Lace-making city of Nottingham, elegant Buxton spa or Skegness by the sea! And then there's Sherwood Forest, haunt of the legendary Robin Hood...

FOR MORE INFORMATION CONTACT:
East Anglia Tourist Board *(Lincolnshire)*
Toppesfield Hall, Hadleigh, Suffolk IP7 5DN
Tel: (01473) 822922 **Fax:** (01473) 823063

Heart of England Tourist Board *(Derbyshire, Nottinghamshire, Leicestershire, Northamptonshire)*
Lark Hill Road, Worcester WR5 2EZ
Tel: (01905) 763436 or 763439
Fax: (01905) 763450

Where to Go in Middle England - see pages 98-101
Where to Stay in Middle England - see pages 102-104

MIDDLE ENGLAND

Where to Go and What to See

You will find hundreds of interesting places to visit during your stay in Middle England, just some of which are listed in these pages. The number against each name will help you locate it on the map (page 101). Contact any Tourist Information Centre in the region for more ideas on days out in Middle England.

1 Gainsborough Old Hall
Parnell Street, Gainsborough,
Lincolnshire DN21 2NB
Tel: (01427) 612669
Late medieval timber-framed manor house built c1460, with fine medieval kitchen. Displays on the building and its restoration.

2 World Of Robin Hood
Haughton, Retford,
Nottinghamshire DN22 8DZ
Tel: (01623) 860210
A hands-on medieval experience including The Crusaders, Medieval Market Place, Sherwood Forest, Castle Dungeons Armoury and the Great Hall.

3 Chatsworth House and Garden
Bakewell, Derbyshire DE45 1PP
Tel: (01246) 582204
Built 1687-1707. Collection of fine pictures, books, drawings, furniture. Garden laid out by Capability Brown with fountains and cascade. Farmyard and adventure playground.

4 Lincoln Cathedral
Lincoln LN2 1PZ
Tel: (01522) 544544
Medieval Gothic cathedral of outstanding historical and architectural merit.

5 Museum of Lincolnshire Life
Burton Road,
Lincoln LN1 3LY
Tel: (01522) 528448
The region's largest social history museum. Agricultural, industrial and social history of Lincolnshire from a teapot to a World War I tank. Victorian room setting.

6 The Heights of Abraham
Matlock Bath,
Matlock,
Derbyshire DE4 3PD
Tel: (01629) 582365
Cable car ride across Derwent Valley gives access to Alpine Centre with refreshments, superb views, woodland, prospect tower and two show caves.

7 The National Tramway Museum
Crich, Matlock,
Derbyshire DE4 5DP
Tel: (01773) 852565
Collection of 50 trams from Britain and overseas built 1873-1957. Tram rides on one-mile route, period street scene, depots, power station, workshops, exhibitions.

8 Midland Railway Centre
Butterley Station, Ripley,
Derby DE5 3QZ
Tel: (01773) 747674
Over 25 locomotives and 80 items of historic rolling stock of Midland and LMS origin. Steam-hauled passenger service, museum site. Country and farm parks.

9 American Adventure
Pit Lane, Ilkeston,
Derbyshire DE7 5SX
Tel: (01773) 531521
American theme park with more than 100 rides including Nightmare Niagara Log Flume, Rocky

Mountain, Rapids Ride, The Missile, Motion Master Simulator Cinema and many other attractions.

10 Southwell Minster
Bishop's Drive,
Southwell,
Nottinghamshire NG25 0JP
Tel: (01636) 812649
Building begun c1108. Saxon tympanum, Norman nave and crossing, early English choir. Outstanding foliage carving in Chapter House. Archbishop's Palace ruins.

11 The Galleries of Justice
Shire Hall,
High Pavement,
Nottingham NG1 1HN
Tel: (0115) 952 0555
Condemned! is the visitor attraction at the Galleries of Justice which offers a major crime and punishment experience. Based in and around former 19thC courthouse.

12 Newstead Abbey
Linby, Nottingham NG15 8GE
Tel: (01623) 793557
800-year-old remains of priory church, converted into country house in 16thC. Home of Lord Byron with possessions and manuscripts. Parkland, lake, gardens.

13 Nottingham Industrial Museum
Courtyard Buildings,
Wollaton Park,
Nottingham NG8 2AE
Tel: (0115) 928 4602
18thC stables presenting history of Nottingham's industries: printing, pharmacy, hosiery and lace. Victorian beam engine, horse gin, transport.

14 Belvoir Castle
Belvoir, Lincolnshire NG32 1PD
Tel: (01476) 870262
The present castle is fourth to be built on this site and dates from 1816. Art treasures including works by Poussin, Rubens, Holbein and Reynolds. Museum of Queen's Royal Lancers.

15 Belton House, Park & Gardens
Belton, Grantham,
Lincolnshire NG32 2LS
Tel: (01476) 66116
The crowning achievement of Restoration country house architecture, built in 1685-88 for Sir John Brownlow. Alterations by James Wyatt in 1777.

16 Sudbury Hall
Sudbury, Derbyshire DE6 5HT
Tel: (01283) 585305
Grand 17thC house. Plasterwork

ceilings, ceiling paintings, carved staircase and overmantel. Museum of Childhood in old servants' wing.

17 Great Central Railway
Great Central Station,
Great Central Road,
Loughborough,
Leicestershire LE11 1RW
Tel: (01509) 230726
Preserved main line steam railway operating over 8.5 miles from Loughborough to Leicester North.

18 Ye Olde Pork Pie Shoppe
Dickinson & Morris Ltd,
10 Nottingham Street,
Melton Mowbray,
Leicestershire LE13 1NW
Pork pie shop and bakery in 17C building. History of shop and Melton Mowbray Pork Pie industry. Demonstrations of traditional craft of hand raising pork pies.

19 Spalding Tropical Forest
Glenside North,
Pinchbeck,
Spalding,
Lincolnshire PE11 3SD
Tel: (01775) 710882
One half-acre glass house enclosing a tropical environment. Four zones including tropical rain forest, Japanese and Australian tropical plants and Mediterranean temperate zone.

20 **Oakham Castle**
Market Place, Oakham,
Leicestershire
Tel: (01572) 723654
*Splendid 12thC Great Hall of
fortified manor house. Unique
horseshoe forfeits left by peers of
the realm.*

21 **Newarke Houses Museum**
The Newarke, Leicester LE2 7BY
Tel: (0116) 247 3222
*Local history and crafts from 1485.
Toys and games, clocks, mechanical
instruments. 19thC street scene,
early 20thC shop. Feature on 19thC
giant Daniel Lambert.*

22 **Twycross Zoo**
Twycross, Near Atherstone,
Warwickshire CV9 3PX
Tel: (01827) 880250
*Gorillas, orangutans, chimpanzees,
modern gibbon complex, elephants,
lions, cheetahs, giraffes, reptile
house. Pets corner. Rides.*

23 **Rockingham Castle**
Rockingham,
Leicestershire LE16 8TH
Tel: (01536) 770240
*Elizabethan house within walls of
Norman castle. Fine pictures.
Extensive views and gardens with
roses and ancient yew hedge.*

24 **Lamport Hall**
Lamport,
Northampton NN6 9HD
Tel: (01604) 686272
*17th/18thC house, home of Isham
family, mainly John Webb and
Francis Smith. Beautiful high room
(1655) fine library (1732). Garden
home to the 1st Gnome in England.*

25 **Holdenby House and
Gardens**
Holdenby,
Northampton NN6 8DJ
Tel: (01604) 770074
*Remains of Elizabethan palace and
gardens. Fragrant border, falconry
centre, armoury, 17thC homestead,
tea room and shop.*

26 **National Dragonfly
Museum**
Ashton Mill, Ashton,
Northampton PE8 5LB
Tel: (01832) 272427
*Discover the wonder and plight of
dragonflies. See also the Victorian
diesel hydro-electric generating
pumping hall and craft exhibitions.
Gift shop.*

27 **Sulgrave Manor**
Sulgrave, Near Banbury,
Oxfordshire OX17 2SD
Tel: (01295) 760205
*Small manor house of Shakespeare's
time, with furniture of period. Fine
kitchen. Early English home of
ancestors of George Washington.*

FIND OUT MORE

Further information about
holidays and attractions in Middle
England is available from either:
East Anglia Tourist Board,
Toppesfield Hall,
Hadleigh,
Suffolk IP7 5DN.
Tel: (01473) 822922
or **Heart of England Tourist
Board**,
Lark Hill Road,
Worcester WR5 2EZ
Tel: (01905) 763436 or 763439

These publications are available
free from the East Anglia Tourist
Board:
■ **Great Escapes** - short breaks
■ **Touring Map**

These publications are available
free from the Heart of England
Tourist Board:
■ **Places to Visit** (chargeable)
■ **Peak District and
Derbyshire Guide**
■ **Rutland, Rockingham Forest
and Stamford Guide**

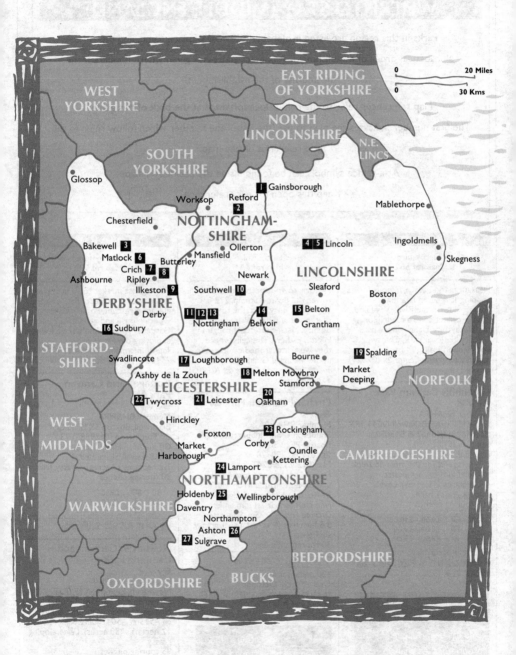

WEST
YORKSHIRE

EAST RIDING
OF YORKSHIRE

0   20 Miles

0   30 Kms

SOUTH
YORKSHIRE

NORTH
LINCOLNSHIRE

N.E.
LINCS

Glossop

Worksop   Retford   **1** Gainsborough

2

Chesterfield   **NOTTINGHAM-**
                    SHIRE

Mablethorpe

Bakewell **3**   Ollerton   **4 5** Lincoln

Ingoldmells

Matlock **6**   Butterley
       Crich **7**   Mansfield   **LINCOLNSHIRE**

Skegness

Ashbourne   Ripley **8**
       Ilkeston **9**   Newark

Southwell **10**

Sleaford

Boston

DERBYSHIRE
       Derby   **11 12 13**   **14**   **15** Belton

Grantham

16 Sudbury   Nottingham   Belvoir

STAFFORD-
SHIRE
       Swadlincote   **17** Loughborough

Bourne   **19** Spalding

Market
Deeping

NORFOLK

Ashby de la Zouch   **18** Melton Mowbray

Stamford

LEICESTERSHIRE

       20
   22 Twycross   **21** Leicester   Oakham

WEST
MIDLANDS   Hinckley

CAMBRIDGESHIRE

Foxton   **23** Rockingham

Market   Corby   Oundle
Harborough   Kettering

24 Lamport

NORTHAMPTONSHIRE

Holdenby **25**   Wellingborough

WARWICKSHIRE   Daventry

Northampton

Ashton **26**
27 Sulgrave

BEDFORDSHIRE

OXFORDSHIRE   BUCKS

101

WHERE TO STAY (MIDDLE ENGLAND)

Parks in this region are listed in alphabetical order of place name, and then in alphabetical order of establishment. A contact address is given where it differs from the address of the establishment.

Map references refer to the colour location maps at the back of this guide. The first number indicates the map to use; the letter and number which follow refer to the grid reference on the map.

At-a-glance symbols can be found inside the back cover flap.

Keep this open for easy reference.

BAKEWELL

Derbyshire
Map ref 5B2

Pleasant market town, famous for its pudding. It is set in beautiful countryside on the River Wye and is an excellent centre for exploring the Derbyshire Dales, the Peak District National Park, Chatsworth and Haddon Hall.
Tourist Information Centre ☎ (01629) 813227

Greenhills Caravan Park
⊖✓✓✓
Member BH&HPA
Crow Hill Lane, Bakewell DE45 1PX
☎ (01629) 813467 & 813052
Fax (01629) 815131
From Bakewell, signposted Buxton, 1 mile north west on the main A6 trunk road and turn left. Signposted.
4.4 hectares (11 acres). Level, sloping, grassy, hard.
100 touring pitches

100	🚐	£9.00—£10.00
100	🚏	£8.00—£9.00
100	▲	£8.00—£9.00

60 units not for hire

Information on accommodation listed in this guide has been supplied by the proprietors. As changes may occur you are advised to check details at the time of booking.

BOSTON

Lincolnshire
Map ref 4A1

Historic town famous for its church tower, the Boston Stump, 272 ft high. Still a busy port, the town is full of interest and has links with Boston, Massachusetts, through the Pilgrim Fathers. The cells where they were imprisoned can be seen in the medieval Guildhall.
Tourist Information Centre ☎ (01205) 356656

Orchard Caravan Park ⚏
⊖✓✓✓
Member BH&HPA
Frampton Lane, Hubberts Bridge, Boston PE20 3QU
☎ (01205) 290328
Fax (01205) 290247
From A17 trunk road, take A1121 towards Boston. At Junction with the B1192 take Hubberts Bridge turn. Frampton Lane is 1st turn on left. Orchard Park is 0.25m. Signposted.
3.6 hectares (9 acres). Level, grassy, sheltered.
30 touring pitches

30	🚏	£7.00—£7.00

120 units not for hire
Open March—October

All accommodation in this guide has been graded, or is awaiting a grading, by a trained Tourist Board inspector.

BUXTON

Derbyshire
Map ref 5B2

The highest market town in England and one of the oldest spas, with an elegant Crescent, Poole's Cavern, Opera House and attractive Pavilion Gardens. An excellent centre for exploring the Peak District.
Tourist Information Centre ☎ (01298) 25106

Cottage Farm Caravan Park ⚏
⊖✓✓✓
Member BH&HPA
Blackwell, Buxton SK17 9TQ
☎ Taddington (0129885) 330
Off the A6, midway between Buxton and Bakewell. Signposted.
1.2 hectares (3 acres). Grassy, hard.
30 touring pitches

30	🚏	£5.50
30	▲	£5.50—£6.50
1	🚐	

Newhaven Caravan and Camping Park
⊖✓✓✓
Member BH&HPA
Newhaven, Buxton SK17 0DT
☎ Hartington (01298) 84300
Halfway between Ashbourne & Buxton on A515 at A5012 Junct. Signposted.
12 hectares (30 acres). Level, sloping, grassy.
95 touring pitches

95	🚐	£7.00—£8.00
95	🚏	£7.00—£8.00
95	▲	£7.00—£8.00

70 units not for hire
Open March–October

🔲🔲🔲🔲🔲🔲🔲🔲🔲🔲🔲🔲🔲🔲
🔲🔲🔲

CASTLE DONINGTON

Leicestershire
Map ref 5C3

A Norman castle once stood here. The world's largest collection of single-seater racing cars is displayed at Donington Park alongside the racing circuit, and an Aeropark Visitor Centre can be seen at nearby East Midlands International Airport.

Park Farmhouse Caravan Park ⚠

⊖✓✓✓

Melbourne Road, Isley Walton, Castle Donington, Derby DE74 2RN
☎ Derby (01332) 862409
Fax (01332) 862364
At Isley Walton on the A453 take the Melbourne turn. The entrance is 0.5 miles on the right adjacent to the Park Farmhouse Hotel. Signposted.
2.8 hectares (7 acres). Grassy, sheltered.
34 touring pitches

26	🚐	£9.00—£12.00
8	🚚	£9.00—£12.00

Open March–December
Cards accepted: Access, Visa

🔲🔲🔲🔲🔲🔲🔲🔲🔲🔲🔲🔲🔲

MABLETHORPE

Lincolnshire
Map ref 5D2

Holiday resort with miles of sandy beaches and many facilities for families, including a wide range of sporting activities, and the Animal Gardens.
Tourist Information Centre ☎ (01507) 472496

Kirkstead Holiday Park

⊖✓✓✓

North Road, Trusthorpe, Mablethorpe LN12 2QD
☎ (01507) 441483
Take the A52 from Sutton-on-Sea or Mablethorpe and enter Trusthorpe. Turn off at the island and look for Kirkstead signs. Signposted.
2 hectares (5 acres). Level.
60 touring pitches

30	🚚	£6.00—£9.00
30	🅰	£4.50—£6.50
7	🛖	£80.00—£250.00

33 units not for hire

🔲🔲🔲🔲🔲🔲🔲🔲🔲🔲🔲🔲🔲🔲
🔲🔲🔲🔲🔲🔲

MANBY

Lincolnshire
Map ref 5D2

Manby Caravan Park ⚠

⊖✓✓✓✓

Manby Middlegate, Manby, Louth LN11 8SX
☎ Louth (01507) 328232
Fax (01507) 328232
After approx 2 miles out of Louth on the A157 turn left at the roundabout onto the B1200, the site is 3 miles on the left. Signposted.
2 hectares (5 acres). Level, grassy, sheltered.
125 touring pitches

125	🚐	£8.00—£8.00
125	🚚	£8.00—£8.00
125	🅰	£8.00—£8.00

Open March–October
Cards accepted: Access, Visa, Diners, Amex, Switch/Delta

🔲🔲🔲🔲🔲🔲🔲🔲🔲🔲🔲🔲🔲🔲
🔲🔲🔲

MARKET RASEN

Lincolnshire
Map ref 5D2

Market town on the edge of the Lincolnshire Wolds. The racecourse and the picnic site and forest walks at Willingham Woods are to the east of the town.

Walesby Woodlands Caravan Park ⚠

⊖✓✓✓✓

Walesby Road, Walesby, Market Rasen LN8 3UN
☎ (01673) 843285
From Market Rasen take the B1203 towards Tealby, turn left after 0.75 miles to Walesby. Signposted.
1 hectares (2.5 acres). Level, grassy, sheltered.
60 touring pitches

60	🚐	£6.50—£7.50
60	🚚	£6.50—£7.50
60	🅰	£6.50—£7.50

Open March–October

🔲🔲🔲🔲🔲🔲🔲🔲🔲🔲🔲🔲🔲🔲
🔲🔲🔲🔲

The symbols in each entry give information about services and facilities. A 'key' to these symbols appears at the back of this guide.

MATLOCK

Derbyshire
Map ref 5B2

The town lies beside the narrow valley of the River Derwent surrounded by steep wooded hills. Good centre for exploring Derbyshire's best scenery.

Darwin Forest Country Park ⚠

⊖✓✓✓✓

Darley Moor, Two Dales, Matlock DE4 5LN
☎ (01629) 732428
Fax (01629) 735015
From A6 turn onto the B5057 towards Chesterfield, 3 miles on the left hand side. Signposted.
17.6 hectares (44 acres). Level, grassy, hard, sheltered.
50 touring pitches

50	🚐	£10.00—£12.00
50	🚚	£10.00—£12.00
25	🅰	£10.00—£12.00

5 units not for hire
Cards accepted: Access, Visa

🔲🔲🔲🔲🔲🔲🔲🔲🔲🔲🔲🔲🔲🔲
🔲🔲🔲🔲🔲🔲🔲🔲

NEWARK

Nottinghamshire
Map ref 5C2

The town has many fine old houses and ancient inns near the large, cobbled market-place. Substantial ruins of the 12th C castle, where King John died, dominate the riverside walk and there are several interesting museums. Sherwood Forest is nearby.
Tourist Information Centre ☎ (01636) 78962

Milestone Caravan Park ⚠

⊖✓✓✓✓✓

Milestone House, North Road, Cromwell, Newark NG23 6JE
☎ (01636) 821244
Leave A1 4.5 m N. Newark as directed by signs for Cromwell.
1.6 hectares (4 acres). Level, grassy, hard.
60 touring pitches

30	🚐	£6.00—£7.50
30	🚚	£6.00—£7.50
10	🅰	£5.00—£7.50

🔲🔲🔲🔲🔲🔲🔲🔲🔲🔲🔲🔲🔲

OAKHAM

Leicestershire
Map ref 5C3

Pleasant former county town of Rutland. Fine 12th C Great Hall, part of its castle, with a historic collection of horseshoes. An octagonal Butter Cross stands in the market-place and Rutland County Museum, Rutland Farm Park and Rutland Water are of interest. *Tourist Information Centre ☎ (01572) 724329*

Hillground Park ⋀⋀
Member BH&HPA
Ranksborough Hall, Langham, Oakham LE15 7SR
☎ (01572) 722984
Fax (01572) 723602
Main A606 at Langham Village Signposted.
14 hectares (35 acres). Grassy, hard, sheltered.
120 touring pitches

120	🚐	£7.50—£10.50
120	🚚	£6.50—£9.50
120	⛺	£7.50—£9.50

120 units not for hire

🚗 P 🖂 🔌 🅰 🛒 🔥 🛆 🕯 🕓 🏴 ✕ 🍽 🛋 🖥 ✂ 🛒 ⊙ 🔍 ⋀ 🥄 ▲

RADCLIFFE-ON-TRENT

Nottinghamshire
Map ref 5C2

Large village adjacent to the A52 Nottingham to Grantham road, perched on the steep, wooded banks of the Trent, with bird sanctuaries and wonderful views.

Thornton's Holt Camping Park ⋀⋀
⊖✓✓✓
Stragglethorpe, Radcliffe-on-Trent, Nottingham NG12 2JZ
☎ Nottingham (0115) 933 2125
Fax (0115) 933 3318
3 miles east of Nottingham on the A52. Turn south at traffic lights on road signed to Cropwell Bishop. Park is 0.5 miles on the left. Signposted.
5.6 hectares (14 acres). Level, grassy, hard, sheltered.
90 touring pitches

90	🚐	£6.50—£7.50
90	🚚	£6.50—£7.50
90	⛺	£6.50—£7.50

🚗 P 🔌 🅰 🛒 🔥 🛆 🕯 🕓 🛒 🛋 🖥 ✂ 🚗 ⊙ 🔍 ⋀ 🥄 🅤 🏴 ▲

SKEGNESS

Lincolnshire
Map ref 5D2

Famous seaside resort with 6 miles of sandy beaches and bracing air. Attractions include swimming pools, bowling greens, gardens, Natureland Marine Zoo, golf-courses and a wide range of entertainment at the Embassy Centre. Nearby is Gibraltar Point Nature Reserve. *Tourist Information Centre ☎ (01754) 764821*

North Shore Holiday Centre ⋀⋀
⊖✓✓✓✓
Roman Bank, Skegness PE25 1SL
☎ (01754) 763815 & 762051
800 yards North of Skegness on A52 Signposted.
16 hectares (40 acres). Level.
250 touring pitches

| 250 | 🚚 | £7.00—£8.00 |
| 15 | 🏠 | £110.00—£275.00 |

380 units not for hire
Open March—October
Cards accepted: Access, Visa

🔌 🚗 🖥 🅰 🛒 🔥 🛆 🕯 🕓 🛒 ✕ 🍽 🖥 ✂ 🛒 ⊙ ⋀ 🔍 🥄 🎵 ▲ ◉

Richmond Holiday Centre ⋀⋀
⊖✓✓✓✓
Member BH&HPA
Richmond Drive, Skegness PE25 3TQ
☎ (01754) 762097
Fax (01754) 765631
A158 from Burgh turn right at the lights on the A52, 1st left past the taxi rank. Signposted.
20 hectares (50 acres). Level, grassy.
186 touring pitches

186	🚐	£7.00—£12.50
186	🚚	£7.00—£12.50
120	🏠	£90.00—£270.00

513 units not for hire
Open March—November
Cards accepted: Access, Visa, Switch/Delta

🚗 🖥 🔌 🅰 🛒 🔥 🛆 🕯 🕓 🛒 ✕ 🍽 📺 🛋 🖥 ✂ 🚗 ⊙ 🔍 ⋀ 🥄 🎵 ▲

SWINDERBY

Lincolnshire
Map ref 5C2

Oakhill Leisure ⋀⋀
⊖✓✓✓✓
Oakhill Farm, Swinderby, Lincoln LN6 9QG
☎ Lincoln (01522) 868771
Fax (01522) 868771
Just off A46 towards Lincoln. Turn down through RAF Swinderby to T junction,

turn right past gravel works, then right down farm track.
30 hectares (75 acres). Level, grassy.
60 touring pitches

60	🚐	£5.00
60	🚚	£5.00
60	⛺	£3.00

P 🔌 🅰 🛒 🔥 🛆 🕯 ✂ 🚗 ⋀ 🅤 🥄 ▲

WORKSOP

Nottinghamshire
Map ref 5C2

Market town close to the Dukeries, where a number of Ducal families had their estates, some of which, like Clumber Park, may be visited. The upper room of the 14th C gatehouse of the priory housed the country's first elementary school in 1628. *Tourist Information Centre ☎ (01909) 501148*

Riverside Caravan Park ⋀⋀
⊖✓✓✓✓✓
Member BH&HPA
Worksop Cricket Club, Central Avenue, Worksop S80 1ER
☎ (01909) 474118
Signed from the junction of the A57 Worksop bypass with the A60 Mansfield road to town centre. Signposted.
1.8 hectares (4.5 acres). Level, grassy, hard.
45 touring pitches

45	🚐	£4.50
45	🚚	£4.50
45	⛺	£4.50

Open January, March—December

🚗 🖥 🔌 🅰 🛒 🔥 🛆 🕯 🕓 🍽 🛋 🖥 ⊙ 🥄 ▲

EAST ANGLIA

East Anglia is the ideal 'get away from it all' destination. Here you can play golf, go fishing, follow the region's nature trails or discover the pastoral beauty of Constable country.

Pretty Hertfordshire villages await you, along with the sleepy charms of the Broads, England's newest National Park.

The untamed coastline boasts a number of much-loved seaside resorts like Great Yarmouth, Clacton and Southend-on-Sea while inland, Aldeburgh hosts a famous music festival.

Discover markets, vineyards and the gourmet delights of Cromer crab, Suffolk ham and Colchester oysters, as memorable as the surroundings in which you'll savour them.

FOR MORE INFORMATION CONTACT:
East Anglia Tourist Board
Toppesfield Hall, Hadleigh, Suffolk IP7 5DN
Tel: (01473) 822922 **Fax:** (01473) 823063

Where to Go in East Anglia - see pages 106-109
Where to Stay in East Anglia - see pages 110-116

EAST ANGLIA

Where to Go and What to See

You will find hundreds of interesting places to visit during your stay in East Anglia, just some of which are listed in these pages. The number against each name will help you locate it on the map (page 109). Contact any Tourist Information Centre in the region for more ideas on days out in East Anglia.

1 Wells Walsingham Railway
Stiffkey Road,
Wells-next-the-Sea,
Norfolk NR23 1QB
Tel: (01328) 856506
Four miles of railway. The longest 10¼ railway in the World. New locomotive Norfolk Hero now in service, largest of its kind ever built.

2 Thursford Collection
Thursford Green,
Thursford, Fakenham,
Norfolk NR21 0AS
Tel: (01328) 878477
Live musical shows, nine mechanical organs and Wurlitzer show starring Robert Wolfe.

3 Pensthorpe Waterfowl Park
Pensthorpe, Fakenham,
Norfolk NR21 0LN
Tel: (01328) 851465
Large waterfowl and wildfowl collection. Information centre, conservation shop, adventure play area, walks and nature trails. Licensed restaurant.

4 Norfolk Lavender
Caley Mill, Heacham,
King's Lynn, Norfolk PE31 7JE
Tel: (01485) 570384
Lavender is distilled from the flowers and the oil made in to a wide range of gifts. Slide show when distillery not working.

5 Sandringham
Sandringham, King's Lynn,
Norfolk PE35 6EN
Tel: (01553) 772675
Country retreat of HM The Queen. Delightful house and 60-acres of grounds and lakes. Museum of vehicles and royal memorabilia.

6 Banham Zoo
The Grove, Banham,
Norwich, Norfolk NR16 2HE
Tel: (01953) 887771
See some of the world's rare and endangered species.

**7 Sainsbury Centre
for Visual Arts**
University of East Anglia,

Norwich, Norfolk NR4 7TJ
Tel: (01603) 456060
The Robert and Lisa Sainsbury Collection of modern and non modern art is wide-ranging and of international importance. Housed in a building purpose designed by N Foster.

8 Sea Life Centre
Marine Parade, Great Yarmouth,
Norfolk NR30 3AH
Tel: (01493) 330631
Walk under a tropical reef. Shark tank, Ray fish and British sharks, plus 25 themed displays depicting British marine life and local settings.

**9 Somerleyton Hall
and Gardens**
Somerleyton, Lowestoft,
Suffolk NR32 5QQ
Tel: (01502) 730224
Anglo-Italian-style building with state rooms, maze. Garden with azaleas and rhododendrons. Miniature railway, shop, light luncheons and teas.

10 East Anglia Transport Museum
Chapel Road, Carlton Colville,
Lowestoft, Suffolk NR33 8BL
Tel: (01502) 518459
A working museum with one of the widest ranges of street transport vehicles on display - and in action!

11 Pleasurewood Hills
Corton, Lowestoft,
Suffolk NR32 5DZ
Tel: (01502) 508200
Log flume, chair lift, cine 180, two railways, pirate ship, fort, Aladdin's cave, parrot and sealion shows, roller coasters, waveswinger, Eye in the Sky, Star Ride Enterprise.

12 Otter Trust
Earsham, Bungay,
Suffolk NR35 2AF
Tel: (01986) 893470
A breeding and conservation headquarters with the largest collection of otters in the world. Also lakes with collection of waterfowl and deer.

13 Bressingham Steam Museum and Gardens
Bressingham, Diss,
Norfolk IP22 2AB
Tel: (01379) 687386
Steam rides through five miles of woodland, garden and nursery.

Mainline locomotives and over 50 steam engines. Alan Bloom's Dell Garden.

14 Sacrewell Farm and Country Centre
Sacrewell, Thornhaugh,
Peterborough,
Cambridgeshire PE8 6HJ
Tel: (01780) 782222
500-acre farm, with working watermill, farmhouse gardens, shrubberies, nature and general interest trails, 18C buildings, displays of farm, rural and domestic bygones.

15 Ely Cathedral
Chapter House,
The College, Ely,
Cambridgeshire CB7 4DN
Tel: (01353) 667735
One of England's finest cathedrals. Fine out buildings. Guided tours and tours of Octagon and West Tower. Brass rubbing and stained glass museum.

16 Pakenham Water Mill
Mill Road,
Grimestone End, Pakenham,
Bury St Edmunds,
Suffolk IP3 2NB
Tel: (01787) 247179
18C working water mill on Domesday site, with oil engine and other subsidiary machinery.

17 Framlingham Castle
Framlingham, Woodbridge,
Suffolk IP13 9BP
Tel: (01728) 724189
12C curtain walls with 13 towers and Tudor brick chimneys. Built by Bigod family, Earls of Norfolk. Wall walk. 17C almshouses. Home of Mary Tudor in 1553.

18 Imperial War Museum
Duxford Airfield, Duxford,
Cambridgeshire CB2 4QR
Tel: (01223) 835000
Over 120 aircraft on display, tanks, vehicles, guns. Ride simulator, adventure playground, shops and restaurant.

19 National Horseracing Museum
99 High Street, Newmarket,
Suffolk CB8 8JL
Tel: (01638) 667333
Five permanent galleries telling the story of horseracing. Opened by the Queen in 1983. British sporting art. Temporary Exhibition Gallery.

20 Ickworth House, Park and Gardens
Ickworth, Bury St Edmunds,
Suffolk IP29 5QE
Tel: (01284) 735270
Extraordinary oval house with flanking wings begun in 1795. Fine paintings and beautiful collection of Georgian silver. Italian garden and park designed by Capability Brown.

21 Helmingham Hall Gardens
Helmingham,
Suffolk IP14 6EF
Tel: (01473) 890363
*Moated and walled garden with
many rare roses and possibly the
best kitchen garden in Britain. Also
highland cattle and safari rides in
park to view red and fallow deer.*

22 Shuttleworth Collection
Old Warden Aerodrome,
Biggleswade,
Bedfordshire SG18 9ER
Tel: (01767) 627288
*Unique historic collection of aircraft
from 1909 Bleriot to 1942 Spitfire
in flying condition. Cars dating from
1898 Panhard.*

23 Audley End House and Park
Saffron Walden,
Essex CB11 4JF
Tel: (01799) 522842
*Palatial Jacobean house remodelled
in the 18-19C. Magnificent Great
Hall. Rooms and furniture by
Robert Adam. Park by Capability
Brown.*

24 Woburn Abbey
Woburn,
Milton Keynes,
Bedfordshire MK43 0TP
Tel: (01525) 290666
*18C Palladian mansion altered by
Henry Holland, the Prince Regent's
architect. Contains a collection of
English silver, French and English
furniture and an important art
collection.*

25 Mountfitchet Castle
Stansted Mountfitchet,
Essex CM24 8SP
Tel: (01279) 813237
*Reconstructed Norman motte-and-
bailey castle and village of
Domesday period. Grand Hall,
church, prison, seige tower and
weapons.*

26 Colchester Castle
Colchester,
Essex CO1 1TJ
Tel: (01206) 282931
*Norman Keep on foundations of
Roman Temple, archaeological
material includes much on Roman
Colchester.*

**27 Whipsnade Wild Animal
Park**
Zoological Society of London,
Dunstable,
Bedfordshire LU6 2LF
Tel: (01582) 872171
*Over 2,500 animals set in 600
acres of beautiful parkland. Great
Whipsnade Railway. Free animal
demonstrations.*

28 Hatfield House
Hatfield Park, Hatfield,
Hertfordshire AL9 5NQ
Tel: (01707) 262823
*Jacobean house built in 1611 and
Old Palace built in 1497. Contains
famous paintings, fine furniture and
possessions of Queen Elizabeth I.
Extensive park and gardens.*

29 The Gardens of the Rose
The Royal National Rose Society,
Chiswell Green,
St Albans,
Hertfordshire AL2 3NR
Tel: (01727) 850461
*The Royal National Rose
Society's Garden, 20 acres of
showground and trial grounds for
new varieties of rose. 30,000
roses of all types with 1,700
different varieties.*

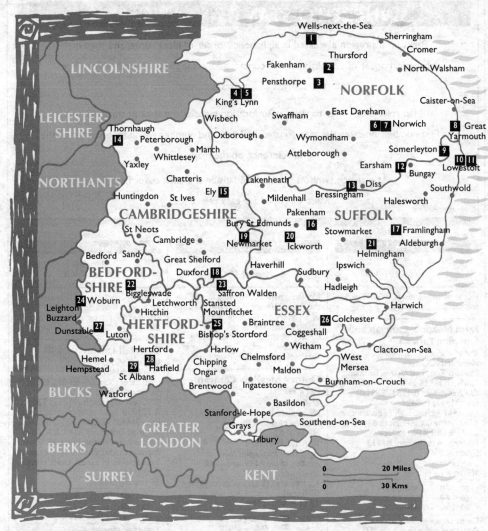

Wells-next-the-Sea
1
Sherringham
Cromer
Thursford
2
North Walsham
Fakenham
Pensthorpe
3
NORFOLK
Caister-on-Sea
4 5
King's Lynn
LINCOLNSHIRE
Wisbech
Swaffham
East Dareham
6 7 Norwich
8 Great Yarmouth
LEICESTER-SHIRE
Thornhaugh
Peterborough
14
Oxborough
Wymondham
Somerleyton
9
March
Attleborough
10 11
Whittlesey
Earsham
12
Bungay
Lowestoft
Yaxley
Bressingham
Diss
Southwold
NORTHANTS
Chatteris
Lakenheath
13
Halesworth
Ely 15
Mildenhall
Huntingdon
St Ives
Pakenham
SUFFOLK
CAMBRIDGESHIRE
Bury St Edmunds
16
St Neots
Stowmarket
17 Framlingham
Cambridge
19
Newmarket
20
Ickworth
Aldeburgh
Ickworth
21
Helmingham
Bedford
Sandy
Great Shelford
Duxford 18
Haverhill
Ipswich
BEDFORD-SHIRE
22
Biggleswade
Sudbury
Hadleigh
Leighton Buzzard
24
Woburn
Letchworth
Stansted
23
Saffron Walden
Harwich
Dunstable
27
Luton
Hitchin
Mountfitchet
25
Braintree
ESSEX
26 Colchester
HERTFORD-SHIRE
Bishop's Stortford
Coggeshall
Hertford
Harlow
Witham
Clacton-on-Sea
Hemel Hempstead
28
Hatfield
Chipping Ongar
Chelmsford
West Mersea
St Albans
Maldon
BUCKS
Watford
Brentwood
Ingatestone
Burnham-on-Crouch
29
GREATER LONDON
Stanford-le-Hope
Basildon
Grays
Southend-on-Sea
BERKS
Tilbury
SURREY
KENT

0   20 Miles
0   30 Kms

FIND OUT MORE

Further information about
holidays and attractions in
East Anglia is available from:
East Anglia Tourist Board,
Toppesfield Hall,
Hadleigh,
Suffolk IP7 5DN.
Tel: (01473) 822922

These publications are available
from the East Anglia Tourist
Board (post free):
■ **Great Escapes** - short breaks
■ **Touring Map** - bed &
breakfast and camping
■ **Freedom Holiday Parks
in Eastern England**

Also available are (prices include
postage and packaging):
■ **East Anglia Guide** £4.50
■ **Gardens to Visit in East
Anglia** £1.99

WHERE TO STAY (EAST ANGLIA)

Parks in this region are listed in alphabetical order of place name, and then in alphabetical order of establishment. A contact address is given where it differs from the address of the establishment.

Map references refer to the colour location maps at the back of this guide.

The first number indicates the map to use; the letter and number which follow refer to the grid reference on the map.

At-a-glance symbols can be found inside the back cover flap.

Keep this open for easy reference.

BANHAM
Norfolk
Map ref 4B1

Home of an extensive wildlife park and monkey sanctuary.

Farm Meadow Caravan and Camping Park ⋀
⊖✓✓✓✓✓
Member NCC
Banham Zoo, The Grove, Banham, Norwich NR16 2HE
☎ Quidenham (01953) 888370
Fax (01953) 888427
From A11 Attleborough to Banham on B1077 New Buckenham to B1113 to Banham. Diss A140 to New Buckenham to Banham B1113. Signposted.
Level, grassy.
100 touring pitches

80	🚐	£6.50—£8.00
80	🚏	£6.50—£8.00
20	⛺	£5.00—£5.00

Cards accepted: Access, Visa
🅿 🖀 🛋 🐾 🔥 ◊ ☎ ⛽ ⚡ ✗ 🍴 🍲 ⬚ ◎ ✓ ☉
✗ ♫ ⚓ ◉

> Please check prices and other details at the time of booking.

> All accommodation in this guide has been graded, or is awaiting a grading, by a trained Tourist Board inspector.

BUNGAY
Suffolk
Map ref 4C1

Market town and yachting centre on the River Waveney with the remains of a great 12th C castle. In the market-place stands the Butter Cross, rebuilt in 1689 after being largely destroyed by fire. Nearby at Earsham is the Otter Trust.

Outney Meadow Caravan Park ⋀
⊖✓✓✓✓
Member BH&HPA
Outney Meadow, Bungay
NR35 1HG
☎ (01986) 892338
Signposted from roundabout at junction of the A144 and A143. Signposted.
3.2 hectares (8 acres). Level, grassy, sheltered.
45 touring pitches

45	🚐	£6.00—£10.00
45	🚏	£6.00—£10.00
45	⛺	£6.00—£10.00

20 units not for hire
Open April–October
🖀 🛋 🐾 🔥 ◊ ☎ ⛽ ⬚ ◎ ✓ ⬛ ☉ ⚓ ✗
⮑ ✗ ♫ ⚓ ◉

> Information on accommodation listed in this guide has been supplied by the proprietors. As changes may occur you are advised to check details at the time of booking.

CAISTER-ON-SEA
Norfolk
Map ref 4C1

Seaside resort close to Great Yarmouth. Remains of Roman commercial port can still be seen here.

Old Hall Leisure Park ⋀
⊖✓✓✓✓ Rose Award
Member BH&HPA
High Street, Caister-on-Sea, Great Yarmouth NR30 5JL
☎ Great Yarmouth (01493) 720400 & 721830
Fax (01493) 720261
Site is on junction of A149 & A1064 next to police station. Entrance opposite Caister Church. Signposted.
1.6 hectares (4 acres). Level, grassy, sheltered.
38 touring pitches

38	🚐	£6.00—£9.00
38	🚏	£6.00—£9.00
34	🏠	£75.00—£290.00

2 units not for hire
Open April–October
Cards accepted: Access, Visa, Switch/Delta
🛋 🅰 🅿 🐾 🔥 ◊ ☎ ⛽ ✗ 🍴 🍲 ⬚ ◎ ✓
🔲 ☉ ◕ 🏔 ⚓ ✗ ♫ ⚓

> The symbols in each entry give information about services and facilities. A 'key' to these symbols appears at the back of this guide.

CAMBRIDGE

Cambridgeshire
Map ref 3D1

A most important and beautiful city on the River Cam with 31 colleges forming one of the oldest universities in the world. Numerous museums, good shopping centre, restaurants, theatres, cinema and fine bookshops.
Tourist Information Centre ☎ (01223) 322640

Highfield Farm Camping Park ⚠

❶✓✓✓✓✓
Member BH&HPA
Long Road, Comberton, Cambridge CB3 7DG
☎ (01223) 262308
Fax (01223) 262308
From Cambridge take A1303/A428 (Bedford), after 3 miles turn left at roundabout, signs to Comberton. From M11 take A603 (Sandy) at junction 12 for 0.5 mile, take B1046 to Comberton. Signposted.
2.8 hectares (7 acres). Level, grassy, hard, sheltered.
120 touring pitches

60	🚐	£7.00—£8.25
60	🚚	£6.75—£8.00
60	⛺	£6.75—£8.00

Open April–October
⚓P🅿🎌📻🔥♨️🛢️⛽🔌×🚽♿💷◉⛺/🚿🔻
⊙/🚻♿
Ad See display advertisement on this page

The ⚠ symbol after an establishment name indicates that it is a Regional Tourist Board member.

CLACTON-ON-SEA

Essex
Map ref 4B3

Developed in the 1870s into a popular holiday resort with pier, pavilion, funfair, theatres and traditional amusements. The Martello Towers on the seafront were built like many others in the early 19th C to defend Britain against Napoleon.
Tourist Information Centre ☎ (01255) 423400

Highfield Holiday Park ⚠

❶✓✓✓✓ Rose Award
Member BH&HPA
London Road, Clacton-on-Sea CO16 9QY
☎ (01255) 424244
Fax (01255) 474646
A12 to Colchester outer limits, then A120 Colchester/Harwich road as far as the A133, A133 to B1441 Clacton-on-Sea, Highfield is on the B1441. Signposted.
18 hectares (45 acres). Sloping, grassy, sheltered.
160 touring pitches

160	🚐	£14.00—£15.00
160	🚚	
82	⛺	

250 units not for hire
Open April–October
Cards accepted: Access, Visa, Switch/Delta
⚓P🅿🎌🔥♨️🛢️⛽×🚽📺💷◉/
🛢️⊙♿♨️🔻×♪♿◎

Valley Farm Caravan Park ⚠

❶✓✓✓✓ Rose Award
Member BH&HPA
Valley Farm Camping Ground Ltd,
Valley Road, Clacton-on-Sea CO15 6LY
☎ (01255) 422484
Fax (01255) 422484
Follow the A133 to the fire station roundabout turn left onto B1027 and follow signs to Valley Farm.

20.8 hectares (52 acres). Sloping, grassy.
39 touring pitches

36	🚐	£7.00—£13.00
36	🚚	£7.00—£13.00
115	⛺	£85.00—£380.00

692 units not for hire
Open March–October
⚓P🅿🎌🔥♨️🛢️⛽🔌×🚽📺💷◉
/🛢️⊙♿♨️🔻×🔺♪♿

CLIPPESBY

Norfolk
Map ref 4C1

Clippesby Holidays ⚠

❶✓✓✓✓✓
Member BH&HPA
Clippesby, Great Yarmouth NR29 3BJ
☎ Great Yarmouth (01493) 369367
Fax (01493) 368181
From the A47 roundabout at Acle, take the A1064 (Caister-on-Sea) Road for 2 miles. Turn left on B1152, 1st left 0.5 miles. From A149 Potter Heigham, 1.5 miles turn right. Turn opposite village sign then 1st drive on right. Signposted.
13.6 hectares (34 acres). Level, grassy, sheltered.
100 touring pitches
Open May–October
Cards accepted: Access, Visa, Switch/Delta
⚓P🅿🎌📻🔥♨️🛢️⛽🔌×🚽💷◉/
🛢️⊙♿♨️🔻🔺♿💷🔺×♿T◎

Map references apply to the colour maps at the back of this guide.

A key to symbols can be found inside the back cover flap.

COLCHESTER

Essex
Map ref 4B2

Britain's oldest recorded town standing on the River Colne and famous for its oysters. Numerous historic buildings, ancient remains and museums. Plenty of parks and gardens, extensive shopping centre, theatre and zoo.
Tourist Information Centre ☎ (01206) 282920

Colchester Camping and Caravanning Park ⋀
☺✓✓✓✓
Cymbeline Way, Lexden, Colchester CO3 4AG
☎ (01206) 45551
A12 then A134 slip road to Colchester, follow Tourist road signs. Signposted.
4.8 hectares (12 acres). Level, grassy, hard.
251 touring pitches

| 251 | 🚐 | £7.00—£9.80 |
| 251 | ▲ | £7.00—£9.80 |

Cards accepted: Access, Visa
🚗🅿📱📶📻♨♀⊙⚡🅿📷🧺 ⊙⛰♨

CROMER

Norfolk
Map ref 4C1

Once a small fishing village and now famous for its fishing boats that still work off the beach and offer freshly caught crabs. Excellent bathing on sandy beaches fringed by cliffs. The town boasts a fine pier, theatre, museum and a lifeboat station.
Tourist Information Centre ☎ (01263) 512497

Forest Park Caravan Site
☺✓✓✓✓
Northrepps Road, Northrepps, Cromer NR27 0JR
☎ (01263) 513290
Fax (01263) 513290
Turn right off A140 at Northrepps, turn immediately left under Railway Bridge to T Junction, turn left. Forest Park entrance on right. Signposted.
34 hectares (85 acres). Sloping, grassy, stony, sheltered.
338 touring pitches

| 338 | 🚐 | £6.50—£10.00 |
| 55 | 🚐 | £6.50—£10.00 |

402 units not for hire
Open March–October
Cards accepted: Access, Visa
🅿📱📶📻♨♀⊙⚡❌📷🧺 ⊙⛰♨⊙✈♀🗙♫♨◎

Seacroft Caravan Park ⋀
☺✓✓✓✓
Member BH&HPA
Runton Road, Cromer NR27 9NJ
☎ (01263) 511722
Fax (01263) 511512
0.25m W. of Cromer on A149 Coast Rd. Signposted.
2 hectares (5 acres). Level, sloping, grassy, sheltered.
120 touring pitches

120	🚐	£8.50—£11.50
120	🚐	£8.50—£11.50
120	▲	£8.50—£11.50

Open March–October
Cards accepted: Access, Visa, Switch/Delta
🚗📶⊙♀📻♨⊙♀⚡❌♀📺🧺📷 ♀🅿⊙♨⛰♨⊙♫♨

DISS

Norfolk
Map ref 4B2

Old market town built around 3 sides of the Mere, a placid water of 6 acres. Although modernised, some interesting Tudor, Georgian and Victorian buildings around the market-place remain. St Mary's church has a fine knapped flint chancel.
Tourist Information Centre ☎ (01379) 650523

Honeypot Camping and Caravan Park
☺✓✓
Wortham, Eye, Suffolk IP22 1PW
☎ Mellis (01379) 783312
Fax (01379) 783293
16 miles east on A143 from Bury St Edmunds, or 4 miles west of Diss on A143. Site entrance on South Side of A143. Signposted.
4 hectares (10 acres). Level, grassy, sheltered.
35 touring pitches

35	🚐	£7.50—£7.50
35	🚐	£7.50—£7.50
35	▲	£5.50—£7.50

Open April–October
Cards accepted: Access
🚗⊙📻♨♀📻♨⊙⚡🧺📷🧺 ♀🅿⊙♫►

National gradings and classifications were correct at the time of going to press but are subject to change. Please check at the time of booking.

DUNWICH

Suffolk
Map ref 4C2

Due to sea erosion Dunwich is now just a small quiet village, but it was once the capital of East Anglia and a thriving port. The main street, containing a museum and inn, leads to the beach. To the south of the village is Dunwich Common (National Trust).

Cliff House (Dunwich) ⋀
☺✓✓✓
Minsmere Road, Dunwich, Saxmundham IP17 3DQ
☎ Westleton (01728) 648282 & 0850 767028
Fax (01728) 648282
A12 to Yoxford. Turn rght s/p Westleton/Dunwich 3 m turn left in West. at T junction. Follow signs Dunwich Heath. Signposted.
12 hectares (30 acres). Level, grassy, sheltered.
95 touring pitches

95	🚐	£8.00—£11.00
95	🚐	£8.00—£11.00
26	▲	£6.50—£8.50
4	🛖	£120.00—£285.00

74 units not for hire
Open April–October
Cards accepted: Access, Visa, Switch/Delta
🚗📱⊙📻♨♀📻♨⊙⚡❌♀🧺📷🧺 ♀🅿⊙♨⛰♫►♨

FAKENHAM

Norfolk
Map ref 4B1

Attractive, small market town dates from Saxon times and was a Royal Manor until the 17th C. Its market place has 2 old coaching inns, both showing traces of earlier work behind Georgian facades, and the parish church has a commanding 15th C tower.

Fakenham Racecourse
☺✓✓✓✓
The Racecourse, Fakenham NR21 7NY
☎ (01328) 862388
Fax (01328) 855908
Site adjoins sports centre 1 mile south of Fakenham off A1065. Signposted.
4.56 hectares (11.4 acres). Level, grassy, sheltered.
150 touring pitches

150	🚐	£8.00—£10.00
150	🚐	£8.00—£10.00
150	▲	£8.00—£10.00

Cards accepted: Access, Visa
🏕🖧👣⚓🛢🐕🚻💺✕🍽📗📠✦🔥
☺🔍📷♠⚒

GREAT YARMOUTH

Norfolk
Map ref 4C1

One of Britain's major seaside resorts with 5 miles of seafront and every possible amenity including an award winning leisure complex offering a huge variety of all-weather facilities. Busy harbour and fishing centre.

The Grange Touring Park
⊖✓✓✓✓✓
Member BH&HPA
Ormesby St Margaret, Great
Yarmouth NR29 3QG
☎ (01493) 730306 & 730023
Fax (01493) 730188
At Junction A149 & B1159 3 miles North of Great Yarmouth. Signposted.
1.4 hectares (3.5 acres). Level, grassy, sheltered.
70 touring pitches

70	🚐	£6.30—£10.00
70	🚃	£6.30—£10.00
70	⛺	£6.30—£10.00

Open April—October
🏕P📗🖧👣⚓🛢🚻💺📠✦🔥📷☺
🔥🚩♠

Grasmere Caravan Park
(T.B.) 🏔
⊖✓✓✓
Bultitudes Loke, Yarmouth Road,
Caister-on-Sea, Great Yarmouth
NR30 5DH
☎ (01493) 720382
Take A149 from Gt. Yarmouth enter Caister at roundabout by Yarmouth stadium after half turn left 100yds past petrol station. Signposted.
2 hectares (5 acres). Level, grassy, stony, hard.
46 touring pitches

46	🚐	£5.10—£7.50
46	🚃	
10	🏠	£80.00—£250.00

53 units not for hire
Open April—October
🛢🏕👣🖧⚓🛢🚻📗📠✦🔥📷☺🔥
🍴🔥♠

Hopton Holiday Village 🏔
⊖✓✓✓✓✓ Rose Award
Member BH&HPA/NCC
Warren Lane, Hopton-on-Sea, Great
Yarmouth NR31 9BW
☎ Reservations/free brochure
(01442) 248668
Fax (01442) 232459
Signposted on A12 midway between Great Yarmouth and Lowestoft.
26 hectares (65 acres). Sloping, grassy.

| 379 | 🏠 | £120.00—£566.00 |

644 units not for hire
Open March—December
Cards accepted: Access, Visa,
Switch/Delta
🏕🛢👣⚓🚻💺✕🍽📗📠✦🔥🛢📷🔍🔥
🏔🥤🔥🎵🔥♠🆃
🅰 See display advertisement inside
front cover

Liffens Holiday Park 🏔
⊖✓✓✓✓ Rose Award
Burgh Castle, Great Yarmouth
NR31 9QB
☎ (01493) 780357
Fax (01493) 782383
From Great Yarmouth follow signs for Beccles and Lowestoft watch for turn left sign for Burgh Castle, turn right at T Junction, then follow tourist signs to Holiday Park. Signposted.
12 hectares (30 acres). Level, grassy.
150 touring pitches

100	🚐	£8.00—£11.00
100	🚃	£8.00—£11.00
50	⛺	£8.00—£11.00
35	🏠	£100.00—£350.00

50 units not for hire
Open April—October

Continued ▶

GREAT YARMOUTH

Continued

Cards accepted: Access, Visa, Switch/Delta

🏕️🚗P🅿️🚻🅰️🎣▲🚰🔌🍴✕♿📺
🍽️🏪🔥🍺🐕🏎️⛵▶️🎵♫🎡
Ad See display advertisement on this page

Vauxhall Holiday Park 🏔️
⊖✓✓✓✓✓ Rose Award
Member BH&HPA
Acle New Road, Great Yarmouth
NR30 1TB
☎ (01493) 857231
Fax (01493) 331122
Just west of Gt. Yarmouth on A47 from Norwich. Signposted.
18.8 hectares (47 acres). Level, grassy.
256 touring pitches

256	🚐	£11.00—£19.00
256	🚕	
398	🏕️	£170.00—£500.00

Open May–September
Cards accepted: Access, Visa

🏕️🚗P🅿️🚻🅰️🎣▲🚰🔌🍴✕♿📺🍽️🏪
🏎️🏪⊙🔥◀️♫🎵🚶✕🎣🎵♫🎡
Ad See display advertisement on page 113

For ideas on places to visit refer to the introduction at the beginning of this section.

The 🏔️ symbol after an establishment name indicates that it is a Regional Tourist Board member.

HARWICH

Essex
Map ref 4C2

Port where the Rivers Orwell and Stour converge and enter the North Sea. The old town still has a medieval atmosphere with its narrow streets. To the south is the seaside resort of Dovercourt with long sandy beaches.
Tourist Information Centre ☎ *(01255) 506139*

Dovercourt Caravan Park 🏔️
Member NCC
Low Road, Dovercourt, Harwich
CO12 3TZ
☎ (01255) 243433
Fax (01255) 241673
A120 from Colchester to Harwich, follow brown tourist signs from Ramsey roundabout. Signposted.
31.6 hectares (79 acres). Level, grassy.
60 touring pitches

60	🚐	£7.00—£11.00
60	🚕	£7.00—£11.00
30	🏕️	£75.00—£295.00

650 units not for hire
Open March–October
Cards accepted: Access, Visa

🏕️🚗🅿️🎣🚻🅰️🚰🔌🍴✕♿📺🍽️🏪🔥
🏎️🔥⊙🔥◀️🚶🚶▶️✕🎣🎵♫🎡🆔

Please check prices and other details at the time of booking.

All accommodation in this guide has been graded, or is awaiting a grading, by a trained Tourist Board inspector.

HODDESDON

Hertfordshire
Map ref 3D1

Several old buildings survive in this modern town including the 17th C Rawdon House, the medieval Chapel of St Katherine and Hogges Hall with its 15th C beams.

Lee Valley Caravan Park 🏔️
⊖✓✓✓✓
Member NCC
Essex Road, Hoddesdon EN11 0AS
☎ (01992) 462090
Off the A10 at the junction for Hoddesdon and turn left at the second roundabout. Signposted.
9.6 hectares (24 acres). Level, grassy, sheltered.
100 touring pitches

100	🚐	£7.29—£10.34
100	🚕	£7.29—£10.34
100	▲	£7.29—£10.34

100 units not for hire
Open April–October
Cards accepted: Access, Visa

🅿️P🚻🚗🎣▲🚰⊙🍽️🏪🔥🚗⊙🚶
🅰️🛒
Ad See display advertisement on page 44

HOUGHTON

Cambridgeshire
Map ref 4A2

Delightful village on the River Ouse popular for boating. There are many picturesque cottages and pleasant walks can be taken along the tree-shaded paths.

Houghton Mill Camping Park
⊖✓✓✓✓
Mill Street, Houghton, Huntingdon
PE17 2BJ
☎ St. Ives (01480) 462413 & 492811
On the A1123 between Huntingdon and St. Ives. Signposted.

3.8 hectares (9.5 acres). Grassy, sheltered.
65 touring pitches

50	🚐	£9.00—£9.50
50	🚚	£9.00—£9.50
25	⛺	£9.00—£9.50

Open April–October

🏕🔲🅰️🚻🛉🔌🟢🔔🦮✏/⊙↖♒↗🔥

Cambridgeshire
Map ref 4A2

Attractive, interesting town which abounds in associations with the Cromwell family. The town is connected to Godmanchester by a beautiful 14th C bridge over the River Great Ouse.
Tourist Information Centre ☎ (01480) 388588

Park Lane (Touring)
Ө✓✓✓✓
Park Lane, Godmanchester,
Huntingdon PE18 8AS
☎ (01480) 453740
Fax (01480) 453740
From A14 T northbound turn off to Godmanchester pick signs on lamp post turn right at Black Bull Pub/Memorial. Park entrance on left. Signposted.
1 hectares (2.5 acres). Level, grassy, sheltered.
50 touring pitches

50	🚐	£8.00—£8.00
50	🚚	£8.00—£8.00
50	⛺	£8.00—£8.00

Open March–October

🏕🔲🅰️🚻🛉🔌🟢🔔🦮🔲✏/🔋⊙🅰️🔥

Suffolk
Map ref 4C1

Seaside village whose church tower has served as a landmark to sailors for generations. Nearby is the Suffolk Wildlife and Country Park.

Heathland Beach Caravan Park 🕍
Ө✓✓✓✓✓ Rose Award
Member BH&HPA
London Road, Kessingland,
Lowestoft NR33 7PJ
☎ Lowestoft (01502) 740337 &
Mobile 0850 571335
Fax (01502) 742355
3 miles north of Kessingland village off old A12.
12 hectares (30 acres). Level, grassy, sheltered.
106 touring pitches

106	🚐	£9.50—£11.50
106	🚚	£9.50—£11.50
106	⛺	£9.50—£11.50
8	⛺	£170.00—£320.00

180 units not for hire
Open April–October
Cards accepted: Access, Visa

🏕🔲🅰️🚻🛉🔌🟢🔔🦮🔲✏🔲/🔋⊙🅰️♒🦮🔥🔥

Norfolk
Map ref 4C1

Beautiful cathedral city and county town on the River Wensum with many fine museums and medieval churches. Norman castle, Guildhall and interesting medieval streets. Good shopping centre and market.
Tourist Information Centre ☎ (01603) 666071

Reedham Ferry Touring and Camping Park
Ө✓✓✓
Reedham Ferry, Norwich
NR13 3HA
☎ Great Yarmouth (01493) 700429
Fax (01493) 700999
B1140 from Acle (A47) or B1140 from Beccles over ferry. Signposted.
1.6 hectares (4 acres). Level, grassy, sheltered.
20 touring pitches

10	🚚	£4.50—£10.00
10	⛺	£4.50—£10.00

Open April–October

🏕🔲🅰️🚻🛉🔌✕🔲✏↖♒🦮🔥

Essex
Map ref 4B3

Beacon Hill Leisure Park 🕍
Ө✓✓✓✓
Member BH&HPA/NCC
St. Lawrence Bay, Southminster
CM0 7LS
☎ Maldon (01621) 779248
Fax (01621) 778106
A141 Nr. Maldon B1018 to Latchingdon, take Bradwell road, 1/5 miles past steeple take left turn to St. Lawrence Bay .5 mile right hand side. Signposted.
10 hectares (25 acres). Level, grassy.
54 touring pitches

54	🚐	£6.00—£8.00
54	🚚	£6.00—£8.00
54	⛺	£6.00—£8.00

500 units not for hire
Open April–October
Cards accepted: Access, Visa,
Switch/Delta

🏕🔲🅰️🚻🛉🔌🟢🔔🦮✕♒📺🔲📠/🔋⊙🔍🅰️♒🔥

Essex
Map ref 4B3

St Osyth was the daughter of the first Christian King of East Anglia. The priory gatehouse and gardens are open to the public during the summer.

The Orchards 🕍
Ө✓✓✓
Member BH&HPA/NCC
St Osyth, Clacton-on-Sea CO16 8LJ
☎ Reservations/free brochure
(01442) 248668
Fax (01442) 232459
From Clacton-on-Sea take the B1027 out of Clacton (signposted Colchester) turn left after petrol station-then over the crossroads in St. Osyth to the park. Signposted.
66 hectares (165 acres). Sloping, grassy.
30 touring pitches

30	🚐	£7.00—£16.50
30	🚚	£7.00—£16.50
250	⛺	£109.00—£400.00

1100 units not for hire
Open March–October
Cards accepted: Access, Visa,
Switch/Delta

🏕P🚻🅰️🛉🔌🟢🔔🦮♒🔲✏/🔋🔋⊙
🔍🅰️♒↗🔥↖U↗🔔🦮♫🅰️🆃
🅰️ See display advertisement inside front cover

Norfolk
Map ref 4C1

Scratby Hall Caravan Park 🕍
Ө✓✓✓✓
Member BH&HPA
Scratby, Great Yarmouth NR29 3PH
☎ Great Yarmouth (01493) 730283
Gt. Yarmouth A149 to Caister. Onto B1159 Scratby, site signed.
2 hectares (5 acres). Level, grassy, sheltered.
108 touring pitches

108	🚐	£4.00—£9.50
108	🚚	£4.00—£9.50
108	⛺	£4.00—£9.50

Open April–October

🏕🔲🅰️🚻🛉🔌🟢🔔🦮🟢🔲✏/🔋⊙🔍🅰️♒🔥

SEA PALLING

Norfolk
Map ref 4C1

Golden Beach Holiday Centre ₳
❷✓✓✓✓
Member BH&HPA/NCC
Beach Road, Sea Palling, Norwich
NR12 0AL
☎ Hickling (01692) 598269
From Stalham take B1159. Signposted.
3.2 hectares (8 acres). Level, grassy, sheltered.
50 touring pitches

50	🚗	£5.50—£8.50
50	🚐	£5.50—£8.50
50	⛺	£5.50—£8.50
10	🏠	£85.00—£230.00

92 units not for hire
Open March–October

SNETTISHAM

Norfolk
Map ref 4B1

Village with a superb Decorated church. The 17th C Old Hall is a distinguished-looking house with Dutch gables over the 2 bays. Snettisham Pits is a reserve of the Royal Society for the Protection of Birds. Red deer herd and other animals, farm trails and nature walks at Park Farm.

Diglea Caravan and Camping Park
❷✓✓✓
Beach Road, Snettisham, King's Lynn
PE31 7RB
☎ Dersingham (01485) 541367
On A149 turn left at sign for Snettisham Beach. Signposted.
6 hectares (15 acres). Level, grassy, sheltered.
200 touring pitches

100	🚗	£5.50—£8.50
100	🚐	£5.50—£8.50
100	⛺	£5.50—£8.50
5	🏠	£150.00—£285.00

150 units not for hire
Open April–October

STANHOE

Norfolk
Map ref 4B1

The Rickels Caravan Site
❷✓✓✓✓
The Rickels, Bircham Road, Stanhoe,
King's Lynn PE31 8PU
☎ Docking (01485) 518671

Signposted.
3.2 hectares (8 acres). Level, sloping, grassy, sheltered.
30 touring pitches

15	🚗	£6.00—£7.00
10	🚐	£6.00—£7.00
5	⛺	£6.00—£6.00

Open March–October

TRIMINGHAM

Norfolk
Map ref 4C1

Woodland Caravan Park
❷✓✓✓✓
Member BH&HPA
Trimingham, Norwich NR11 8AL
☎ Southrepps (01263) 833144
Fax (01263) 833071
From Norwich to Cromer A140, join coast road B1159, site 4 miles south east of Cromer. Signposted.
8 hectares (20 acres). Level, grassy, sheltered.
110 touring pitches

| 98 | 🚐 | £6.50—£9.00 |
| 12 | 🚐 | |

150 units not for hire
Open April–October

WEST MERSEA

Essex
Map ref 4B3

Weatherboarded and Georgian brick cottages still remain as evidence of the old fishing, oyster and sailing centre and the small museum includes fishing exhibits.

Waldegraves Holiday Park ₳
❷✓✓✓✓
Member BH&HPA/NCC
Mersea Island, Colchester CO5 8SE
☎ Colchester (01206) 382898
Fax (01206) 385359
B1025 from Colchester left to East Mersea. Second on right. Follow brown tourist signs.
10 hectares (25 acres). Level, grassy, sheltered.
60 touring pitches

40	🚗	£7.00—£11.00
40	🚐	£7.00—£11.00
20	⛺	£7.00—£11.00
10	🏠	£130.00—£320.00

195 units not for hire
Open March–October
Cards accepted: Access, Visa, Switch/Delta

WOODBRIDGE

Suffolk
Map ref 4C2

Once a busy seaport, the town is now a sailing centre on the River Deben. There are many buildings of architectural merit including the Bell and Angel Inns. The 18th C Tide Mill is now restored and open to the public.

Tangham Campsite
❷✓✓✓
Butley, Woodbridge IP12 3NP
☎ Orford (01394) 450707
6m E. Woodbridge on B1084 to Orford. Signposted.
2.8 hectares (7 acres).
90 touring pitches

90	🚗	£7.00—£8.50
90	🚐	£7.00—£8.50
90	⛺	£7.00—£8.50

Open April–December

WEST COUNTRY

The West Country is famous for its wildness and beauty, legends and magic... but mostly for the breathtaking variety of its scenery.

From titanic cliffs overlooking sparkling beaches to the vastness of Dartmoor and Exmoor, then on to cosy villages nestling in verdant countryside, this most compelling of regions has inspired generations of writers and artists.

Tintagel Castle, traditionally the home of King Arthur, stares out to sea from the rugged North Cornwall coast. Stonehenge stands silent. Maritime Plymouth waits to welcome its next tide of visitors while elegant Bath and lively Salisbury bustle with life in this land of many mysteries.

FOR MORE INFORMATION CONTACT:
West Country Tourist Board
60 St Davids Hill, Exeter EX4 4SY
Tel: (01392) 425426 Fax: (01392) 420891

Where to Go in the West Country -
see pages 118-122
Where to Stay in the West Country -
see pages 123-144

WEST COUNTRY

Where to Go and What to See

You will find hundreds of interesting places to visit during your stay in the West Country, just some of which are listed in these pages. The number against each name will help you locate it on the map (pages 120-121). Contact any Tourist Information Centre in the region for more ideas on days out in the West Country.

1 Great Western Railway Museum
Faringdon Road, Swindon,
Wiltshire SN1 5BJ
Tel: (01793) 493189
Historic Great Western Railway locomotives, wide range of nameplates, models, illustrations, posters and tickets.

2 Dyrham Park
Dyrham,
Chippenham,
Wiltshire SN14 8ER
Tel: (0117) 937 2501
Mansion built between 1691 and 1710 for William Blathwayt. Rooms have been little changed. A herd of deer roams the 263-acre parkland.

3 Bristol Zoo Gardens
Clifton, Bristol BS8 3HA
Tel: (0117) 973 8951
Set in beautiful gardens, the zoo provides a haven for some of the world's most endangered wildlife. Plenty of activities and special events throughout the year.

4 The Exploratory Hands-on Science Centre
Bristol Old Station,
Temple Meads,
Bristol BS1 6QU
Tel: (0117) 925 2008
Exhibition of lights, lenses, lasers, bubbles, bridges, illusions, gyroscopes and much more all housed in Brunel's original engine shed and drawing office.

5 Harveys Wine Museum
12 Denmark Street,
Bristol BS1 5DQ
Tel: (0117) 927 5036
Wine museum in original 13thC cellars displaying artefacts connected with production and enjoyment of wines, especially glass, silver and corkscrews.

6 Bowood House and Gardens
Bowood Estate,
Calne, Wiltshire SN11 0LZ
Tel: (01249) 812102
18thC house by Robert Adam, collections of paintings, watercolours,

Victoriana, Indiana and porcelain. Landscaped park with lake, terraces, waterfall and grottos.

7 Weston-super-Mare Sea Life Centre
Marine Parade,
Weston-super-Mare,
North Somerset BS23 1BE
Tel: (01934) 641603
All aspects of British marine life housed on Britain's first pier for 85 years.

8 Museum of Costume
Assembly Rooms, Bennett Street,
Bath BA1 2QH
Tel: (01225) 477789
Designed by John Wood the Younger in 1769. One of Bath's finest Georgian buildings. Museum of Costume housed in basement.

9 Cheddar Showcaves and Gorge
Cheddar, Somerset BS27 3QF
Tel: (01934) 742343
Beautiful caves located in Cheddar

Gorge. Gough's Cave with its cathedral-like caverns and Cox's Cave with stalagmites and stalactites. Also "The Crystal Quest" fantasy adventure.

10 Secret World
New Road Farm, East Huntspill, Highbridge, Somerset TA9 3PZ
Tel: (01278) 783250
300-year-old farm, many breeds of animals including rare breeds. Old and modern farm machinery on display. Play areas, gardens. Somerset Levels Visitor Centre.

11 Wookey Hole Caves and Papermill
Wookey Hole,
Wells,
Somerset BA5 1BB
Tel: (01749) 672243
Spectacular caves and legendary home of the Witch of Wookey. Working Victorian papermill including Fairground Memories, Old Penny Arcade, Magical Mirror Maze and Cave Diving Museum.

12 Longleat
Warminster,
Wiltshire BA12 7NW
Tel: (01985) 844400
Great Elizabethan house with lived-in atmosphere. Important libraries and Italian ceilings. Capability Brown designed parkland. Safari Park.

13 Stourhead House and Garden
Stourton, Warminster,
Wiltshire BA12 6QH
Tel: (01747) 840348
Landscaped garden laid out in 1741-80, with lakes and temples, rare trees and plants. House begun in 1721 by Colen Campbell contains fine paintings and Chippendale furniture.

14 Wilton House
Wilton, Wiltshire SP2 0BJ
Tel: (01722) 743115
Home of the Earls of Pembroke for nearly 450 years. Famous Double and Single Cube rooms. Art collection. Adventure playground. Woodland walk. Wareham Bears.

15 Salisbury and South Wiltshire Museum
The King's House, 65 The Close, Salisbury, Wiltshire SP1 2EN
Tel: (01722) 332151
Grade 1 listed building. Stonehenge collection, Salisbury Giant, Early man. History of Old Sarum, Salisbury, Romans to Saxons, ceramics, Wedgwood, pictures, costume exhibitions.

16 West Somerset Railway
The Railway Station, Minehead, Somerset TA24 5BG
Tel: (01643) 704996
Preserved steam railway operating between Minehead and Bishops Lydeard, near Taunton. Longest independent railway in Britain (20 miles).

17 Clovelly Village
Clovelly, Bideford,
Devon EX39 5SY
Tel: (01237) 431200
Unspoilt fishing village on North Devon coast with steep cobbled street and no vehicular access. Donkeys and sledges only means of transport. Visitor centre.

18 Dartington Crystal
Linden Close, Torrington,
Devon EX38 7AN
Tel: (01805) 622321
Manufacture of hand-made crystal table glassware by skilled craftsmen. Glass centre and glassware exhibition. Visitors can watch glass blowers "hand blowing" glassware.

19 Rosemoor Garden - Royal Horticultural Society's Garden
Rosemoor, Great Torrington,
Devon EX38 8PH
Tel: (01805) 624067
Garden of rare horticultural interest. Trees, shrubs, roses, alpines and arboretum. Nursery of uncommon and rare plants. 8 acres being expanded to 40 acres.

20 **Haynes Motor Museum**
Sparkford, Yeovil,
Somerset BA22 7LH
Tel: (01963) 440804
*Motor vehicles and memorobilia
covering the years from the turn of
the century to the present day.
Video cinema, exhibition track.*

21 **Montacute House**
Montacute, Yeovil,
Somerset TA15 6XP
Tel: (01935) 823289
*Late 16thC house built of local
golden Ham stone, by Sir Edward
Phelips. The Long Gallery houses
a collection of Tudor and
Jacobean portraits. Formal gardens
and park.*

22 **Sherborne Castle**
Sherborne, Dorset
Tel: (01935) 813182
*Built by Sir Walter Raleigh in 1594
to replace the old castle. The
Elizabethan Hall and Jacobean Oak
Room show two of the many styles
of architecture.*

24 **The Dinosaur Museum**
Icen Way,
Dorchester,
Dorset DT1 1EW
Tel: (01305) 269880
*Only museum in Britain devoted
exclusively to dinosaurs. Fossils,
actual-size dinosaur reconstructions,
audio-visual, "hands on".
Video gallery and computerised
displays.*

26 **Weymouth Sea Life Park**
Lodmoor Country Park,
Weymouth, Dorset DT4 7SX
Tel: (01305) 761070
*Spectacular displays of British
marine life where visitors come face
to face with a wide variety of
creatures. Also an exciting tropical
jungle full of birds.*

23 **Athelhampton House and
Gardens**
Athelhampton, Dorset DT2 7LG
Tel: (01305) 848363
*Legendary site of King Athelstan's
Palace. Family home for five
centuries. Fine example of 15thC
architecture. Gardens with
fountains, pools and waterfalls.*

25 **Brewers' Quay and
Timewalk**
Hope Square, Weymouth,
Dorset DT4 8TR
Tel: (01305) 777622
*Former brewery now housing The
Timewalk, depicting 600 years of
Weymouth's history, also The
Brewer's Tale exhibition and
shopping village with restaurants.*

27 **Abbotsbury Swannery**
New Barn Road, Abbotsbury
Weymouth, Dorset DT3 4JG
Tel: (01305) 871684
*The only place in the world where
over 600 swans can be visited
during the nesting and hatching
time (end May-end June). Audio-
visual presentation. Ugly duckling
trail.*

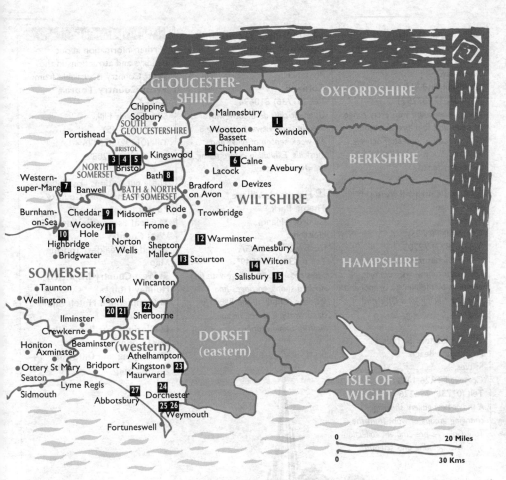

Map labels:

GLOUCESTER-SHIRE

OXFORDSHIRE

Chipping Sodbury

SOUTH GLOUCESTERSHIRE

Portishead

Malmesbury

Wootton Bassett

1

Swindon

2 Chippenham

BRISTOL

BERKSHIRE

3 4 5 Kingswood

NORTH SOMERSET   Bristol

6 Calne

Western-super-Mare **7**   Banwell

Bath **8**

Lacock

Avebury

BATH & NORTH EAST SOMERSET

Bradford on Avon

Devizes

WILTSHIRE

Burnham-on-Sea

Cheddar **9**   Midsomer

Rode

Trowbridge

Wookey Hole **11**

10

Frome

Highbridge

Norton Wells

Shepton Mallet

12 Warminster

Bridgwater

Amesbury

13 Stourton

Wilton

14

SOMERSET

Wincanton

Salisbury **15**

Taunton

Wellington

Yeovil

22

Ilminster

20 21   Sherborne

Crewkerne

DORSET (western)

DORSET (eastern)

Honiton

Beaminster

Axminster

Athelhampton

Ottery St Mary   Bridport   Kingston Maurward **23**

Seaton

Lyme Regis

Sidmouth   Abbotsbury **27**   Dorchester **24**

Fortuneswell

25 26 Weymouth

ISLE OF WIGHT

HAMPSHIRE

0 _____ 20 Miles

0 _____ 30 Kms

---

28 Killerton House
Broadclyst, Exeter,
Devon EX5 3LE
Tel: (01392) 881345
18thC house built for the Acland
family. Now houses a collection of
costumes shown in various room
settings. 15 acres of hillside garden
with rare trees and shrubs.

29 Babbacombe Model Village
Hampton Avenue, Babbacombe,
Torquay, Devon TQ1 3LA
Tel: (01803) 328669
Hundreds of models and figures
laid out in 4 acres of beautiful
gardens to represent a model
English countryside with modern

town, villages and rural areas. Scale
to 1/12th.

30 Woodlands Leisure Park
Blackawton, Totnes,
Devon TQ9 7DQ
Tel: (01803) 712598
A full day of variety set in 60 acres
of countryside. 12 venture
playzones including 500-metre
toboggan run, commando course.
34000 sq ft indoor play area,
toddlers' areas and animals.

31 Plymouth Dome
The Hoe, Plymouth,
Devon PL1 2NZ
Tel: (01752) 603300

Purpose-built visitor interpretation
centre showing the history of
Plymouth and its people from
Stone Age beginnings to satellite
technology. Situated on Plymouth
Hoe.

32 Cotehele
St Dominick,
Saltash,
Cornwall PL12 6TA
Tel: (01579) 351346
Medieval granite house. Working
watermill. Quay on River Tamar
with small shipping museum. Sailing
barge "Shamrock". Formal and
valley gardens, pools, dovecote.
Woodland walks.

33 Newquay Pearl
Southway,
Quintrell Downs,
Newquay,
Cornwall TR8 4LE
Tel: (01637) 872991
A large showroom with every range of pearl and semi-precious stone, with workshops and staff actively working. Pick your own pearl from our oyster tanks.

34 Royal Cornwall Museum
River Street,
Truro,
Cornwall TR1 2SJ
Tel: (01872) 72205
World famous mineral collection, Old Master drawings, ceramics, oil paintings by the Newlyn School and others, including John Opie and Hogarth. Geneaology library.

35 Tate Gallery St Ives
Porthmeor Beach,
St Ives,
Cornwall TR26 1TG
Tel: (01736) 796226
A major new gallery showing changing groups of work from the Tate Gallery's pre-eminent collection of St Ives painting and sculpture.

36 The Minack Theatre and Exhibition Centre
Porthcurno,
Penzance,
Cornwall
Tel: (01736) 810694
Open-air cliffside theatre with breathtaking views, presenting a 16 week season of plays and musicals. Exhibition centre telling the theatre's story.

37 Flambards Village Theme Park
Culdrose Manor,
Helston,
Cornwall TR13 0GA
Tel: (01326) 574549
Life-sized Victorian village with fully stocked shops, carriages and fashions. 'Britain in the Blitz' life-sized wartime street, historic aircraft. Exploratorium.

FIND OUT MORE

Further information about holidays and attractions in the West Country is available from:
West Country Tourist Board,
60 St Davids Hill,
Exeter EX4 4SY.
Tel: (01392) 425426
Fax: (01392) 420891

These publications are available free from the West Country Tourist Board:
■ **Great Escapes in England's West Country**
■ **Bed & Breakfast Touring Map**
■ **West Country Inspected Holiday Homes**
■ **Commended Hotels and Guesthouses**
■ **Glorious Gardens of the West Country**
■ **Camping and Caravan Touring Map**

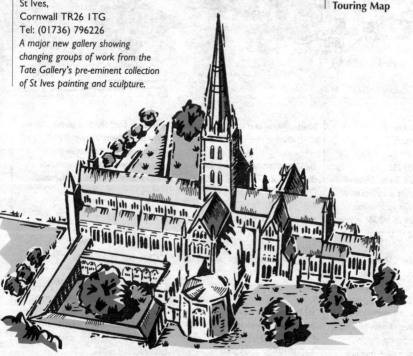

WHERE TO STAY (WEST COUNTRY)

Parks in this region are listed in alphabetical order of place name, and then in alphabetical order of establishment. A contact address is given where it differs from the address of the establishment.

Map references refer to the colour location maps at the back of this guide.

The first number indicates the map to use; the letter and number which follow refer to the grid reference on the map.

At-a-glance symbols can be found inside the back cover flap.

Keep this open for easy reference.

ASHBURTON

Devon
Map ref 2C2

Formerly a thriving wool centre and important as one of Dartmoor's four stannary towns. Today's busy market town has many period buildings. Ancient tradition is maintained in the annual ale-tasting and bread-weighing ceremony. Good centre for exploring Dartmoor or the South Devon coast.

Ashburton Caravan Park ⚠
☻✓✓✓✓✓ Rose Award
Member BH&HPA
Waterleat, Ashburton, Newton Abbot TQ13 7HU
☎ (01364) 652552
Off A38 to centre Ashburton, turn into North Street, bear right before bridge, signed Waterleat with camping logo. One and a half miles north towards moor. Signposted.
1.6 hectares (4 acres). Level, grassy, sheltered.
35 touring pitches

35	🚐	£7.00—£9.00
35	⛺	£7.00—£9.00
9	🏠	£100.00—£260.00

---

27 units not for hire
Open April–September
🅿 P ⊕ 🐕 ❄ ⊙ ⚡ 🛒 📶 🗑 ✂ 🚐 ☺
⚠
Ad See display advertisement on this page

Parkers Farm Holidays ⚠
☻✓✓✓✓
Higher Mead Farm, Ashburton, Newton Abbot TQ13 7LJ
☎ (01364) 652598
Fax (01364) 654004
Take A38 from Exeter to Plymouth. When you see sign 26 miles to Plymouth take 2nd left marked Woodland and Denbury. Signposted.
148 hectares (370 acres). Level, grassy.
40 touring pitches

40	🚐	£4.50—£8.00
40	🚍	£4.50—£8.00
40	⛺	£4.50—£8.00
25	🏠	£90.00—£270.00

Open March–October
Cards accepted: Access
🅿 🔌 ⊕ 🐕 ❄ ⊙ ⚡ 🛒 🍴 📶 🗑 ✂ 🚐
☺ ❓ ⚠ Ů ⚡
Ad See display advertisement on page 124

Please check prices and other details at the time of booking.

River Dart Country Park ⚠
☻✓✓✓✓✓✓
Holne Park, Ashburton, Newton Abbot TQ13 7NP
☎ (01364) 652511
Fax (01364) 652020
Exeter or Plymouth take A38 to Ashburton. Follow brown signs. Signposted.
36 hectares (90 acres). Level, grassy, sheltered.
120 touring pitches

50	🚐	£10.00—£12.00
50	🚍	£10.00—£12.00
120	⛺	£10.00—£12.00

Open April–September and Christmas
Cards accepted: Access, Visa, Switch/Delta
🅿 P 🔌 ⊕ 🐕 ❄ ⊙ ⚡ 🛒 ❌ 🍴 📺 📶
🗑 ✂ 🚐 ❓ ⚠ 🔺 Ů ⚡ ✂ 🚗 ☐ ⊤

The map references refer to the colour maps towards the end of the guide. The first figure is the map number; the letter and figure which follow indicate the grid reference on the map.

ASHBURTON CARAVAN PARK
Waterleat, Ashburton, Devon TQ13 7HU   Tel: 01364-652552
★ Luxury 6-berth Rose Award caravans
★ Award winning camping facilities
★ A tranquil haven within the scenic surrounds of Dartmoor National Park

BRITISH GRADED HOLIDAY PARKS

ROSE AWARD
CARAVAN HOLIDAY PARK

AXMINSTER

Devon
Map ref 2D2

This tree-shaded market town on the banks of the River Axe was one of Devon's earliest West Saxon settlements, but is better known for its carpet making. Based on Turkish methods, the industry began in 1755, declined in the 1830s and was revived in 1937.

Andrewshayes Caravan Park

⊖✓✓✓✓Rose Award
Member BH&HPA
Dalwood, Axminster EX13 7DY
☎ Wilmington (01404) 831225
Fax (01404) 831225
150 yards off A35 signposted Dalwood, Stockland. Three miles Axminster, 6 miles Honiton. Signposted.
4 hectares (10 acres). Sloping, grassy, hard.
90 touring pitches

60	🚐	£8.00—£10.00
10	🚏	£6.00—£10.00
20	▲	£6.00—£10.00
30	🛏	£85.00—£360.00

50 units not for hire
Open January, March–December
Cards accepted: Access, Visa

🔌🚽⊖🅿🐕♨💧⊙⚡✖📺📱🔟✓
�︎⊙🔍⚠🔧♨

BATH

Bath & North East Somerset
Map ref 3B2

Georgian spa city beside the River Avon. Important Roman site with impressive reconstructed baths, uncovered in 19th C. Bath Abbey built on site of monastery where first king of England was crowned (AD 973). Fine architecture in mellow local stone. Pump Room and museums.
Tourist Information Centre ☎ (01225) 462831

Bath Marina and Caravan Park ⚠

⊖✓✓✓✓✓
Brassmill Lane, Bath BA1 3JT
☎ (01225) 428778
Fax (01225) 428778
M4 junction 18, follow A46 to Bath. One and a half miles from city centre,

opposite Newbridge Park and Ride bus terminus on the A4 Bristol Road. Signposted.
1.6 hectares (4 acres). Level, hard, sheltered.
88 touring pitches

| 64 | 🚐 | £10.50—£13.50 |
| 88 | 🚏 | £10.50—£13.50 |

Cards accepted: Access, Visa

🔌🚽⊖🅿🐕♨💧⊙⚡🔟✓🔌⊙⚠
�︎🔧♨

Newton Mill Camping

⊖✓✓✓✓✓
Newton Road, Bath BA2 9JF
☎ (01225) 333909
Fax (01225) 461556
A4 Bath/Bristol left at Globe Inn to Newton Road on left at bottom of hill signed Twerton (B3110). Signposted.
17.2 hectares (43 acres). Level, grassy, hard.
195 touring pitches

90	🚐	£10.50—£12.95
90	🚏	£9.50—£11.95
105	▲	£8.50—£9.95

Cards accepted: Access, Visa, Amex, Switch/Delta

🔌🚽🚽⊖🅿🐕♨💧⊙⚡🍴✖🍷📺📱🔟
✓🔌⚠🔧♨

Ad See display advertisement on page 125

BLACKWATER

Cornwall
Map ref 2B3

Trevarth Holiday Park

⊖✓✓✓✓Rose Award
Member BH&HPA
Blackwater, Truro TR4 8HR
☎ Truro (01872) 560266
Fax (01872) 560266
Three hundred metres from Blackwater exit off Chiverton roundabout on A30. Four and a half miles north east of Redruth. Signposted.
1.8 hectares (4.5 acres). Level, grassy, sheltered.
30 touring pitches

30	🚐	£4.75—£6.75
30	🚏	£4.75—£6.75
30	▲	£4.75—£6.75
20	🛏	£85.00—£315.00

Open April–October
Cards accepted: Access, Visa, Amex

🔌🚽🐕♨💧⊙⚡📱🔟✓🔌⊙🔍⚠
🔧♨

Ad See display advertisement on page 125

BREAN

Somerset
Map ref 2D1

Caravans and holiday bungalows by sand dunes on the flat shoreline south of Brean Down. This rocky promontory has exhilarating cliff walks, bird-watching and an Iron Age fort.

Holiday Resort at Unity Farm

⊖✓✓✓✓
Member BH&HPA/NCC
Coast Road, Brean Sands, Burnham-on-Sea TA8 2RB
☎ Brean Down (01278) 751235
Fax (01278) 751539
M5 junction 22. Follow signs for Berrow and Brean. Site on right. Four and a half miles from M5. Signposted.
32 hectares (80 acres). Level, grassy.
800 touring pitches

400	🚐	£3.00—£13.00
100	🚏	£3.00—£13.00
300	▲	£3.00—£10.00
120	🛏	£80.00—£480.00

400 units not for hire
Open March–November
Cards accepted: Access, Visa, Switch/Delta

⚡🅿🔌🚽⊖🐕♨💧⊙⚡🍴✖🍷📱🔟✓
🔌⊙🔍⚠🔧♨⟳∪🏊♥🏕♪♨

BRIDPORT

Dorset
Map ref 3A3

Market town and chief producer of nets and ropes just inland of dramatic Dorset coast. Old, broad streets built for drying and twisting and long gardens for rope-walks. Grand arcaded Town Hall and Georgian buildings. Local history museum has Roman relics.
Tourist Information Centre ☎ *(01308) 424901*

Binghams Farm Touring Caravan Park ⋈
☺✓✓✓✓✓
Member BH&HPA
Binghams Farm, Melplash, Bridport DT6 3TT
☎ (01308) 488234
Turn off A35 at Bridport at roundabout onto A3066 signed Beaminster. After approximately 2 miles turn left into Binghams Farm. Signposted.
12 hectares (30 acres). Level, grassy, hard.
40 touring pitches

40	🚐	£8.00—£10.50
40	🚙	£8.00—£10.50
40	⛺	£8.00—£10.50

Freshwater Beach Holiday Park ⋈
☺✓✓✓✓
Member BH&HPA
Burton Bradstock, Bridport DT6 4PT
☎ Burton Bradstock (01308) 897317
Fax (01308) 897336
From Bridport take B3157, situated 2 miles on the right. Signposted.
12 hectares (30 acres). Level, grassy.
425 touring pitches

425	🚐	£6.25—£15.00
425	🚙	£6.25—£15.00
425	⛺	£6.25—£15.00
60	🏕	£100.00—£450.00

190 units not for hire
Open March–November
Cards accepted: Access, Visa, Switch/Delta

Ad See display advertisement on page 126

Golden Cap Holiday Park ⋈
☺✓✓✓✓✓ Rose Award
Member BH&HPA
Seatown, Bridport DT6 6JX
☎ (01308) 422139
Fax (01308) 425672
In Chideock turn south for Seatown. Signposted.
8.4 hectares (21 acres). Level, sloping, grassy, hard.
150 touring pitches

150	🚐	£7.50—£11.50
150	🚙	£7.50—£11.50
150	⛺	£7.50—£11.50
9	🏕	£119.00—£390.00

185 units not for hire
Open March–November
Cards accepted: Access, Visa

Highlands End Holiday Park ⋈
☺✓✓✓✓✓ Rose Award
Member BH&HPA
Eype, Bridport DT6 6AR
☎ (01308) 422139
Fax (01308) 425672
Two miles south west Bridport on A35 turn south for Eype. Signposted.
11.2 hectares (28 acres). Level, grassy, hard.
195 touring pitches

120	🚐	£7.50—£11.50
120	🚙	£7.50—£11.50
75	⛺	£7.50—£11.50
17	🏕	£119.00—£390.00

144 units not for hire
Open March–November
Cards accepted: Access, Visa

BUDE

Cornwall
Map ref 2C2

Resort on dramatic Atlantic coast. High cliffs give spectacular sea and inland views. Golf-course, cricket pitch, folly, surfing, coarse-fishing and boating. Mother-town Stratton was base of Royalist Sir Bevil Grenville.
Tourist Information Centre ☎ *(01288) 354240*

Budemeadows Touring Holiday Park
☺✓✓✓✓✓
Bude EX23 ONA
☎ Widemouth Bay (01288) 361646
Signposted on A39 3.5 miles south of Bude. Signposted.
3.8 hectares (9.5 acres). Level, sloping, grassy, hard, sheltered.
100 touring pitches

100	🚐	£7.20—£10.00
100	🚙	£7.20—£10.00
100	⛺	£7.20—£10.00

Sandymouth Bay Holiday Park
☺✓✓✓✓
Member BH&HPA
Sandymouth Bay, Bude EX23 9HW
☎ (01288) 352563 & Mobile 0831 213932
Fax (01288) 352563
Take junction 27 off M5. Continue to A39. After 30 miles pass through village of Kilkhampton. Turn right at signpost. Signposted.
5.6 hectares (14 acres). Level, grassy.
53 touring pitches

Continued ▶

BUDE
Continued

53	🚐	£6.25—£10.50
53	🚎	£6.25—£10.50
53	⛺	£6.25—£10.50
80	🏠	£80.00—£420.00

50 units not for hire
Open March–September
Cards accepted: Access, Visa,
Switch/Delta

🏕🅿🚿📶🛁🍴🛒🛗✕☎📺
📺🚰🔥🛒❓⛰🎣⛵♫🅰🆃

Upper Lynstone Caravan and Camping Site
⊖✓✓✓✓
Member BH&HPA
Lynstone, Bude EX23 0LP
☎ (01288) 352017
0.5 miles south of Bude on coastal road to Widemouth Bay. Signposted.
2.4 hectares (6 acres). Level, sloping, grassy.
90 touring pitches

90	🚐	£5.80—£8.50
90	🚎	£5.80—£8.50
90	⛺	£5.80—£8.50
14	🏠	£94.00—£223.25

30 units not for hire
Open April–September

🏕🚿📶🛁🍴🛒🛗📶📺🔥🚰☀⛰

Wooda Farm Park 🏕
⊖✓✓✓✓✓
Poughill, Bude EX23 9HJ
☎ (01288) 352069
Fax (01288) 355258
From A39 at Stratton take coast road to Combe Valley. Signposted.
44.8 hectares (112 acres). Level, sloping, grassy, hard.
160 touring pitches

160	🚐	£6.00—£9.00
160	🚎	£6.00—£9.00
160	⛺	£6.00—£9.00
54	🏠	£90.00—£390.00

2 units not for hire
Open April–October
Cards accepted: Access, Visa,
Switch/Delta

🏕🚿📶🛁🍴🛒🛗✕📶📺🔥🚰☀
🚰🎣🔥🅰◎

BURNHAM-ON-SEA
Somerset
Map ref 2D1

Small Victorian resort famous for sunsets and sandy beaches, a few minutes from junction 22 of the M5. Ideal base for touring Somerset, Cheddar and Bath. Good sporting facilities, championship golf-course. *Tourist Information Centre* ☎ *(01278) 787852*

Burnham-on-Sea Holiday Village
⊖✓✓✓
Member BH&HPA
Marine Drive, Burnham-on-Sea
TA8 1LA
☎ Reservations/free brochure
(01442) 248668
Fax (01442) 232459
Off M5 junction 22, A38 to Highbridge, B3139 to Burnham. Signposted from there.
38 hectares (95 acres). Level, grassy.

400	🏠	£178.00—£462.00

Open March–November
Cards accepted: Access, Visa,
Switch/Delta

🏕🚿📶🛁🍴🛒🛗✕📶📺🔥📶
🚰⛵🎣⛵🍴♫🅰🆃
Ad See display advertisement inside front cover

CHARMOUTH
Dorset
Map ref 2D2

Set back from the fossil-rich cliffs, a small coastal town where Charles II came to the Queen's Armes when seeking escape to France. Just south at low tide, the sandy beach rewards fossil-hunters; at Black Ven an ichthyosaurus (now in London's Natural History Museum) was found.

Monkton Wylde Farm Caravan and Camping Park
⊖✓✓✓✓
Charmouth, Bridport DT6 6DB
☎ Axminster (01297) 34525
Fax (01297) 33594
Take A35 west from Charmouth. At Greenway head 2.5 miles turn right signed Marshwood. Site 0.5 miles on left. Signposted.
80 hectares (200 acres). Level, grassy, sheltered.
60 touring pitches

60	🚐	£6.25—£8.75
10	🚎	£6.25—£8.75
60	⛺	£6.25—£8.75
1	🏠	

Open March–October

🅿📶🚿📶🛁🍴🛒🛗📶📺🔥🚰☀⛰
🚰🐕

Wood Farm Caravan and Camping Park
⊖✓✓✓✓✓
Axminster Road, Charmouth,
Bridport DT6 6BT
☎ (01297) 560697
Directly off the main A35 to the west of Charmouth. Signposted.
7.6 hectares (19 acres). Level, sloping, grassy, hard, sheltered.
216 touring pitches

166	🚎	£7.50—£12.00
50	⛺	£7.50—£12.00
6	🏠	£180.00—£300.00

78 units not for hire
Open April–October

P ⊟ ▦ ◑ ▦ ▯ ◊ ⊙ ⊙ ⚌ ▯◙ ⁄ ◢ ⊙
◖ ☜ ◖ ♪ ↑ ✕ ♤

Somerset
Map ref 2D1

Large village at foot of Mendips just south of the spectacular Cheddar Gorge. Close by are Roman and Saxon sites and famous show caves. Traditional Cheddar cheese is still made here.

Broadway House Holiday Touring Caravan and Camping Park ⚠

⊖✓✓✓✓✓
Member BH&HPA
Cheddar BS27 3DB
☎ (01934) 742610
Fax (01934) 744950
Midway between Cheddar and Axbridge on A371. M5 junction 22. Signposted.
12 hectares (30 acres). Sloping, grassy, sheltered.
200 touring pitches

200	🚐	£4.50—£11.00
200	🚚	£4.50—£9.00
200	▲	£4.50—£11.00
34	⊞	£110.00—£390.00

Open March–November
Cards accepted: Access, Visa, Diners, Amex, Switch/Delta

▦ ◑ ▦ ▯ ◊ ⊙ ⊙ ⚌ ▮ TV ▯◙ ⁄ ◢
⊙ ◖ ♤ ☜ ↷ ✦ ∪ ♪ ↑ T

Devon
Map ref 2D2

Surrounded by fertile farmland, this small riverside town was an early Saxon settlement. Medieval prosperity from the wool trade built the grand church tower with its octagonal lantern and the church's fine west window.

Leacroft Touring Park

⊖✓✓✓✓✓
Member BH&HPA
Colyton Hill, Colyton EX13 6HY
☎ Seaton (01297) 552823
Off A3052 at Stafford Cross, approximately 2 miles west of Colyford and 18 miles east of Exeter. Signposted.
4 hectares (10 acres). Sloping, grassy.
138 touring pitches

118	🚐	£6.00—£8.00
118	🚚	£6.00—£8.00
20	▲	£5.00—£7.00

Open March–October
Cards accepted: Access, Visa

P ⊟ ▦ ◑ ▦ ▯ ◊ ⊙ ⊙ ⚌ ▮ ▯◙ ⁄ ◢ ⊙
◖ ♤ ✕ ♤

Somerset
Map ref 2D1

Village at the foot of the Quantock Hills, with an early medieval market cross. The church is adorned with rich 16th C bench-ends and the fine church house is of about the same period. A large Georgian house, Crowcombe Court, stands next to the church.

Quantock Orchard Caravan Park

⊖✓✓✓✓✓
Member BH&HPA
Crowcombe, Taunton TA4 4AW
☎ (01984) 618618
Fax (01984) 618618
Follow A358 from Taunton to Minehead for approximately 10 miles. Turn left at Flaxpool Garage signposted 50 yards.
1.4 hectares (3.5 acres). Level, grassy, hard, sheltered.
75 touring pitches

55	🚐	£6.90—£9.75
55	🚚	£6.90—£9.75
20	▲	£6.90—£9.75

▦ ◑ ▦ ▯ ◊ ⊙ ⊙ ⚌ TV ▯◙ ⁄ ◢ ⊙
◖ ♤ ↷ ↑ ✕ ♤

Devon
Map ref 2D2

Small resort, developed in Regency and Victorian periods beside Dawlish Water. Town centre has ornamental riverside gardens with black swans. One of England's most scenic stretches of railway was built by Brunel alongside jagged red cliffs between the sands and the town.
Tourist Information Centre ☎ (01626) 863589

Cofton Country Holiday Park ⚠

⊖✓✓✓✓✓
Member BH&HPA
Starcross, Exeter EX6 8RP
☎ Starcross (01626) 890111
Fax (01626) 891572
A379 Exeter/Dawlish road, 3 miles Exeter side of Dawlish. Signposted.
6.4 hectares (16 acres). Level, grassy, sheltered.
450 touring pitches

450	🚚	£5.00—£9.50
450		£5.00—£9.50
62	⊞	£75.00—£399.00

Open March–October
Cards accepted: Access, Visa

▮ ▦ ◑ ▦ ▯ ◊ ⊙ ⊙ ✕ ⚌ ▯◙ ⁄ ◢
⊙ ◖ ♤ ↷ ↑ ✕ ♤

Golden Sands Holiday Park ⚠

⊖✓✓✓✓ Rose Award
Member BH&HPA
Week Lane, Dawlish EX7 0LZ
☎ (01626) 863099
Fax (01626) 867149
Leave M5 at junction 30. Take A379 to Dawlish. Signposted.
4.8 hectares (12 acres). Level, sloping, grassy, sheltered.
75 touring pitches

75	🚐	£5.50—£12.50
75	🚚	£5.50—£12.50
112	⊞	£60.00—£380.00

Open April–October
Cards accepted: Access, Visa, Switch/Delta

▮ ▦ P ◑ ▦ ▯ ◊ ⊙ ⊙ ✕ ⚌ ▯◙ ⁄
◢ ⊙ ◖ ♤ ↷ ↑ ✕ ♪ ♤

Ladys Mile Touring and Camping Park ⚠

⊖✓✓✓✓✓
Dawlish EX7 0LX
☎ (01626) 863411
Fax (01626) 888689
A379 Exeter to Dawlish road, 1 mile Exeter side of Dawlish. Signposted.
6.4 hectares (16 acres). Level, sloping, grassy, sheltered.
486 touring pitches

486	🚐	£5.50—£10.50
486	🚚	£5.50—£10.50
486	▲	£5.50—£10.50
1	⊞	£120.00—£255.00

Open March–October
Cards accepted: Access, Visa, Switch/Delta

▮ ▦ ◑ ▦ ▯ ◊ ⊙ ⊙ ✕ ⚌ ▯◙ ⁄
◢ ⊙ ◖ ♤ ↷ ↑ ♤

Ad See display advertisement on page 128

The map references refer to the colour maps towards the end of the guide.
The first figure is the map number; the letter and figure which follow indicate the grid reference on the map.

DAWLISH WARREN

Devon
Map ref 2D2

Popular with campers and caravanners, a sandy spit of land at the mouth of the River Exe. The sand dunes with their golf links are rich in plant and bird life. Brunel's atmospheric railway once ran along the dramatic line between jagged red cliffs and sandy shore.

Dawlish Sands Holiday Park ▲▲
⊖✓✓✓✓✓
Member BH&HPA
Warren Road, Dawlish Warren,
Dawlish EX7 0PG
☎ Starcross (01626) 890111
Fax (01626) 891572
Take A379 from M5, through Starcross, left at harbour bridge at Cockwood. At Dawlish Sands, situated on the left in Warren Road.
4.8 hectares (12 acres). Level, grassy, hard.

179	🚐	£60.00—£365.00

2 units not for hire
Open March–September
Cards accepted: Access, Visa
🚗🏠🚻♿🛒✕🍴📺📶🚮🔌🔥🚘☀🔍
⛰🏕🎣🎵⚓

Peppermint Park ▲▲
⊖✓✓✓✓✓
Member BH&HPA
Warren Road, Dawlish Warren,
Dawlish EX7 0PQ
☎ Dawlish (01626) 863436
Exit M5 at junction 30, onto A379 signed Dawlish, after 9 miles left turn signed Dalwish Warren. One mile on right to park entrance. Signposted.
7 hectares (17.5 acres). Level, sloping, grassy, hard.
240 touring pitches

192	🚐	£5.00—£9.50
192	🚏	£5.00—£9.50
48	▲	£5.00—£9.50
30	🚐	£55.00—£400.00

Open April–September
Cards accepted: Access, Visa, Switch/Delta

🚜🏠🚻♿🛒🚽🔌🔥🍴📶🚮🔥🔌
☀🔍⛰🏕🎣🎵⚓

DEVIZES

Wiltshire
Map ref 3B2

Old market town standing on the Kennet and Avon Canal. Rebuilt Norman castle, good 18th C buildings. St John's Church has 12th C work and Norman tower. Museum of Wiltshire's archaeology and natural history reflects wealth of prehistoric sites in the county. *Tourist Information Centre* ☎ *(01380) 729408*

The Bell Caravan and Camping Park
⊖✓✓✓✓
Member BH&HPA
Andover Road, Lydeway, Devizes
SN10 3PS
☎ (01380) 840230
Three miles south east of Devizes on A342 near Urchfont. Signposted.
1.2 hectares (3 acres). Level, grassy, sheltered.
30 touring pitches

30	🚐	£6.95—£8.95
30	🚏	£6.95—£8.95
30	▲	£6.95—£8.95

Open April–September
Cards accepted: Access
🅿️🚗🏠🚻♿🛒🚽🔌📺📶🚮🔥🚘☀
🔍⛰🏕🎣🎵⚓

Lakeside
⊖✓✓✓
Devizes Road, Rowde, Devizes
SN10 2LX
☎ (01380) 722767

From Devizes town centre take A342 towards Chippenham. Signposted. 2.6 hectares (6.5 acres). Level, grassy, sheltered.
55 touring pitches

55	🚐	£6.50—£7.00
55	🚏	£6.50—£7.00
55	▲	£6.50—£7.00

Open April–October
🚗🏠🚻♿🛒🚽🔌🔥🚮🔌☀🔍⛰🎣🏕⚓

DORCHESTER

Dorset
Map ref 3B3

Busy medieval county town destroyed by fires in 17th and 18th C. Cromwellian stronghold and scene of Judge Jeffreys' Bloody Assize after Monmouth Rebellion of 1685. Tolpuddle Martyrs were tried in Shire Hall. Museum has Roman and earlier exhibits and Hardy relics. *Tourist Information Centre* ☎ *(01305) 267992*

Giants Head Caravan and Camping Park
⊖✓✓✓
Member BH&HPA
Old Sherborne Road, Cerne Abbas,
Dorchester DT2 7TR
☎ Cerne Abbas (01300) 341242
Into Dorchester, avoiding bypass, at top of town roundabout, take Sherborne road, after 500 yards take right hand fork at Loder garage. From Cerne Abbas take Buckland Newton road. Signposted.
1.6 hectares (4 acres). Level, grassy, sheltered.
50 touring pitches

50	🚐	£5.00—£6.50
50	🚏	£5.00—£6.50
50	▲	£5.00—£6.50

Open March–October
🚗🚘🅿️🚻🏠🚽♿🛒🔌🔥🍴📺🚮
🚮🚘☀

DREWSTEIGNTON

Devon
Map ref 2C2

Pretty village of thatched cottages overlooking the steep, wooded Teign valley at the northern edge of Dartmoor. The tree-shaded square shelters a fine 15th C church. To the west is Sir Edwin Lutyens' dramatic Castle Drogo in a romantic setting high over the Teign Gorge.

Clifford Bridge Park Ѧ
ѳ✓✓✓
Member BH&HPA
Clifford, Drewsteignton, Exeter
EX6 6QE
☎ Cheriton Bishop (01647) 24226
M5 junction 31 west along A30 to Woodleigh junction and turn left signed Cheriton Bishop. At Old Thatch Inn follow 'brown tent' signs to Clifford Bridge.
3.2 hectares (8 acres). Level, grassy, sheltered.
64 touring pitches

24	🚐	£6.95—£10.75
64	🚍	£6.25—£9.95
40	⛺	£6.95—£10.75
3	🏠	£78.00—£269.00

Open April–September

Ad See display advertisement on this page

EAST WORLINGTON

Devon
Map ref 2C2

Yeatheridge Farm Caravan Park Ѧ
ѳ✓✓✓✓
Member NCC
East Worlington, Crediton
EX17 4TN
☎ Tiverton (01884) 860330
Fax (01884) 860330
B3137, take B3042 before Witheridge. Site 3.5 miles on left.
3.6 hectares (9 acres). Level, sloping, grassy, sheltered.
85 touring pitches

85	🚐	£6.50—£7.75
85	🚍	£6.50—£7.75
85	⛺	£6.50—£7.75
2	🏠	£95.00—£215.00

Open April–September
Cards accepted: Access, Visa

EXETER

Devon
Map ref 2D2

University city rebuilt after the 1940s around its cathedral. Attractions include 13th C cathedral with fine west front; notable waterfront buildings; Maritime Museum; Guildhall; Royal Albert Memorial Museum; underground passages; Northcott Theatre.
Tourist Information Centre ☎ (01392) 265700

Kennford International Caravan Park
ѳ✓✓✓✓✓
Member BH&HPA
Kennford, Exeter EX6 7YN
☎ (01392) 833046
Fax (01392) 833046
Half a mile from end of M5 on A38, 4 miles south of Exeter. Signposted.
3.2 hectares (8 acres). Level, grassy, hard, sheltered.
120 touring pitches

120	🚐	£9.00
120	🚍	£9.00
120	⛺	£9.00

Cards accepted: Access, Visa

FALMOUTH

Cornwall
Map ref 2B3

Busy port and fishing harbour, popular resort on the balmy Cornish Riviera. Henry VIII's Pendennis Castle faces St Mawes Castle across the broad natural harbour and yacht basin, Carrick Roads, which receives 7 rivers.
Tourist Information Centre ☎ (01326) 312300

Maen Valley Park Ѧ
ѳ✓✓✓✓ Rose Award
Member BH&HPA
Falmouth TR11 5BJ
☎ (01326) 312190
Fax (01326) 211120

From A39 Truro/Falmouth road, follow signs to Maenporth beach, straight for 1 mile look for Maen Valley sign, turn right. Signposted.
7.2 hectares (18 acres). Level, grassy, sheltered.
130 touring pitches

130	🚐	£6.00—£12.00
130	🚍	£6.00—£11.00
130	⛺	£6.00—£11.00
60	🏠	£70.00—£400.00

16 units not for hire
Open March–October
Cards accepted: Access, Visa

Ad See display advertisement on page 130

Pennance Mill Touring Park Ѧ
ѳ✓✓✓
Maenporth, Falmouth TR11 5HJ
☎ (01326) 312616 & 317431
A39 to Falmouth, follow International Camping sign to Maenporth beach, situated 0.5 miles on left hand side. Signposted.
28 hectares (70 acres). Level, grassy, sheltered.
50 touring pitches

30	🚐	£7.50—£8.50
20	⛺	£7.50—£8.50

Open March–December

The Ѧ symbol after an establishment name indicates that it is a Regional Tourist Board member.

The symbols in each entry give information about services and facilities. A 'key' to these symbols appears at the back of this guide.

OS Ref. SX782897

CLIFFORD BRIDGE Park
SEE ENTRY UNDER "DREWSTEIGNTON"

Small, level, family-run picturesque country estate in Dartmoor National Park surrounded by woodland, bordered by River Teign. Pitches for **touring/motor caravans (24)**, tents **(40)**. **Three holiday caravans for hire.** All set in 8 acres of outstanding natural beauty. HEATED SWIMMING POOL. Small shop by farmhouse. Electric hook-ups. Flush toilets and free showers. Fly-fishing on site. Golf at Moretonhampstead.

AA 3 Pennant   RAC Appointed
Write or phone for colour brochure. Nr. Drewsteignton, Devon EX6 6QE. Tel: (01647) 24226

GLASTONBURY

Somerset
Map ref 3A2

Market town associated with Joseph of Arimathea and the birth of English Christianity. Built around its 7th C abbey said to be the site of King Arthur's burial. Glastonbury Tor with its ancient tower gives panoramic views over flat country and the Mendip Hills.
Tourist Information Centre ☎ (01458) 832954

The Old Oaks Touring Park ⚠
⊖✓✓✓✓✓
Member BH&HPA
Wick Farm, Wick, Glastonbury
BA6 8JS
☎ (01458) 831437
From Glastonbury 2 miles towards Shepton Mallet on A361, signed for Wick, site 1 mile. From Wells left after roundabout entering Glastonbury at sign for Wick. Site 1.5 miles. Signposted.
40 hectares (100 acres). Level, sloping, grassy, hard, sheltered.
40 touring pitches

20	🚐	£6.50—£8.00
20	🚛	£6.50—£8.00
20	▲	£6.50—£8.00

Open March—October

🔌🅿🛠🔥💧🔵⚡🔌📻⏚⟋🔌☺🔍⚠
〰🍴✕❄

GOONHAVERN

Cornwall
Map ref 2B2

Silverbow Park ⚠
⊖✓✓✓✓✓ Rose Award
Member BH&HPA
Goonhavern, Truro TR4 9NX
☎ Truro (01872) 572347
On the A3075 0.5 miles south of Goonhavern village. Signposted.
9.6 hectares (24 acres). Grassy, hard.
90 touring pitches

90	🚛	£5.50—£12.50
90	▲	£5.50—£12.50
14	🏠	£120.00—£415.00

Open April—October

🔌🚫🅿🔥💧🔵⚡🔌🔌⟋🔌☺
🔍⚠〰🔄🔍✦✕❄♨

GORRAN

Cornwall
Map ref 2B3

Tregarton Farm Caravan and Camping Park
⊖✓✓✓✓
Member BH&HPA
Gorran, St Austell PL26 6NF
☎ Mevagissey (01726) 843666
Fax (01726) 843666
Take B3273 turn right at crossroads to Gorran. Signposted.
4 hectares (10 acres). Level, sloping, grassy, sheltered.
150 touring pitches

150	🚐	£7.50—£10.50
150	🚛	£7.50—£10.50
150	▲	£7.50—£10.50

Open April—October
Cards accepted: Access, Visa, Switch/Delta

🅿🚫⚡🔥🛠💧🔵⚡🔌📻🔌⟋🔌☺
⚠〰✕❄♨

GWINEAR

Cornwall
Map ref 2B3

Parbola Holiday Park
⊖✓✓✓✓ Rose Award
Member BH&HPA
Wall, Gwinear, Hayle TR27 5LE
☎ Praze (01209) 831503
Fax (01209) 831503
Leave A30 at Hayle, at roundabout leave by 1st exit to Connor Downs, at end of village turn right to Carnhell Green, right at T-junction, Parbola is 1 mile on left. Signposted.
7 hectares (17.5 acres). Level, grassy, sheltered.
120 touring pitches

70	🚐	£6.50—£10.00
70	🚛	£6.50—£10.00
40	▲	£6.50—£10.00
19	🏠	£109.00—£369.00

Open April—October
Cards accepted: Access, Visa

🔌🚫🅿🚫⚡🔥🛠💧🔵⚡🔌📺📻🔌
⟋🔌☺⚠〰✕❄♨

Please check prices and other details at the time of booking.

HAYLE

Cornwall
Map ref 2B3

Former mining town with modern light industry on the Hayle Estuary. Most buildings are Georgian or early Victorian, with some Regency houses along the canal.

Beachside Holiday Park
⊖✓✓✓✓
Member BH&HPA
Hayle TR27 5AW
☎ (01736) 753080
Leave A30 at the large roundabout at the approach to Hayle, take the Hayle road, turn right beside the putting green and signposted showing beach, situated approximately 0.5 miles on right. Signposted.
16 hectares (40 acres). Sloping, grassy.
90 touring pitches

90	🚐	£6.00—£15.00
90	🚛	£6.00—£15.00
90	▲	£6.00—£15.00

Open May—September
Cards accepted: Access, Visa, Switch/Delta

🔌🚌🅿🚫⚡🔥🛠💧🔵⚡🔌📻🔌⟋🔌
☺🔍⚠〰✕❄🎵🔌T

St Ives Bay Holiday Park ⚠
⊖✓✓✓✓
Member BH&HPA
73 Loggans Road, Upton Towans, Hayle TR27 5BH
☎ (01736) 752274
Fax (01736) 754523
Exit A30 at Hayle, turn immediately right. Park entrance 500 metres on the left. Signposted.
40 hectares (100 acres). Level, grassy.
300 touring pitches

300	🚐	£5.00—£15.00
300	🚛	£5.00—£15.00
300	▲	£5.00—£15.00
250	🏠	£99.00—£439.00

Open May—September
Cards accepted: Access, Visa, Switch/Delta

🔌🚌🅿🚫⚡🔥🛠💧🔵⚡🔌📻📺🔌
🔌⟋🔌☺⚠〰🔍✦🎵🔌T

MAEN VALLEY HOLIDAY PARK

Falmouth, Cornwall TR11 5BJ. Tel: (01326) 312190 Fax: (01326) 211120
Camping and Holiday Caravans for hire in sheltered wooded valley. 1 mile from safe sandy beach, 2 miles from historic Falmouth and its Port. Electric hook-ups, club, shop. Sailing, diving and fishing nearby.

AA ▶ ▶ ▶ ▶
RAC Approved

HELSTON

Cornwall
Map ref 2B3

Handsome town with steep, main street and narrow alleys. In medieval times it was a major port and stannary town. Most buildings date from Regency and Victorian periods. The famous May dance, the Furry, is thought to have pre- Christian origins. A museum occupies the old Butter Market.
Tourist Information Centre ☎ *(01326) 565431*

Boscrege Caravan Park ⚠

☻✓✓✓✓✓ Rose Award
Ashton, Helston TR13 9TG
☎ Penzance (01736) 762231
Helston to Penzance road, A394, turn by side of Ashton post office, turn left after 1.5 miles. Signposted.
3 hectares (7.5 acres). Level, grassy, sheltered.
50 touring pitches

50	🚐	£4.50—£8.50
50	🚎	£4.50—£8.50
50	⛺	£4.50—£8.50
26	⊡	£85.00—£330.00

Open April–October
Cards accepted: Access, Visa

ISLES OF SCILLY

Map ref 2A3

Picturesque group of islands and granitic rocks south-west of Land's End. Peaceful and unspoilt, they are noted for natural beauty, romantic maritime history, silver sands, early flowers and sub-tropical gardens on Tresco. Main island is St Mary's.
Tourist Information Centre ☎ *(01720) 422536*

Saint Martins Campsite

☻✓✓✓
St Martin's, Isles of Scilly TR25 0QN
☎ Scillonia (01720) 422888
Ferry, helicopter or plane from Penzance/Lands End to St Mary's. Launch from St Mary's to St Martin's.
Level, grassy, sheltered.
50 touring pitches

| 50 | ⛺ | £5.60—£6.60 |

Open April–October

Please mention this guide when making your booking.

KENTISBEARE

Devon
Map ref 2D2

Pretty village at the foot of the Blackdown Hills. The church has a magnificent carved 15th C screen, and nearby is a medieval priest's house with a minstrels' gallery and oak screens.

Forest Glade Holiday Park ⚠

☻✓✓✓✓✓
Member BH&HPA
Kentisbeare, Cullompton EX15 2DT
☎ Broadhembury (01404) 841381
Fax (01404) 841593
From Honiton take Dunkerswell road and follow Forest Glade signs. Signposted.
6 hectares (15 acres). Level, grassy, hard, sheltered.
80 touring pitches

80	🚐	£5.75—£11.00
80	🚎	£5.75—£11.00
80	⛺	£5.75—£11.00
23	⊡	£95.00—£310.00

16 units not for hire
Open March–October
Cards accepted: Access, Visa

LACOCK

Wiltshire
Map ref 3B2

Village of great charm. Medieval buildings of stone, brick or timber-frame have jutting storeys, gables, oriel windows. Magnificent church has Perpendicular fan-vaulted chapel with grand tomb to benefactor who, after Dissolution, bought Augustinian nunnery, Lacock Abbey.

Piccadilly Caravan Site

☻✓✓✓✓✓
Member BH&HPA
Folly Lane (West), Lacock, Chippenham SN15 2LP
☎ Chippenham (01249) 730260
Turn right off A350 Chippenham/Melksham road, signposted to Gastard (Folly Lane West), with caravan symbol, situated 300 yards on the left. Signposted.
1.2 hectares (3 acres). Level, grassy, hard.
43 touring pitches

40	🚐	£7.00—£8.50
40	🚎	£7.00—£8.50
32	⛺	£7.00—£8.50

Open April–October

LOOE

Cornwall
Map ref 2C2

Small resort developed around former fishing and smuggling ports occupying the deep estuary of the East and West Looe Rivers. Narrow winding streets, with old inns; museum and art gallery are housed in interesting old buildings. Shark fishing centre, boat trips; busy harbour.

Tencreek Caravan Park

☻✓✓✓✓
Member BH&HPA
Looe PL13 2JR
☎ (01503) 262447 & Mobile 0831 411843
Fax (01503) 262447
A387 Looe-Polperro road, 400 yards from signpost. Signposted.
5.6 hectares (14 acres). Level, grassy.
254 touring pitches

100	🚐	£6.75—£11.00
54	🚎	£6.75—£11.00
100	⛺	£6.75—£11.00
45	⊡	£90.00—£325.00

Cards accepted: Access, Visa, Switch/Delta

Treble B Holiday Centre ⚠

☻✓✓✓✓
Polperro Road, Looe PL13 2JS
☎ (01503) 262425
Fax (01503) 262425
2.5 miles from Looe on A387 on right hand side, site entrance down private road. Signposted.
8.8 hectares (22 acres). Level, grassy.
557 touring pitches

557	🚐	£6.80—£10.00
557	🚎	£6.80—£10.00
557	⛺	£6.80—£10.00
30	⊡	£63.00—£313.00

Open May–September
Cards accepted: Visa

Ad See display advertisement on page 132

Tregoad Farm Touring Caravan and Camping Park

☻✓✓✓
Member BH&HPA
St Martin's, Looe PL13 1PB
☎ (01503) 262718
Fax (01503) 262718
Plymouth to Looe road, 1.5 miles from Looe. Signposted.

Continued ▶

131

LOOE

Continued

22 hectares (55 acres). Level, sloping, grassy, sheltered.
150 touring pitches

100	⚏	£6.00—£12.00
50	▲	£6.00—£12.00
3	⌷	£70.00—£330.00

Open April—October

🎣P🅿️⚘♨️◐⚡️⛴️🗑️🔲∥🛒☺️🔍
⚘▲Ⓐ®

LUXULYAN

Cornwall
Map ref 2B2

Croft Farm Park ⋀
⊖✓✓✓✓
Member BH&HPA
Luxulyan, Bodmin PL30 5EQ
☎ St Austell (01726) 850228
Fax (01726) 850498
From A390 (Liskeard to St Austell) turn right just past level crossing in St Blazey (signed Luxulyan). Turn right at next junction, right again at next T-junction. Park is on your left approximately 0.5 miles on.
7 hectares (17.5 acres). Level, grassy, sheltered.
50 touring pitches

50	⚏	£5.15—£9.30
20	⚎	£5.15—£9.30
20	▲	£5.15—£9.30

Open March—October
Cards accepted: Access, Visa

⚎📻⚘♨️◐⚡️🔲∥🛒☺️⛰️✈️🆃

COLOUR MAPS

Colour maps at the back of this guide pinpoint all places in which you will find accommodation listed.

LYNTON

Devon
Map ref 2C1

Hilltop resort on Exmoor coast linked to its seaside twin, Lynmouth, by a water-operated cliff railway which descends from the town hall. Spectacular surroundings of moorland cliffs with steep chasms of conifer and rocks through which rivers cascade.
Tourist Information Centre ☎ *(01598) 752225*

Channel View Caravan Park
⊖✓✓✓✓
Member BH&HPA
Manor Farm, Barbrook, Lynton EX35 6LD
☎ (01598) 753349
A39 2 miles outside Lynton. Signposted.
3.2 hectares (8 acres). Level, grassy, stony.
70 touring pitches

70	⚏	£7.50
70	⚎	£7.00
70	▲	£3.50—£7.50
10	⌷	£85.00—£222.00

21 units not for hire
Open April—October
Cards accepted: Access, Visa

⚎📻⚘♨️◐⚡️🛒🔲∥🛒☺️✈️

For ideas on places to visit refer to the introduction at the beginning of this section.

All accommodation in this guide has been graded, or is awaiting a grading, by a trained Tourist Board inspector.

MALMESBURY

Wiltshire
Map ref 3B2

Overlooking the River Avon, an old town dominated by its great church, once a Benedictine abbey. The surviving Norman nave and porch are noted for fine sculptures, 12th C arches and musicians' gallery.
Tourist Information Centre ☎ *(01666) 823748*

Burton Hill Caravan and Camping Park ⋀
⊖✓✓✓
Member BH&HPA
Burton Hill, Malmesbury SN16 0EH
☎ (01666) 822585
Fax (01666) 822585
Off A429 0.25 miles south, Malmesbury to Chippenham road, opposite hospital, Arches Lane. Signposted.
0.8 hectares (2 acres). Level, grassy, sheltered.
30 touring pitches

30	⚏	£6.00
30	⚎	£6.00
30	▲	£6.00

Open April—November

⚎📻⚘♨️◐⚡️🔲🛒☺️🍴✈️♨️

MARTOCK

Somerset
Map ref 3A3

Small town with many handsome buildings of hamstone and a beautiful old church with tie-beam roof. Medieval treasurer's house, Georgian market house, 17th C manor.

Southfork Caravan Park ⋀
⊖✓✓✓✓✓
Member BH&HPA/NCC
Parrett Works, Martock TA12 6AE
☎ (01935) 825661
Fax (01935) 825122

A303 east of Ilminster. At roundabout take road signposted to South Petherton. Follow camping signs. Signposted.
1 hectares (2.5 acres). Level, grassy.
30 touring pitches

30	🚐	£7.00—£7.00
30	🚏	£7.00—£7.00
30	⛺	£7.00—£7.00
2	⛲	£90.00—£220.00

P❂✆📞⛳🔥♨⚑⛴🏕📷⚡🚿 ⛽☉⚠ ⛵✗⚓

MEVAGISSEY

Cornwall
Map ref 2B3

Small fishing town, a favourite with holidaymakers. Earlier prosperity came from pilchard fisheries, boat-building and smuggling. By the harbour are fish cellars, some converted, and a local history museum is housed in an old boat-building shed. Handsome Methodist chapel; shark fishing, sailing.

Sea View International
❂✓✓✓✓✓ Rose Award
Member BH&HPA
Boswinger, Gorran, St Austell
PL26 6LL
☎ St Austell (01726) 843425
Fax (01726) 843358
From St Austell roundabout take B3273 to Mevagissey. Prior to village turn right and follow signs to Gorran and Gorran Haven. Signposted.
6.4 hectares (16 acres). Level, grassy, hard, sheltered.
165 touring pitches

	🚐	£6.00—£15.90
	🚏	£6.00—£15.90
	⛺	£6.00—£15.90
39	⛲	£90.00—£460.00

Open April—September
Cards accepted: Access, Visa, Switch/Delta

⚡❂✆📞⛳🔥♨⚑⛴📷⚡🚿⚓ ☉⚠ ⚓🎣✗⚓

A key to symbols can be found inside the back cover flap.

The 𝕄 symbol after an establishment name indicates that it is a Regional Tourist Board member.

MINEHEAD

Somerset
Map ref 2D1

Victorian resort with spreading sands developed around old fishing port on the coast below Exmoor. Former fishermen's cottages stand beside the 17th C harbour; cobbled streets climb the hill in steps to the church. Boat trips, steam railway. Hobby Horse festival 1 May.
Tourist Information Centre ☎ (01643) 702624

The Beeches Holiday Park
❂✓✓✓✓ Rose Award
Member BH&HPA
Blue Anchor Bay, Minehead
TA24 6JW
☎ Washford (01984) 640391
From M5 junction 23, A39 to Minehead. 1st right after West Quantoxhead and follow signs to Blue Anchor on B3191. Signposted.
4 hectares (10 acres). Sheltered.

40	⛲	£104.00—£298.00

100 units not for hire
Open March—October
Cards accepted: Access, Visa

⚓🔥♨⚑⛴📷⚡🚿⚓☉⚠✗⚓

MULLION

Cornwall
Map ref 2B3

Small holiday village with a golf-course, set back from the coast. The church has a serpentine tower of 1500, carved roof and beautiful medieval bench-ends. Beyond Mullion Cove, with its tiny harbour, wild untouched cliffs stretch south-eastward toward Lizard Point.

Franchis Holiday Park
❂✓✓✓✓ Rose Award
Member BH&HPA
Cury Cross Lanes, Mullion, Helston
TR12 7AZ
☎ (01326) 240301
Take A3083 Helston to The Lizard road. Franchis is 6 miles from Helston. Signposted.
6.7 hectares (16.75 acres). Level, sloping, grassy, sheltered.
70 touring pitches

70	🚐	£6.00—£7.00
70	🚏	£6.00—£7.00
70	⛺	£6.00—£7.00
7	⛲	£105.00—£380.00

Open March—October

⚡❂P❂🔥♨⚑⛴📷⚡🚿⚓☉ ✗⚓

Mullion Holiday Park 𝕄
❂✓✓✓✓✓
Member BH&HPA
Mullion, Helston TR12 7LJ
☎ Exeter (Bookings) (01392) 447447 & Mullion (Touring and Tents) (01326) 240000
Fax (01392) 445202
Main A3083 from Helston to Lizard. Opposite B3296 turning to Mullion. Signposted.
19.6 hectares (49 acres). Level, sloping, grassy.
167 touring pitches

57	🚏	£7.70—£14.50
110	⛺	£7.70—£14.50
290	⛲	£105.00—£549.00

Open April—October
Cards accepted: Access, Visa, Switch/Delta

⚡❂P❂✆📞🔥♨⚑⛴⚡✗♨📺📷 📷🚿☉⚓⚠✎🦐⚓UP♫⚓T

NEWQUAY

Cornwall
Map ref 2B2

Popular resort spread over dramatic cliffs around its old fishing port. Many beaches with abundant sands, caves and rock pools; excellent surf. Pilots' gigs are still raced from the harbour and on the headland stands the stone Huer's House from the pilchard-fishing days.
Tourist Information Centre ☎ (01637) 871345

Crantock Beach Holiday Park
❂✓✓✓✓✓
Member BH&HPA
Crantock, Newquay TR8 5RH
☎ (01637) 871111
Fax (01637) 850818
From A30 turn right signed Perranporth. Right at Goonhavern onto A3075. 3rd left to Crantock, 0.5 miles turn right, follow signs to park.
3.2 hectares (8 acres). Level, grassy.

147	⛲	£92.00—£437.00

Open April—October
Cards accepted: Access, Visa

⚓P⚑♨✎⛴📷⚡🚿⚓☉⚠U✗⚓◉

Hendra Holiday Park 𝕄
❂✓✓✓✓✓ Rose Award
Member BH&HPA
Newquay TR8 4NY
☎ (01637) 875778
Fax (01637) 879017
A30 to Indian Queens, A392 to Newquay, situated on A392 1.5 miles before Newquay. Signposted.
16 hectares (40 acres). Level, sloping, grassy, hard, sheltered.

Continued ▶

133

NEWQUAY
Continued

600 touring pitches

600	🚐	£6.88—£10.60
600	�caravan	£6.88—£10.60
600	⛺	£6.88—£10.60
160	🏠	£108.00—£440.00

Open April–October
Cards accepted: Access, Visa, Switch/Delta

🅰️ See display advertisement on this page

Holywell Bay Holiday Park ⚲
❂✓✓✓✓✓
Member BH&HPA
Holywell Bay, Newquay TR8 5PR
☎ (01637) 871111
Fax (01637) 850818
Turn right off the A3075, signposted Holywell Bay, 3 miles west of Newquay. Signposted.
12 hectares (30 acres). Level, grassy, sheltered.
75 touring pitches

75	🚐	£6.80—£11.30
75	�caravan	£6.80—£11.30
75	⛺	£6.80—£11.30
143	🏠	£117.00—£492.00

Open April–October
Cards accepted: Access, Visa

Newperran Tourist Park
❂✓✓✓✓✓
Rejerrah, Newquay TR8 5QJ
☎ Truro (01872) 572407
Fax (01872) 571254
From A30 take B3285 Perranporth road, 2 miles past Mitchell village. Right onto A3075 Newquay road at Goonhavern. Site is 400 yards on left. Signposted.
10 hectares (25 acres). Level, grassy.
270 touring pitches

270	🚐	£5.90—£9.20
270	�caravan	£5.40—£8.40
270	⛺	£5.90—£9.20

Open May–September
Cards accepted: Access, Visa, Switch/Delta

🅰️ See display advertisement on page 135

Newquay Holiday Park ⚲
❂✓✓✓✓✓
Member BH&HPA
Newquay TR8 4HS
☎ (01637) 871111
Fax (01637) 850818

Follow A30 Newquay/Redruth after Iron Bridge, turn right signed RAF St Mawgan, 7 miles and 1 roundabout, signs to Newquay Holiday Park.
16 hectares (40 acres). Level, sloping, grassy, hard, sheltered.
259 touring pitches

259	🚐	£6.80—£11.00
259	🚐caravan	£6.80—£11.00
259	⛺	£6.80—£11.00
112	🏠	£112.00—£417.00

Open May–September
Cards accepted: Access, Visa

🅰️ See display advertisement on page 135

Treloy Tourist Park
❂✓✓✓✓
Member BH&HPA/NCC
Newquay TR8 4JN
☎ (01637) 872063 & 876279
Fax (01637) 872063
Just off the A3059 St Columb Major to Newquay road. Signposted.
4.6 hectares (11.5 acres). Level, sloping, grassy, hard.
141 touring pitches

141	🚐	£5.00—£8.60
141	�caravan	£5.00—£8.60
141	⛺	£5.00—£8.60

Open April–September
Cards accepted: Access, Visa

Trenance Caravan and Chalet Park

⊖✓✓✓✓
Member BH&HPA
Edgcumbe Avenue, Newquay
TR7 2JY
☎ (01637) 873447
On Newquay A3075 Truro road, situated 0.5 miles from Newquay town centre. Signposted.
4.8 hectares (12 acres). Sloping, grassy.
50 touring pitches

50	🚐	£5.00—£9.50
20	⛺	£5.00—£9.50
134	🛖	£110.00—£330.00

56 units not for hire
Open April–October
Cards accepted: Access, Visa, Switch/Delta

Trethiggey Touring Park

⊖✓✓✓✓
Member BH&HPA
Quintrell Downs, Newquay
TR8 4LG
☎ (01637) 877672

From A30 at Indian Queens take the A392 to Newquay, at Quintrell Downs roundabout turn left on A3058, site signposted 0.5 miles on the left.
6 hectares (15 acres). Level, grassy, sheltered.
157 touring pitches

57	🚐	£5.15—£7.75
50	🚎	£4.40—£7.00
50	⛺	£5.15—£7.75
12	🛖	£150.00—£300.00

Open March–December

Trevella Caravan and Camping Park 🏔

⊖✓✓✓✓ Rose Award
Member BH&HPA
Crantock, Newquay TR8 5EW
☎ (01637) 830308
Fax (01872) 571254
Take A3075 Redruth road from Newquay. After 1.5 miles turn right into road signposted Crantock. Signposted.
8 hectares (20 acres). Level, sloping, grassy, hard.
270 touring pitches

270	🚐	£5.90—£9.80
270	🚎	£5.40—£9.00
270	⛺	£5.90—£9.80
56	🛖	£135.00—£489.00

Open March–October
Cards accepted: Access, Visa, Switch/Delta

Ad See display advertisement on this page

Trevornick Holiday Park

⊖✓✓✓✓✓
Member BH&HPA
Holywell Bay, Newquay TR8 5PW
☎ Crantock (01637) 830531
Fax (01637) 831000
Off A3075 4 miles from Newquay follow signs to Holywell Bay. Signposted.
16 hectares (40 acres). Level, sloping, grassy, hard.
450 touring pitches

450	🚐	£5.50—£10.30
450	🚎	£5.50—£10.30
450	⛺	£5.50—£10.30
50	🛖	

Open May–September
Cards accepted: Access, Visa, Amex

NEWTON ABBOT

Devon
Map ref 2D2

Lively market town at the head of the Teign Estuary. A former railway town, well placed for moorland or seaside excursions. Interesting old houses nearby include Bradley Manor, dating from the 15th C, and Forde House, visited by Charles I and William of Orange.
Tourist Information Centre ☎ (01626) 67494

Dornafield ⚐
☉✓✓✓✓✓
Member BH&HPA
Dornafield Farm, Two Mile Oak, Newton Abbot TQ12 6DD
☎ Ipplepen (01803) 812732
Take A381 (Newton Abbot - Totnes). In 2.5 miles at Two Mile Bar Inn turn right. In 0.5 miles 1st turn to left. Site 200 yards on right. Signposted.
12 hectares (30 acres). Level, grassy, hard, sheltered.
135 touring pitches

135	🚐	£6.50—£11.50
135	🚚	£6.50—£11.50
135	⛺	£6.50—£11.50

Open March–October
P🖽🍴🏧🚿🅿🔥⛽🛒📺🛁🚮 🏪
☉🔍⚠️🛶↺🎣✗🎣🐴🛒

OWERMOIGNE

Dorset
Map ref 3B3

Sandyholme Holiday Park ⚐
☉✓✓✓✓
Member BH&HPA
Moreton Road, Owermoigne, Dorchester DT2 8HZ
☎ Warmwell (01305) 852677
One mile inland off A352. Through village of Owermoigne, 1 mile. Signposted.
2.4 hectares (6 acres). Level, grassy, sheltered.
65 touring pitches

65	🚐	£5.00—£10.00
65	🚚	£5.00—£10.00
65	⛺	£5.00—£10.00
30	🏠	£95.00—£295.00

5 units not for hire
Open April–October
Cards accepted: Access, Visa
P🖽🍴🏧🚿🅿🔥⛽🛒✗🎣🛁📺🛒🚮 🏪
☉🔍🛶🎣🐴🛒

PADSTOW

Cornwall
Map ref 2B2

Old town encircling its harbour on the Camel Estuary. The 15th C church has notable bench-ends. There are fine houses on North Quay and Raleigh's Court House on South Quay. Tall cliffs and golden sands along the coast and ferry to Rock. Famous 'Obby 'Oss Festival on 1 May.
Tourist Information Centre ☎ (01841) 533449

Carnevas Holiday Park ⚐
☉✓✓✓✓✓ Rose Award
Member BH&HPA
St Merryn, Padstow PL28 8PN
☎ (01841) 520230
In St Merryn, at crossroads take B3276 towards Newquay for 2 miles. Just before Porthcothan Bay turn right towards Treyarnon opposite Tredrea Inn. Signposted.
3.2 hectares (8 acres). Level, sloping, grassy.
198 touring pitches

198	🚚	£5.00—£8.00
198	⛺	£5.00—£8.00
9	🏠	£100.00—£340.00

Open April–October
🛖🍴🖽🏧🚿🅿🔥⛽🛒🛁🚮 🏪☉
🔍⚠️🛒

For ideas on places to visit refer to the introduction at the beginning of this section.

All accommodation in this guide has been graded, or is awaiting a grading, by a trained Tourist Board inspector.

PAIGNTON

Devon
Map ref 2D2

Lively seaside resort with a pretty harbour on Torbay. Bronze Age and Saxon sites are occupied by the 15th C church, which has a Norman door and font. The beautiful Chantry Chapel was built by local landowners, the Kirkhams.
Tourist Information Centre ☎ (01803) 558383

Beverley Park ⚐
☉✓✓✓✓✓ Rose Award
Member BH&HPA/NCC
Goodrington Road, Paignton TQ4 7JE
☎ Churston (01803) 843887
Fax (01803) 845427
From end of M5 take A380 to Torbay. Then A3022 for 2 miles south of Paignton. Turn left into Goodrington Road. Signposted.
9.2 hectares (23 acres). Level, sloping, grassy, hard.
194 touring pitches

194	🚐	£8.50—£13.00
50	🚚	£7.00—£11.50
120	⛺	£7.00—£11.50
203	🏠	£65.00—£490.00

16 units not for hire
Open March–October
Cards accepted: Access, Visa, Switch/Delta
P🖽🍴🏧🚿🅿🔥⛽🛒✗🎣🛁📺🛒🚮 🏪
☉🔍⚠️🍴🎣🎣✗🎣🎵🛒📺 🏪
🆎 See display advertisement on this page

Byslades Camping and Touring Park ⚐
☉✓✓✓✓✓
Member BH&HPA
Totnes Road, Paignton TQ4 7PY
☎ (01803) 555072
On main A385 Paignton-Totnes road. Signposted.
9.2 hectares (23 acres). Level, sloping, grassy, sheltered.
170 touring pitches

80	🚐	£5.50—£10.00
90	⛺	£5.00—£9.00

Open April–September
🛖🍴🖽🏧🚿🅿🔥⛽🛒✗🎣🛁📺🛒🚮 🏪☉🔍⚠️🎣🎣🐴🛒

Ramslade Touring Park ⚠

⊖✓✓✓✓✓
Member BH&HPA
Stoke Road, Stoke Gabriel, Totnes
TQ9 6QB
☎ Stoke Gabriel (01803) 782575
Fax (01803) 782828
From M5 follow A380 towards Torquay. Turn right into Paignton ring road. At traffic lights turn right (A385). Second left at Parkers Arms, signposted Stoke Gabriel. Signposted.
3.4 hectares (8.5 acres). Level, sloping, grassy.
135 touring pitches

135	🚐	£7.50—£10.50
135	🚚	£7.50—£10.50
135	⛺	£7.50—£10.50

Open March–October
🚰🛇🔥🗼🚿🔌🛒📺🛏🗑✎ ▰☺🔍
🛆🍴🎯⊛

POLPERRO

Cornwall
Map ref 2C3

Picturesque fishing village clinging to steep valley slopes about its harbour. A river splashes past cottages and narrow lanes twist between, the harbour mouth, guarded by jagged rocks, is closed by heavy timbers during storms.

Killigarth Caravan Park ⚠

⊖✓✓✓✓✓
Member BH&HPA
Polperro, Looe PL13 2JQ
☎ Looe (01503) 72216
From Tamar Bridge A38 at roundabout at Trerulefoot left onto A387 to Looe. Cross bridge to Polperro 3.5 miles turn left at junction just past bus shelter. Signposted.
12 hectares (30 acres). Level.
202 touring pitches

202	🚐	£7.80—£10.60
202	🚚	£7.80—£10.60
202	⛺	£7.80—£10.60
144	⛺	£95.00—£450.00

Open March–October
Cards accepted: Access, Visa
🚰🛇🔥🗼🔌🛇🛒🚿✗🛒📺🛏🗑
✎▰☺🔍🛆🍴🎯🔥🏠⊛
🆎 See display advertisement on this page

POLRUAN-BY-FOWEY

Cornwall
Map ref 2B3

Old village linked to Fowey across its estuary by a passenger ferry. Twin medieval forts guard village and town at the river's mouth.

Polruan Holiday Centre ⚠

⊖✓✓✓
Member BH&HPA
Townsend Road, Polruan-by-Fowey, Fowey PL23 1QH
☎ Polruan (01726) 870263
Fax (01726) 870263
A38 to Dobwalls, left on A390 to East Taphouse. Left on B3359 after 4.5 miles turn right signposted Polruan. Signposted.
1.2 hectares (3 acres). Level, sloping, grassy, hard, sheltered.
32 touring pitches

7	🚐	£5.50—£7.50
7	🚚	£5.50—£7.50
25	⛺	£5.50—£7.50
11	⛺	£95.00—£295.00

Open April–September
🛇🚰🛇🔥🗼🔌🛇🛒🛏🗑▰☺🛆🛆
⊛

Information on accommodation listed in this guide has been supplied by the proprietors. As changes may occur you are advised to check details at the time of booking.

PORLOCK

Somerset
Map ref 2D1

Village set between steep Exmoor hills and the sea at the head of beautiful Porlock Vale. The narrow street shows a medley of building styles. South westward is Porlock Weir with its old houses and tiny harbour and further along the shore at Culbone is England's smallest church. ·

Burrowhayes Farm Caravan and Camping Site and Riding Stables

⊖✓✓✓✓
Member BH&HPA
West Luccombe, Porlock, Minehead
TA24 8HU
☎ (01643) 862463
From Minehead take A39 to within 1 mile Porlock turn left. Site 0.25 miles on right before hump back bridge. Signposted.
3.2 hectares (8 acres). Level, sloping, grassy, sheltered.
120 touring pitches

54	🚐	£5.50—£7.00
54	🚚	£5.50—£7.00
66	⛺	£5.50—£7.00
20	⛺	£90.00—£225.00

Open March–October
🛒🚰🛇🔥🗼🔌🛇🛒🛏🗑✎▰☺U
🍴🛆

Porlock Caravan Park ⚠

⊖✓✓✓✓
Member BH&HPA
Highbanks, Porlock, Minehead
TA24 8NS
☎ (01643) 862269
A39 from Minehead to Lynton. Take B3225. Site signposted.
2 hectares (5 acres). Level, grassy, sheltered.
40 touring pitches

Continued ▶

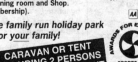

PORLOCK

Continued

40	🚐	£6.00—£6.50
40	🚎	£5.00—£5.50
40	⛺	£5.00—£6.50
15	🏚	£140.00—£325.00

41 units not for hire
Open March—October

ST AGNES

Cornwall
Map ref 2B3

Small town in a once-rich mining area on the north coast. Terraced cottages and granite houses slope to the church. Some old mine workings remain, but the attraction must be the magnificent coastal scenery and superb walks. St Agnes Beacon offers one of Cornwall's most extensive views.

Beacon Cottage Farm Touring Park
⊖✓✓✓✓✓
Member BH&HPA
Beacon Drive, St Agnes TR5 0NU
☎ Truro (01872) 552347
From A30 take B3277 to St Agnes, follow signs to park.
48 hectares (120 acres). Level, grassy, sheltered.
50 touring pitches

50	🚐	£5.00—£11.00
50	🚎	£5.00—£11.00
50	⛺	£5.00—£11.00

Open May—September

ST AUSTELL

Cornwall
Map ref 2B3

Leading market town, the meeting point of old and new Cornwall. One mile from St Austell Bay with its sandy beaches, old fishing villages and attractive countryside. Ancient narrow streets, pedestrian shopping precincts. Fine church of Pentewan stone and Italianate Town Hall.

River Valley Holiday Park
⊖✓✓✓✓ Rose Award
Member BH&HPA
Pentewan Road, London Apprentice, St Austell PL26 7AP
☎ St Austell (01726) 73533
Fax (01726) 73533
Take B3273 from St Austell to Mevagissey. When entering London

Apprentice, site is on left hand side. Signposted.
4 hectares (10 acres). Level, grassy, sheltered.
20 touring pitches

20	🚐	£5.00—£12.00
20	🚎	£5.00—£12.00
20	⛺	£5.00—£12.00
40	🏚	£80.00—£325.00

Open March—October
Cards accepted: Access, Visa

ST IVES

Cornwall
Map ref 2B3

Old fishing port, artists' colony and holiday town with good surfing beach. Fishermen's cottages, granite fish cellars, a sandy harbour and magnificent headlands typify a charm that has survived since the 19th C pilchard boom. Tate Gallery opened in 1993.
Tourist Information Centre ☎ (01736) 796297

Ayr Holiday Park ♠
⊖✓✓✓✓✓ Rose Award
Member BH&HPA
Higher Ayr, St Ives TR26 1EJ
☎ Penzance (01736) 795855
Fax (01736) 798797
B3306, 0.5 miles from town centre turn into Carnellis Road. Follow signs to Ayr Holiday Park (0.25 miles).
1.6 hectares (4 acres). Sloping, grassy.
40 touring pitches

40	🚐	£8.75—£14.00
20	🚎	£8.00—£13.00
20	⛺	£8.75—£14.00
43	🏚	£150.00—£540.00

Open April—October and Christmas
Cards accepted: Access, Visa, Switch/Delta

Polmanter Tourist Park
⊖✓✓✓✓✓
Member BH&HPA
St Ives TR26 3LX
☎ Penzance (01736) 795640
Fax (01736) 795640
B3074 to St Ives from A30 1st left at mini roundabout take 'HR' route to St Ives (Halsetown) turn right at inn, signposted.
4.8 hectares (12 acres). Grassy.
240 touring pitches

75	🚐	£6.00—£12.00
75	🚎	£6.00—£12.00
165	⛺	£6.00—£12.00

Open April—October
Cards accepted: Access, Visa, Switch/Delta

Trevalgan Family Camping Park ♠
⊖✓✓✓
Member BH&HPA
Trevalgan Farm, St Ives TR26 3BJ
☎ St Ives (01736) 796433
Fax (01736) 796433
From A30 take holiday route to St Ives, junction B3306 turn left, park 0.25 miles. Signposted.
1.96 hectares (4.9 acres). Level, grassy.
120 touring pitches

40	🚐	£6.00—£10.00
40	🚎	£6.00—£10.00
40	⛺	£6.00—£10.00

Open May—September

ST MERRYN

Cornwall
Map ref 2B2

Old roadside village with later development around its crossroads and a beautiful church opposite a pub and some stone cottages. The 15th C arcade is of locally-quarried cataleuse slate.

Harlyn Sands Holiday Park
⊖✓✓✓✓
Lighthouse Road, Trevose Head, St Merryn, Padstow PL28 8SQ
☎ Padstow (01841) 520720 &
Saltash (01752) 847949
On Trevose Head, 300 yards from Harlyn Bay. Signposted.
8.4 hectares (21 acres). Level, grassy.
150 touring pitches

150	🚐	£4.00—£8.00
150	🚎	£4.00—£8.00
150	⛺	£4.00—£8.00
100	🏚	£95.00—£360.00

250 units not for hire
Open April—October

Ad See display advertisement on page 139

The ♠ symbol after an establishment name indicates that it is a Regional Tourist Board member.

SALTASH

Cornwall
Map ref 2C2

Old fishing port with a busy waterfront and much modern development. In a square at the top of the town the 17th C pillared Guildhall stands near the parish church, which has granite arcades and medieval carving on the roofs.

Notter Bridge Caravan and Camping Park
⊖✓✓✓✓
Notter Bridge, Saltash PL12 4RW
☎ Plymouth (01752) 842318
A38 from Tamar Bridge follow signs for Landrake, Tideford and Liskeard, from Carkell roundabout, approximately 2.5 miles on the right. Signposted.
1.8 hectares (4.5 acres). Level, grassy, sheltered.
55 touring pitches

55	🚐	£5.00—£7.00
55	🚗	£5.00—£7.00
55	⛺	£3.00—£6.00
12	🚍	£80.00—£180.00

Open April–October

SEVERN BEACH

South Gloucestershire
Map ref 3A2

Salthouse Farm Caravan and Camp Park
⊖✓✓✓✓
Member BH&HPA
Severn Beach, Bristol BS12 3NH
☎ Pilning (01454) 632274 & 632699
From M48 exit 1 take A403 (Avonmouth) for 3 miles to Pilning. At traffic lights turn right B4064 to Severn Beach. Site 1 mile on right. Alternatively M5 exit 17 to Pilning. Signposted.
4 hectares (10 acres). Level, grassy, sheltered.
50 touring pitches

50	🚐	£7.00—£7.50
50	⛺	£7.00—£7.50

40 units not for hire
Open April–October

SIDMOUTH

Devon
Map ref 2D2

Charming resort set amid lofty red cliffs where the River Sid meets the sea. The wealth of ornate Regency and Victorian villas recalls the time when this was one of the south coast's most exclusive resorts. Museum; August International Festival of Folk Arts.
Tourist Information Centre ☎ (01395) 516441

Salcombe Regis Camping and Caravan Park
⊖✓✓✓✓✓ Rose Award
Member BH&HPA
Salcombe Regis, Sidmouth EX10 0JH
☎ (01395) 514303
Fax (01395) 514303
1.5 miles east of Sidmouth signposted off the A3052 coast road.
6.4 hectares (16 acres). Level, grassy, hard, sheltered.
100 touring pitches

40	🚐	£6.00—£9.00
40	🚗	£6.00—£9.00
60	⛺	£6.00—£9.00
10	🚍	£98.00—£315.00

Open April–October
Cards accepted: Access, Visa
[Ad] See display advertisement on this page

Please mention this guide when making your booking.

SOUTH BRENT

Devon
Map ref 2C2

Small town on the southern edge of Dartmoor National Park, just off the A38. Norman to 15th C church with carved Norman font, and the old toll-house in the square still displays toll charges for livestock.

Edeswell Farm Country Caravan Park 🏕
⊖✓✓✓✓
Member BH&HPA
Rattery, South Brent TQ10 9LN
☎ (01364) 72177
A38 at Marley Head junction take A385 to Paignton, site 0.5 miles on right. Signposted.
8 hectares (20 acres). Level, sloping, grassy.
46 touring pitches

46	🚐	£7.00—£9.00
46	🚗	£7.00—£9.00
46	⛺	£7.00—£9.00
18	🚍	£100.00—£350.00

Open April–October
[Ad] See display advertisement on page 140

SPARKFORD

Somerset
Map ref 3A3

Long Hazel Caravan and Camping Park
⊖✓✓✓✓
Member BH&HPA
High Street, Sparkford, Yeovil BA22 7JH
☎ North Cadbury (01963) 440002
Fax (01963) 440002
Four hundred yards from roundabout on A303/A359 at Sparkford. Proceed into village along the High Street, entrance on the left. Signposted.
Continued ▶

SPARKFORD

Continued

1.2 hectares (3 acres). Level, grassy, sheltered.
58 touring pitches

58	🚐	£6.50—£7.00
58	🚛	£6.50—£7.00
58	⛺	£6.50—£7.00

Open March–November
P🏠🔥🛈☎🍴⊙⛰✗❄

TAUNTON

Somerset
Map ref 2D1

County town, well-known for its public schools, sheltered by gentle hill-ranges on the River Tone. Medieval prosperity from wool has continued in marketing and manufacturing and the town retains many fine period buildings.
Tourist Information Centre ☎ *(01823) 336344*

Ashe Farm Caravan and Campsite ⚠

⊝✓✓✓✓
Ashe, Thornfalcon, Taunton
TA3 5NW
☎ (01823) 442567
Fax (01823) 443372
M5 junction 25. Take A358 southeastwards for 2.5 miles, turn right at Nags Head, site 0.25 miles on right. Signposted.
160 hectares (400 acres). Level, grassy, hard, sheltered.
30 touring pitches

20	🚐	£6.00—£7.50
20	🚛	£6.00—£7.50
10	⛺	£6.00—£7.50
2	🏚	£110.00—£140.00

Open April–October
P🏠🔥🛈☎⊙🛒💲🍴⊙🔥 ⊙🍴🔍
✗🗺

Holly Bush Park

⊝✓✓✓✓
Culmhead, Taunton TA3 7EA
☎ (01823) 421515
Fax (01823) 421885
M5 junction 25, follow signs for Taunton, Corfe and racecourse on B3170. Three and a half miles after Corfe, turn right at crossroads, then right again at T-junction. Site on left. Signposted.
0.8 hectares (2 acres). Level, grassy, hard, sheltered.
40 touring pitches

40	🚐	£6.00—£7.00
40	🚛	£6.00—£7.00
40	⛺	£6.00—£7.00

P🏠🔥🛈☎🍴🛒💲🍴⊙✗ ⊝U
🍴✗🗺

TAVISTOCK

Devon
Map ref 2C2

Old market town beside the River Tavy on the western edge of Dartmoor. Developed around its 10th C abbey, of which some fragments remain, it became a stannary town in 1305 when tin-streaming thrived on the moors. Tavistock Goose Fair, October.
Tourist Information Centre ☎ *(01822) 612938*

Harford Bridge Holiday Park ⚠

⊝✓✓✓✓✓ Rose Award
Member BH&HPA
Peter Tavy, Tavistock PL19 9LS
☎ Mary Tavy (01822) 810349
Fax (01822) 810028
Tavistock A386 north for 2 miles to Peter Tavy, site on right. Signposted.
6.4 hectares (16 acres). Level, grassy, sheltered.
120 touring pitches

40	🚐	£6.00—£9.00
40	🚛	£6.00—£9.00
40	⛺	£6.00—£9.00
10	🏚	£110.00—£290.00

45 units not for hire
Open March–November and Christmas
🔥P🏠🔥🛈🔥🛒💲🍴📺🍴🔍 🔥⊙🔥🛒🔍🍴✗🔨⊙

TORQUAY

Devon
Map ref 2D2

Devon's grandest resort, developed from a fishing village. Smart apartments and terraces rise from the seafront and Marine Drive along the headland gives views of beaches and colourful cliffs.
Tourist Information Centre ☎ *(01803) 297428*

Widdicombe Farm Caravan Park ⚠

⊝✓✓✓✓✓
Member BH&HPA
Ring Road (A380), Compton,
Paignton TQ3 1ST
☎ (01803) 558325
Fax (01803) 558325
A380 Torquay to Paignton ring road. Signposted.
8 hectares (20 acres). Level, grassy, hard, sheltered.
200 touring pitches

156	🚐	£5.00—£10.00
44	⛺	£5.00—£10.00
3	🏚	£80.00—£250.00

Open March–October
🔥🏠🔥🛈🔥🛒💲🍴✗🍴🍴🔍🔥🛒 ⊙🔍⛰🍴✗🗺

> The symbols in each entry give information about services and facilities. A 'key' to these symbols appears at the back of this guide.

TOTNES

Devon
Map ref 2D2

Old market town steeply built near the head of the Dart Estuary. Remains of medieval gateways, a noble church, 16th C Guildhall and medley of period houses recall former wealth from cloth and shipping, continued in rural and water industries.
Tourist Information Centre ☎ *(01803) 863168*

Higher Well Farm Holiday Park ᴀᴧ
⊖✓✓✓
Member BH&HPA
Stoke Gabriel, Totnes TQ9 6RN
☎ Stoke Gabriel (01803) 782289
From Paignton A385 to Totnes turn left at Parkers Arms for Stoke Gabriel, 1.5 miles turn left to Waddeton, situated 200 yards down the road. Signposted.
3.2 hectares (8 acres). Level, sloping, grassy, sheltered.
45 touring pitches

30	🚐	£5.80—£5.80
30	🚚	£5.80—£5.80
15	⛺	£5.80—£5.80
18	🏠	£120.00—£285.00

Open April–October
⚓P🔌🍴🔧🚿🛒🔥⛽🍳✗🚮🛒✗🚮⊙

TRURO

Cornwall
Map ref 2B3

Cornwall's administrative centre and cathedral city, set at the head of Truro River on the Fal Estuary. A medieval stannary town, it handled mineral ore from west Cornwall; fine Georgian buildings recall its heyday as a society haunt in the second mining boom.
Tourist Information Centre ☎ *(01872) 74555*

Leverton Place
⊖✓✓✓✓✓ Rose Award
Member BH&HPA
Greenbottom, Truro TR4 8QW
☎ (01872) 560462
Fax (01872) 560668
A390 to Truro, 1st roundabout turn right, then right again at 2nd roundabout, situated 100 yards on the right. Signposted.
3.8 hectares (9.5 acres). Level, sloping, grassy, hard, sheltered.
107 touring pitches

107	🚐	£7.00—£13.50
107	🚚	£7.00—£13.50
107	⛺	£7.00—£13.50
15	🏠	£100.00

Cards accepted: Access, Visa, Switch/Delta
⚓⚓P🔌🔧🍴🚿🛒⊙⚡✗🛒📺
🔥🍳🚮🛒🔍🔧🚿🛒⚡🚮✗🛁🚮⊙

Liskey Touring Park
⊖✓✓✓✓✓
Greenbottom, Truro TR4 8QN
☎ (01872) 560274
Fax (01872) 560274
Turn left off the A30 onto A390 at Chiverton Cross roundabout, at next roundabout turn right, signposted Threemilestone, right at mini roundabout, 2nd site 600 yards on the right. Signposted.
3.2 hectares (8 acres). Level, sloping, grassy, hard, sheltered.
68 touring pitches

68	🚐	£5.40—£9.00
68	🚚	£5.40—£9.00
68	⛺	£5.40—£9.00

Open April–September
🔧🍴🔧🚿🛒⚡🔥📺🛒🚮🔥🚮⊙⚡
🛖🛁🚮

WADEBRIDGE

Cornwall
Map ref 2B2

Old market town with Cornwall's finest medieval bridge, spanning the Camel at its highest navigable point. Twice widened, the bridge is said to have been built on woolpacks sunk in the unstable sands of the river bed.

Little Bodieve Holiday Park ᴀᴧ
⊖✓✓✓✓
Wadebridge PL27 6EG
☎ (01208) 812323
Situated on B3314 half a mile from A39 trunk road, 1 mile north of Wadebridge town centre. Signposted.
8.2 hectares (20.5 acres). Level, grassy.
195 touring pitches

195	🚐	£6.00—£9.00
195	🚚	£6.00—£9.00
195	⛺	£6.00—£9.00
17	🏠	£100.00—£390.00

43 units not for hire
Open March–October
Cards accepted: Access, Visa, Switch/Delta
⚓P🔌🔧🍴🔧🚿🛒⚡🔥✗🛒📺🚮
🔥⊙🔍🚿🛁🍳🚮

Valley Caravan Park ᴀᴧ
⊖✓✓
Polzeath, Wadebridge PL27 6SS
☎ Trebetherick (01208) 862391
From Wadebridge take the B3314 to Old Polzeath. Signposted.
4 hectares (10 acres). Level, grassy, sheltered.
65 touring pitches

30	🚐	£8.00—£12.00
10	🚚	£6.00—£10.00
25	⛺	£8.00—£12.00
40	🏠	£80.00—£420.00

10 units not for hire
Open March–October
⚓P🔧🍴🔧🚿🛒⚡✗🛒📺🔥🚮🔥⊙
🔍🛁🚿🍳🛁🎵🚮

WELLS

Somerset
Map ref 3A2

Small city set beneath the southern slopes of the Mendips. Built between 1180 and 1424, the magnificent cathedral is preserved in much of its original glory and with its ancient precincts forms one of our loveliest and most unified groups of medieval buildings.
Tourist Information Centre ☎ *(01749) 672552*

Mendip Heights Camping and Caravan Park ᴀᴧ
⊖✓✓✓✓
Member BH&HPA
Townsend, Priddy, Wells BA5 3BP
☎ (01749) 870241
Fax (01749) 870241
On A39 north of Wells. Left at Green Ore crossroads onto B3135 to Cheddar. Follow signs. Signposted.
1.8 hectares (4.5 acres). Level, sloping, grassy, hard.
90 touring pitches

15	🚐	£5.90—£6.40
15	🚚	£5.90—£6.40
75	⛺	£5.90—£6.40
1	🏠	£120.00—£225.00

Open April–October
⚓🔧🍴🔧🚿🛒⚡🔥📺🚮🔥⊙🛖
🛁🚮◎

WESTON-SUPER-MARE

North Somerset
Map ref 2D1

Large, friendly resort developed in the 19th C. Traditional seaside attractions include theatres and a dance hall. The museum shows a Victorian seaside gallery and has Iron Age finds from a hill fort on Worleybury Hill in Weston Woods. *Tourist Information Centre ☎ (01934) 888800*

Country View Caravan Park

✆✓✓✓✓ Rose Award
Sand Road, Sand Bay,
Weston-super-Mare BS22 9UJ
☎ (01934) 627595 & Mobile 0385 245461
Fax (01934) 627595
Junction 21 off M5. Right at Sainsbury's Homebase onto Queensway, into Lower Norton Lane. Right into Sand Road. Entrance on right. Signposted.
3.2 hectares (8 acres). Level, grassy.
120 touring pitches

120	🚐	£6.50—£12.00
120	🚛	£6.50—£12.00
120	⛺	£4.00—£12.00
15	🏠	£90.00—£295.00

50 units not for hire
Open March–October
Cards accepted: Access, Visa

P🅿🕿♿🛈⚲🅿⚡🍴🛒🖳⌨ / 🚮☺☕
⚒🏕⚓
Ad See display advertisement on this page

West End Farm/Caravan and Camping Park

✆✓✓✓✓
Member BH&HPA
Locking, Weston-super-Mare BS24 8RH
☎ (01934) 822529
M5 to junction 21, along A370 to Helicopter Museum and follow signs to site.
4 hectares (10 acres). Sheltered.
75 touring pitches

75	🚛	£7.00—£8.50
75	⛺	£7.00—£8.50

20 units not for hire

🚐♿🕿🛈⚲🅿🍴🛒🖳⌨ / 🚮☺🔍
🏕⚓

WEYMOUTH

Dorset
Map ref 3B3

Ancient port and one of the south's earliest resorts. Curving beside a long, sandy beach, the elegant Georgian esplanade is graced with a statue of George III and a cheerful Victorian Jubilee clock tower. *Tourist Information Centre ☎ (01305) 765221 or 785747*

Bagwell Farm Touring Park 🏍

✆✓✓✓✓
Member BH&HPA
Chickerell, Weymouth DT3 4EA
☎ (01305) 782575
Four miles west of Weymouth on the B3157. 500 yards past Victoria Inn on left hand side. Signposted.
5.6 hectares (14 acres). Sloping, grassy.
320 touring pitches

150	🚐	£5.00—£9.00
150	🚛	£5.00—£9.00
170	⛺	£4.00—£8.00

Open March–October

🚐🕿♿🛈⚲🅿🍴🛒🖳⌨ / 🚮☺🔍🏕
⚒⚓

Pebble Bank Caravan Park

✆✓✓✓
Member BH&HPA
90 Camp Road, Wyke Regis,
Weymouth DT4 9HF
☎ (01305) 774844
From harbour roundabout, up Boot Hill, turn right at mini roundabout opposite pub onto Wyke Road. Camp Road 1 mile on left bottom of hill on right bend. Park entrance 400 yards on left. Signposted.
3.2 hectares (8 acres). Level, sloping, grassy.
75 touring pitches

40	🚐	£6.00—£10.25
10	🚛	£5.00—£9.25
35	⛺	£5.00—£9.00
15	🏠	£125.00—£305.00

75 units not for hire
Open April–September

🚐♿🕿🛈⚲🅿🍴🛒🖳⌨ / 🚮☺🏕⚓
⚒⚓

WHIDDON DOWN

Devon
Map ref 2C2

Dartmoor View Caravan and Camping Park 🏍

✆✓✓✓✓✓
Member BH&HPA
Whiddon Down, Okehampton EX20 2QL
☎ (01647) 231545
Fax (01647) 231654
Half a mile off A30 (Merrymeet roundabout). Turn left for Whiddon Down. 0.75 miles on the right hand side. Signposted.
2.2 hectares (5.5 acres). Level, grassy, hard.
75 touring pitches

75	🚐	£6.40—£7.45
75	🚛	£6.40—£7.45
75	⛺	£6.40—£7.45
6	🏠	£105.00—£299.00

Open March–November
Cards accepted: Access, Visa

🚐🅿🕿♿🛈⚲🅿🍴🛒🖳⌨ / 🚮
🖳⚡🚮☺🔍🏕⚒🕯⚓🏕⚓

WHITEPARISH

Wiltshire
Map ref 3B3

Hillcrest Campsite

✆✓✓✓
Southampton Road (A36),
Whiteparish, Salisbury SP5 2QW
☎ (01794) 884471
On left side of Southampton road, A36 7 miles from Salisbury. One and a half miles from junction with A27. Signposted.
0.8 hectares (2 acres). Level, sloping, grassy, sheltered.
35 touring pitches

5	🚐	£6.50—£6.50
30	⛺	£6.50—£6.50

🚐🕿♿🛈⚲🅿🖳⌨ / ☺🕯🏕⚓

All accommodation in this guide has been graded, or is awaiting a grading, by a trained Tourist Board inspector.

TOUR & EXPLORE *from* "COUNTRY VIEW"

"at the gateway to this lovely corner of the West of England...or just relax on our quiet, level, family caravan park adjoining open fields"

♦ Licensed Clubroom
♦ Shop, Showers, Launderette
♦ Heated Pool ♦ Long Term Tourers
♦ 'Bright Lights' of Weston 3 miles
♦ Close to National Trust Headland

♦ 400 Yds Beach ♦ 10 mins M5
♦ **Touring Caravans, Tents, Motorhomes** (& dogs!) all welcome
♦ *Holiday Homes to Let*
♦ *Holiday Homes for Sale*

Sand Road, Sand Bay, Weston-super-Mare. Telephone 01934 627595

WILLITON

Somerset
Map ref 2D1

Large village on the edge of the Quantock Hills.

Home Farm Holiday Centre
◉✓✓✓✓
Member BH&HPA
St Audries Bay, Williton, Taunton
TA4 4DP
☎ (01984) 632487
Off M5 at Bridgwater, A39 towards Minehead for 17 miles to West Quantoxhead, 1st right after St Audries garage, entrance on right after 0.5 miles after mock Tudor lodge. Signposted.
14 hectares (35 acres). Level, sloping, grassy, hard, sheltered.
40 touring pitches

30	🚐	£4.00—£8.00	
5	🚗	£4.00—£8.00	
5	▲	£4.00—£8.00	
4	🏚	£80.00—£175.00	

205 units not for hire
🔌⚡🅿🍴🔥🌳🚿💧🚰☕🐕🍽🛒🍺📺🖥✳
🔌⊙🏔♪♫♨

WINSFORD

Somerset
Map ref 2D1

Small village on the River Exe in splendid walking country under Winsford Hill. On the other side of the hill is a Celtic standing stone, the Caratacus Stone, and nearby across the River Barle stretches an ancient packhorse bridge, Tarr Steps, built of great stone slabs.

Halse Farm 🏔
◉✓✓✓✓
Member BH&HPA
Winsford, Minehead TA24 7JL
☎ (01643) 851259

From Dulverton take B3223 for Lynton, on Winsford Hill turn right, campsite 0.5 miles. From B396 Tiverton/Minehead road turn off for Winsford, in village take lane in front of Royal Oak Inn. After 1 mile entrance on left after cattle grid. Signposted.
1.2 hectares (3 acres). Level, grassy, sheltered.
44 touring pitches

22	🚐	£5.00—£7.00	
22	🚗	£5.00—£7.00	
22	▲	£5.00—£7.00	

Open March–October
🔌⚡🍴🔥🌳🚿💧🚰☕🖥✳🔌⊙🏔🍽
♨

WOODBURY

Devon
Map ref 2D2

Attractive village, with Woodbury Common to the east, affording a panoramic coastal view from Berry Head to Portland Bill.

Webbers Farm Caravan Park
◉✓✓✓✓✓
Member BH&HPA
Castle Lane, Woodbury, Exeter
EX5 1EA
☎ (01395) 232276
Fax (01395) 233389
Leave M5 at junction 30 and follow A376 (Exmouth). At 2nd roundabout take B3179 (Budleigh Salterton/Woodbury). From Woodbury village centre follow official signs.
3 hectares (7.5 acres). Level, sloping, grassy.
115 touring pitches

115	🚐	£6.75—£8.75	
115	🚗	£6.75—£8.75	
115	▲	£6.75—£8.75	

Open April–September
🔌⚡🍴🔥🌳🚿💧🚰☕🖥✳🔌⊙🏔U
▶♨

WOOLACOMBE

Devon
Map ref 2C1

Between Morte Point and Baggy Point, Woolacombe and Mortehoe offer 3 miles of the finest sand and surf on this outstanding coastline.

Woolacombe Sands Holiday Park
◉✓✓✓✓
Member BH&HPA
Station Road, Woolacombe
EX34 7AF
☎ (01271) 870569
Fax (01271) 870569
M5 junction 27 to Barnstaple. A361 to Mullacott Cross then B3343 to Woolacombe. Left just before Woolacombe. Signposted.
Level, sloping, grassy, sheltered.
300 touring pitches

200	🚐	£6.75—£16.50	
200	🚗	£6.75—£16.50	
100	▲	£5.75—£15.50	
60	🏚	£99.00—£380.00	

Open April–September
Cards accepted: Access, Visa, Switch/Delta
🔌⚡🍴🔥🌳🚿💧🚰☕✳🍽🛒🍺📺🖥✳
🔌⊙🏔♨U♪♫
Ad See display advertisement on this page

USE YOUR *i*'s

There are more than 550 Tourist Information Centres throughout England offering friendly help with accommodation and holiday ideas as well as suggestions of places to visit and things to do. There may well be a centre in your home town which can help you before you set out. You'll find the address of your nearest Tourist Information Centre in your local Phone Book.

AT-A-GLANCE SYMBOLS

Symbols at the end of each accommodation entry give useful information about services and facilities. A key to symbols can be found inside the back cover flap.

Keep this open for easy reference.

COUNTRY CODE

Always follow the Country Code ⚘ Enjoy the countryside and respect its life and work ⚘ Guard against all risk of fire ⚘ Fasten all gates ⚘ Keep your dogs under close control ⚘ Keep to public paths across farmland ⚘ Use gates and stiles to cross fences, hedges and walls ⚘ Leave livestock, crops and machinery alone ⚘ Take your litter home ⚘ Help to keep all water clean ⚘ Protect wildlife, plants and trees ⚘ Take special care on country roads ⚘ Make no unnecessary noise

SOUTH OF ENGLAND

The South of England is a region of contrast and fascination. While the New Forest and Chiltern Hills offer mile upon mile of unspoilt countryside, there is much to please those who prefer town life - not to mention smart little Thameside villages crammed with antiques shops, quaint tea shops and exclusive boutiques.

Historic Oxford, Winchester and Windsor fall within the region, as does Henley, home of the famous Regatta.

The bucolic charms of Dorset await - along with the delightful seaside resorts of Poole, Weymouth and Bournemouth. And don't overlook the pretty Isle of Wight, just a ferry ride away.

FOR MORE INFORMATION CONTACT:
Southern Tourist Board
40 Chamberlayne Road, Eastleigh,
Hampshire SO50 5JH
Tel: (01703) 620555 **Fax:** (01703) 620010·

Where to Go in the South of England -
see pages 146-149
Where to Stay in the South of England -
see pages 150-159

SOUTH OF ENGLAND

Where to Go and What to See

You will find hundreds of interesting places to visit during your stay in the South of England, just some of which are listed in these pages. The number against each name will help you locate it on the map (page 149). Contact any Tourist Information Centre in the region for more ideas on days out in the South of England.

1 Broughton Castle
Banbury, Oxfordshire OX15 5EB
Tel: (01295) 262624
Medieval moated house built in 1300 and enlarged between 1550-1600. The home of Lord and Lady Saye and Sele and family home for 600 years. Civil War connections.

2 Blenheim Palace
Woodstock,
Oxfordshire OX20 1PX
Tel: (01993) 811091
Birthplace of Sir Winston Churchill, designed by Vanbrugh. Park designed by Capability Brown. Adventure play area, maze, butterfly house and Churchill exhibition.

3 The Oxford Story
6 Broad Street, Oxford OX1 3AJ
Tel: (01865) 728822
Heritage centre depicting eight centuries of history in sights, sounds, personalities and smells. Visitors are transported in moving desks with commentary of their choice.

4 Didcot Railway Centre
Great Western Society, Didcot,
Oxfordshire OX11 7NJ
Tel: (01235) 817200
Living museum recreating the golden age of the Great Western Railway. Steam locomotives and trains, engine shed and small relics museum.

5 Bekonscot Model Village
Warwick Road, Beaconsfield,
Buckinghamshire HP9 2PL
Tel: (01494) 672919
A complete model village of the 1930's, with outdoor gauge 1 model railway. Zoo, cinema, minster, cricket match and 1,400 inhabitants.

6 Beale Park
The Child-Beale Wildlife Trust
Lower Basildon,
Berkshire RG8 9NH
Tel: (01734) 845172
Established 38 years ago, the park features wildfowl, pheasants,

highland cattle, rare sheep, llamas, narrow guage railway and pet corner.

7 Windsor Castle
Windsor, Berkshire SL4 1NJ
Tel: (01753) 868286
Official residence of HM The Queen and royal residence for nine centuries. State apartments, Queen Mary's Dolls' House, exhibition of The Queen's presents and carriages.

8 Legoland Windsor
Winkfield Road, Windsor,
Berkshire SL4 4AY
Tel: (0990) 626375
A unique family park with hands-on activities, rides, themed playscapes and more Lego bricks than you ever dreamed possible.

9 Museum of Army Flying
Middle Wallop,
Hampshire SO20 8DY
Tel: (01980) 674421
Award-winning and unique collection of flying machines and

displays depicting the role of army flying since the late 19thC.

10 Jane Austen's House
Chawton, Hampshire GU34 1SD
Tel: (01420) 83262
17thC house where Jane Austen lived from 1809-1817, and wrote or revised her six great novels. Letters, pictures, memorabilia, garden.

11 Winchester Cathedral
5 The Close, Winchester,
Hampshire SO23 9LS
Tel: (01962) 853137
Originally Norman with 16thC additions. Old Saxon site adjacent. Tombs, library and medieval wall paintings.

12 The Sir Harold Hillier Gardens and Arboretum
Jermyns Lane, Ampfield,
Hampshire SO51 0QA
Tel: (01794) 368787
The largest collection of trees and shrubs of its kind in the British Isles planted within an attractive landscape of over 166 acres.

13 Marwell Zoological Park
Colden Common, Winchester,
Hampshire SO21 1JH
Tel: (01962) 777407
Set in 100 acres of parkland surrounding Marwell Hall. Venue suitable for all age groups including disabled.

14 Broadlands
Romsey, Hampshire SO51 9ZD
Tel: (01794) 517888
Home of the late Lord Mountbatten. Magnificent 18thC house and contents. Superb views across River Test. Mountbatten exhibition and audio-visual presentation.

15 Paultons Park
Ower, Romsey,
Hampshire SO51 6AL
Tel: (01703) 814442
A whole day out for all the family in beautiful surroundings. Over 40 different attractions including rides, museums, birds, animals and entertainment.

16 Exbury Gardens
Exbury, Southampton SO4 1AZ
Tel: (01703) 891203
Over 200 acres of woodland garden, including the Rothschild collection of rhododendrons, azaleas, camellias and magnolias.

17 Tudor House Museum
St. Michael's Square, Bugle Street,
Southampton SO14 2AD
Tel: (01703) 332513
Large half-timbered Tudor house with exhibitions on Tudor, Georgian, and Victorian domestic and local history. Unique Tudor garden.

18 Royal Signals Museum
Blandford Camp,
Blandford Forum,
Dorset DT11 8RH
Tel: (01258) 482248
History of Army communication from Crimean War to Gulf War. Vehicles, uniforms, medals and badges on display.

19 The New Forest Owl Sanctuary
Crow Lane, Crow,
Ringwood,
Hampshire BH24 1EA
Tel: (01425) 476487
All the barn owls are destined to be released into the wild. The sanctuary includes an incubation room, hospital unit and 100 aviaries of various size.

20 National Motor Museum
Beaulieu,
Hampshire SO42 7ZN
Tel: (01590) 612345
Motor museum with over 200 exhibits showing history of motoring from 1895. Palace House, Wheels Experience, abbey ruins with a display of monastic life.

Collection of paintings. 250 acres wooded park, herd of Devon cattle.

26 Brownsea Island
Poole Harbour, Poole,
Dorset BH15 1EE
Tel: (01202) 707744
An island of 500 acres of woodland with beaches, glades and nature reserve. Site of Lord Baden Powell's first scout camp.

27 Compton Acres
Canford Cliffs Road,
Canford Cliffs, Poole,
Dorset BH13 7ES
Tel: (01202) 700778
Nine separate and distinct gardens of the world. The gardens include Italian, Japanese, sub tropical glen, rock, water and heather garden. Collection of statues.

28 Poole Pottery
The Quay, Poole,
Dorset BH15 1RF
Tel: (01202) 666200
Factory tour, self-guided commentary includes museum, cinema, factory and craft area. 'Have-a-go area', craft village, throwing, painting, plus craft demonstrations.

29 Corfe Castle
Corfe Castle, Wareham,
Dorset BH20 5EZ
Tel: (01929) 481294
Ruins of former Royal Castle sieged and "slighted" in 1646 by Parliamentary forces.

30 The Tank Museum
Bovington Camp, Wareham,
Dorset BH20 6JG
Tel: (01929) 405096
Largest and most comprehensive museum collection of armoured fighting vehicles in the world. Over 300 vehicles on show with supporting displays and video theatres.

21 HMS Victory
Portsmouth Historic Ships,
HM Naval Base,
Portsmouth PO1 3LJ
Tel: (01705) 839766
Vice Admiral Lord Nelson's flagship at Trafalgar. See his cabin, the "cockpit," where he died. Memorable tours of the sombre gun decks where men lived.

22 Osborne House
East Cowes,
Isle of Wight PO32 6JY
Tel: (01983) 200022
Queen Victoria and Prince Albert's seaside holiday home. Swiss Cottage where royal children learnt cooking and gardening. Victorian carriage service to Swiss Cottage.

23 Carisbrooke Castle
Newport,
Isle of Wight PO30 1XY
Tel: (01983) 522107

A splendid Norman castle, where Charles I was imprisoned. Governors' lodge houses the county museum, wheelhouse operated by donkeys.

24 Alice in Wonderland Maze and Family Park
Merritown Farm, Hurn,
Christchurch, Dorset BH23 6BA
Tel: (01202) 483444
Hedge maze, Mad Hatter's tea garden, Queen of Heart's croquet lawn, Cheshire Cat's adventure playground, Duchess' rose and herb garden, rare breeds farmyard and bouncy colour maze.

25 Kingston Lacy
Wimborne Minster,
Dorset BH21 4EA
Tel: (01202) 883402
17thC house designed for Sir Ralph Bankes by Sir Roger Pratt, altered by Sir Charles Barry in the 19thC.

HEREFORD & WORCESTER

WARWICKSHIRE

NORTHANTS

Newport Pagnell

Wolverton

Milton Keynes

BEDS

Cropredy

1 Banbury

Buckingham

Bletchley

Chipping Norton

Bicester

2 Woodstock

BUCKINGHAM-SHIRE

GLOUCESTERSHIRE

Witney

Oxford **3**

Aylesbury

Wendover

Chesham

Thame

Princes Risborough

High Wycombe

OXFORDSHIRE

Faringdon

Abingdon

Wallingford

Beaconsfield **5**

Wantage

Didcot **4**

Henley on-Thames

Marlow

Slough

Lower Basildon **6**

Maidenhead

7 **8**

Twyford

Windsor

BERKSHIRE

Reading

Hungerford

Newbury

Wokingham

Bracknell

WILTSHIRE

Stratfield Saye

Farnborough

Fleet

Aldershot

Basingstoke

Alton

HAMPSHIRE

SURREY

9 Middle Wallop

Chawton **10**

11 Winchester

Liss

Ampfield

Colden Common

12

13

Petersfield

Gillingham

Shaftesbury

14 **15**

Romsey

Eastleigh

WEST SUSSEX

Fordingbridge

Totton

16 Southampton

DORSET (eastern)

Lyndhurst

17

Waterlooville

Blandford Forum **18**

Ringwood **19**

Brockenhurst

Fawley

Locks Heath

Lee-on-the-Solent

Wimborne Minster **25**

West Moors

Beaulieu

20

Lymington

East Cowes

Gosport

21 Portsmouth

Poole **26** **27** **28**

Christchurch

Newport **22** **23** Ryde

29 **30**

Bournemouth

Yarmouth

ISLE OF WIGHT

Sandown

Wareham

Freshwater

Shanklin

Ventnor

Swanage

0 _____ 20 Miles

0 _____ 30 Kms

FIND OUT MORE

Further information about holidays and attractions in the South of England is available from:

Southern Tourist Board,
40 Chamberlayne Road,
Eastleigh,
Hampshire SO50 5JH.
Tel: (01703) 620555

WHERE TO STAY (SOUTH OF ENGLAND)

Parks in this region are listed in alphabetical order of place name, and then in alphabetical order of establishment. A contact address is given where it differs from the address of the establishment.

Map references refer to the colour location maps at the back of this guide.

The first number indicates the map to use; the letter and number which follow refer to the grid reference on the map.

At-a-glance symbols can be found inside the back cover flap.

Keep this open for easy reference.

BANBURY

Oxfordshire
Map ref 3C1

Famous for its cattle market, cakes and nursery rhyme Cross. Founded in Saxon times, it has some fine houses and interesting old inns. A good centre for touring Warwickshire and the Cotswolds. *Tourist Information Centre ☎ (01295) 259855*

Bo-Peep Farm Caravan Park ⚠
☺✓✓✓✓✓
Bo-Peep Farm, Aynho Road, Adderbury, Banbury OX17 3NP
☎ (01295) 810605
Fax (01295) 812060
Look for international caravan sign on B4100 half a mile east of Adderbury traffic lights. Signposted.
2.4 hectares (6 acres). Level, sloping, grassy, sheltered.
50 touring pitches

50	🚐	£6.00—£7.00
40	🚍	
5	⛺	

Open March–October
🔌🗄🏪🔫♨🚰🔥🍴🛒🎢📺🚿🚗☺
🚣🏕

BEACONSFIELD

Buckinghamshire
Map ref 3D2

Former coaching town with several inns still surviving. The old town has many fine houses and an interesting church. Beautiful countryside and beech woods nearby.

Highclere Farm Country Touring Park ⚠
☺✓✓✓✓
Member BH&HPA
Newbarn Lane, Seer Green, Beaconsfield HP9 2QZ
☎ Chalfont St Giles (01494) 874505
Fax (01494) 875238
A40 to Potkiln Lane and pick signs up to site. M40 Junction 2 to Beaconsfield, A355 signed Amersham 1 mile, right to Seer Green. Signposted.
1 hectares (2.5 acres). Level, grassy, hard, sheltered.
60 touring pitches

45	🚐	£8.50—£9.50
45	🚍	£8.50—£9.50
15	⛺	£7.50—£9.50

Open January, March–December
Cards accepted: Access, Visa, Switch/Delta
🔌🅿🗄🏪🔫♨🚰🔥🍴🛒🎢📺🚿🚗
☺🏕
🆑 See display advertisement on this page

BERE REGIS

Dorset
Map ref 3B3

This watercress-growing village was in the Middle Ages famed for its fairs and being a resort of kings on their way to the south-west; its former splendour is well commemorated by the medieval church.

Rowlands Wait Touring Park
☺✓✓✓✓
Member BH&HPA
Rye Hill, Bere Regis, Wareham BH20 7LP
☎ Wareham (01929) 471958
From A35 (Poole/Dorchester road) at Bere Regis take Wool/ Bovington Tank Museum road. About half a mile up Rye Hill turn right, site 300 yards. Signposted.
3.2 hectares (8 acres). Level, sloping, grassy, sheltered.
71 touring pitches

30	🚐	£5.60—£8.60
6	🚍	£5.60—£8.60
35	⛺	£5.60—£8.60

Open January, March–December
🔌🗄🏪🔫♨🚰🔥🍴🛒🎢📺🚿🚗☺
🔍🏕☾☺

Dorset
Map ref 3B3

Almost completely destroyed by fire in 1731, the town was rebuilt in a handsome Georgian style. The church is large and grand and the town is the hub of a rich farming area.
Tourist Information Centre ☎ (01258) 454770

The Inside Park ⚠
●✓✓✓✓✓
Member BH&HPA
Blandford Forum DT11 9AD
☎ (01258) 453719 & Mobile 0378 313293
Fax (01258) 454026
Follow signs from Blandford St Mary exit off Blandford bypass, one and three quarters of a mile from roundabout. Signposted.
4.8 hectares (12 acres). Level, sloping, grassy, sheltered.
125 touring pitches

125	🚐	£7.00—£12.00
125	🚙	£7.00—£12.00
125	▲	£7.00—£12.00

Open April–October
Cards accepted: Access, Visa

BOURNEMOUTH

Dorset
Map ref 3B3

Seaside town set among the pines with a mild climate, sandy beaches and fine coastal views. The town has wide streets with excellent shops, a pier, a pavilion, museums and conference centre.
Tourist Information Centre ☎ (01202) 451700

Cara Touring Park ⚠
●✓✓✓✓✓
Member BH&HPA
Old Bridge Road, Iford,
Bournemouth BH6 5RQ
☎ (01202) 482121
On main A35 Bournemouth to Christchurch road. Signposted.
2.4 hectares (6 acres). Level, grassy, hard, sheltered.
36 touring pitches

36	🚐	£6.35—£8.50
36	🚙	£5.30—£7.25

77 units not for hire

CHARLBURY

Oxfordshire
Map ref 3C1

Large Cotswold village with beautiful views of the Evenlode Valley just outside the village and close to the ancient Forest of Wychwood.

Cotswold View Caravan & Camping Site
●✓✓✓✓✓
Enstone Road, Charlbury, Oxford OX7 3JH
☎ (01608) 810314
Fax (01608) 811891
2 miles off A44 on B4022. Signposted.
21.6 hectares (54 acres). Level, sloping, grassy, hard.
90 touring pitches

64	🚙	£8.00—£10.50
26	▲	£8.00—£10.50

Open April–October

CHRISTCHURCH

Dorset
Map ref 3B3

Tranquil town lying between the Avon and Stour just before they converge and flow into Christchurch Harbour. A fine 11th C church and the remains of a Norman castle and house can be seen.
Tourist Information Centre ☎ (01202) 471780

Beaulieu Gardens Holiday Park ⚠
●✓✓✓✓✓ Rose Award
Member BH&HPA
Beaulieu Avenue, Christchurch BH23 2EB
☎ Bournemouth (01202) 486215
Fax (01202) 483878
From Christchurch A35, west for 1 mile, turn left into Beaulieu Road. Signposted.
1.2 hectares (3 acres). Level, grassy, hard.

59	🛏	£110.00—£350.00

3 units not for hire
Open March–October
Cards accepted: Access, Visa, Switch/Delta

Grove Farm Meadow Holiday Park ⚠
●✓✓✓✓✓ Rose Award
Member BH&HPA
Stour Way, Christchurch BH23 2PQ
☎ Bournemouth (01202) 483597
Fax (01202) 483878
A35 from Christchurch, west one and a half miles, turn right at Crooked Beam Restaurant into the Grove, site third left. Signposted.
4 hectares (10 acres). Level, grassy, hard, sheltered.
44 touring pitches

44	🚐	£6.50—£13.00
44	🚙	£6.50—£13.00
77	🛏	£120.00—£380.00

116 units not for hire
Open March–October
Cards accepted: Access, Visa, Switch/Delta

Mount Pleasant Touring Park ⚠
●✓✓✓✓✓
Member BH&HPA
Matchams Lane, Hurn, Christchurch BH23 6AW
☎ (01202) 475474
From M27, take A31, first left after passing Ringwood 4 miles left. Signposted.
2.88 hectares (7.2 acres). Level, grassy, sheltered.
145 touring pitches

145	🚐	£6.50—£11.00
145	🚙	£6.50—£11.00
95	▲	£6.50—£11.00

Open March–October
Cards accepted: Access, Visa, Switch/Delta

CORFE CASTLE

Dorset
Map ref 3B3

One of the most spectacular ruined castles in Britain. Norman in origin, the castle was a Royalist stronghold during the Civil War and held out until 1645. The village had a considerable marble-carving industry in the Middle Ages.

Knitson Tourers' Site
Knitson Farm, Corfe Castle, Swanage BH20 5JB
☎ (01929) 422836
A351 to Swanage, first left opposite Royal Oak, left at T-junction, proceed for half a mile, site on left. Signposted.
Continued ▶

151

CORFE CASTLE

Continued

3 hectares (7.5 acres). Sloping, grassy, sheltered.
60 touring pitches

30	🚐	£3.00—£6.00
30	🚏	
30	⛺	

Open April–October
🚗 ▣ 🚿 🅿 ♿ ⛰ ∪

DOWNTON

Hampshire
Map ref 3B3

Hamlet on the A337, 4 miles south-west of Lymington.

Shorefield Country Park ⚠
⊖✓✓✓✓✓ Rose Award
Member BH&HPA/NCC
Shorefield Road, Downton,
Lymington SO41 0LH
☎ Lymington (01590) 642513
Fax (01590) 645610
From M27 take Lyndhurst exit 1 onto A337 to Downton, turn left at Royal Oak public house. Signposted.
40 hectares (100 acres). Level, grassy, stony.

80	🚐	£145.00—£725.00

449 units not for hire
Open March–December
Cards accepted: Access, Visa, Switch/Delta
🔥 🚗 🅿 🚿 ⚓ ⏰ ∪ ⚡ ✕ 🍽 🛒 📷 ▣ ⚡ 🛢
⊙ 🔍 ⛰ 🎣 ∪ 🔧 🎵 🎶 🔲 ⊚

[Ad] See display advertisement on this page

GOSPORT

Hampshire
Map ref 3C3

From a tiny fishing hamlet, Gosport has grown into an important centre with many naval establishments, including HMS Dolphin, the submarine base, with the Naval Submarine Museum which preserves HMS Alliance and Holland I.
Tourist Information Centre ☎ (01705) 522944

Kingfisher Caravan Park ⚠
⊖✓✓✓✓✓
Member BH&HPA/NCC
Browndown Road, Stokes Bay,
Gosport PO13 9BE
☎ Portsmouth (01705) 502611
Fax (01705) 583583
M27 junction 11, A32 to Gosport (3 miles approximately) and follow signs to Stokes Bay. Midway between

Gosport and Lee on Solent on coast road. Signposted.
5.6 hectares (14 acres). Level, grassy.
110 touring pitches

90	🚏	£13.00—£15.00
20	⛺	£8.50—£15.00
20	🚐	£180.00—£350.00

Open February–November
Cards accepted: Access, Visa, Amex, Switch/Delta
🚗 🅿 ▣ 🚿 ⚓ ⏰ ♿ 🛒 ✕ 🍽 📺 🛒 📷 ⚡
🛢 ⊙ 🔍 ⛰ 🎵 🎶 🔲

HAMBLE

Hampshire
Map ref 3C3

Set almost at the mouth of the River Hamble, this quiet fishing village has become a major yachting centre.

Riverside Park ⚠
⊖✓✓✓
Member BH&HPA
Satchell Lane, Hamble, Southampton SO31 4HR
☎ Southampton (01703) 453220 & 457414
Fax (01703) 457414
Junction 8 off M27, take B3397 south to Hamble. Signposts from Hamble Lane to Riverside Park. Signposted.

BEST OF BOTH WORLDS

ONLY 2½ miles from Shorefield Country Park, Lytton Lawn is set in beautiful natural parkland, close to Milford Beach and the historic New Forest.

Individual pitches have plenty of space for the car, caravan or tent, awning and barbecue.

Facilities include: Electricity hook up, showers, purpose-built launderette, "Premier" pitches and a children's area.

Plus FREE Leisure Club Membership:
Indoor/Outdoor pools, dance studio, tennis courts, top class restaurant, sauna, solarium, spa bath and nightly entertainment.

WINNER
1990

SHOREFIELD
COUNTRY PARKS

Shorefield Road, Downton, Lymington, Hants SO41 0LH

01590 642513

Quote WTST

ROSE
AWARD
CARAVAN
HOLIDAY
PARK
1997

2.24 hectares (5.6 acres). Level, sloping, grassy, sheltered.
17 touring pitches

17	🚐	£7.50—£9.50
17	🚗	£7.50—£9.50
17	⛺	£7.50—£9.50
8	🏠	£147.00—£420.00

24 units not for hire
Open March–October and Christmas
Cards accepted: Access, Visa
🛢🛎️P🅿🔥🏕️♨🚾🏪📶📱🔌⚡🚗☺🔥
🔥🏠♿

HENLEY-ON-THAMES

Oxfordshire
Map ref 3C2

The famous Thames Regatta is held in this prosperous and attractive town at the beginning of July each year. The town has many Georgian buildings and old coaching inns and the parish church has some fine monuments.
Tourist Information Centre ☎ *(01491) 578034*

Swiss Farm International Camping ⚠️
🛢✓✓✓
Member NCC
Swiss Farm, Marlow Road, Henley-on-Thames RG9 2HY
☎ (01491) 573419
From Henley take A4155 north towards Marlow, half a mile from centre. Signposted.
18.4 hectares (46 acres). Sloping, grassy, hard, sheltered.
180 touring pitches

60	🚐	£8.00—£9.75
60	🚗	£8.00—£9.75
60	⛺	£8.00—£9.75
6	🏠	£140.00—£220.00

Open March–October
🚗☺🔥📶🔥🏕️♨🚾🏪⚡🍴📱♿
🛢☺🔥🔥🍴♿

HURLEY

Berkshire
Map ref 3C2

Hurley Farm Caravan & Camping Park ⚠️
🛢✓✓✓✓
Member BH&HPA
Shepherds Lane, Hurley, Maidenhead SL6 5NE
☎ Littlewick Green (01628) 823501
From M4 junction 8/9, take A404M, then A4130 to Henley, travel north for 5 miles and turn right, 1 mile past East Arms pub, into Shepherds Lane. From M40 J4 take A404 south then A4130 to Henley and as above. Signposted.
160 hectares (400 acres). Level, grassy, sheltered.
200 touring pitches

138	🚐	£5.50—£10.00
138	🚗	£5.50—£10.00
62	⛺	£5.50—£9.00
6	🏠	£120.00—£260.00

450 units not for hire
Open March–October
Cards accepted: Access, Visa
🛢P🅿🔥🏕️♨🚾🏪📶📱🔌🚗☺♿🍴♿
🏕️♿📶

Ad See display advertisement on this page

MILFORD-ON-SEA

Hampshire
Map ref 3C3

Victorian seaside resort with shingle beach and good bathing, set in pleasant countryside and looking out over the Isle of Wight. Nearby is Hurst Castle, built by Henry VIII.

Downton Holiday Park ⚠️
🛢✓✓✓✓✓
Member BH&HPA
Shorefield Road, Milford-on-Sea, Lymington SO41 0LH
☎ Ringwood (01425) 476131 & Lymington (01590) 642515

Turn from B3058 into Downton Lane, then first right, or from A337 into Downton Lane then first left.
1.4 hectares (3.5 acres). Level, grassy, sheltered.

21	🏠	£70.50—£399.50

53 units not for hire
Open March–October
🚗P🅿🔥🏕️♨🚾🏪📶📱🔌⚡🚗☺🔥
🔥♿♿

NEW MILTON

Hampshire
Map ref 3B3

New Forest residential town on the mainline railway.

Glen Orchard Holiday Park ⚠️
🛢✓✓✓✓✓
Member BH&HPA
Walkford Lane, New Milton BH25 5NH
☎ (01425) 616463
Fax (01425) 638655
Signposted.
0.46 hectares (1.15 acres). Sloping, grassy, sheltered.

19	🏠	£95.00—£315.00

Open March–October
🚗P🏕️🔥♨🚾📶📱🔌⚡🚗☺🔥
🔥🏠♿

OWER

Hampshire
Map ref 3C3

New Forest hamlet lying close to the important road junction of the A36 and the M27.

Green Pastures Caravan Park ⚠️
🛢✓✓✓
Green Pastures Farm, Ower, Romsey SO51 6AJ
☎ Southampton (01703) 814444

Continued ▶

OWER

Continued

Between Cadnam and Romsey just off A31 west of junction with A36, exit 2 off M27. Follow signs to Paultons Park. Signposted.
2 hectares (5 acres). Level, grassy.
45 touring pitches

45	£7.50—£7.50
45	£7.50—£7.50
45	£7.50—£7.50

Open March–October

OXFORD

Oxfordshire
Map ref 3C1

Beautiful university town with many ancient colleges, some dating from the 13th C, and numerous buildings of historic and architectural interest. The Ashmolean Museum has outstanding collections. Lovely gardens and meadows with punting on the Cherwell.
Tourist Information Centre ☎ (01865) 726871

Cassington Mill Caravan Park

✓✓✓
Member BH&HPA
Eynsham Road, Cassington, Witney OX8 1DB
☎ (01865) 881081
Fax (01865) 880577
Take the second turn left, two and a half miles west of Oxford, on the A40 towards Witney. Signposted.
1.6 hectares (4 acres). Grassy, sheltered.
83 touring pitches

83	£7.00—£7.00
83	£7.00—£7.00
83	£7.00—£7.00

35 units not for hire
Open April–October
Cards accepted: Access, Visa, Diners, Amex, Switch/Delta

Oxford Camping International

✓✓✓✓✓
Member BH&HPA
426 Abingdon Road, Oxford OX1 4XN
☎ (01865) 246551
Fax (01865) 240145
Situated on the south side of Oxford. Take the A4144 to the city centre and follow campsite signs. Signposted.
2 hectares (5 acres). Level, grassy.
129 touring pitches

99	£7.85
99	£7.85
129	£7.85

Cards accepted: Access, Visa, Amex

POOLE

Dorset
Map ref 3B3

Tremendous natural harbour makes Poole a superb boating centre. The harbour area is crowded with historic buildings including the 15th C Town Cellars housing a maritime museum.
Tourist Information Centre ☎ (01202) 673322

Beacon Hill Touring Park

✓✓✓✓
Member BH&HPA
Blandford Road North, Lytchett Minster, Poole BH16 6AB
☎ Lytchett Minster (01202) 631631
On A350, a quarter of a mile from junction of A35 and A350 towards Blandford. Approximately 3 miles north of Poole. Signposted.
12 hectares (30 acres). Level, grassy, hard, sheltered.
170 touring pitches

120	£7.40—£14.00
120	£6.60—£14.00
50	£6.60—£14.00

Open April–September

Organford Manor Caravans & Holidays

✓✓✓
Member BH&HPA
Organford, Poole BH16 6ES
☎ Lytchett Minster (01202) 622202
Take first turning left off A35 after roundabout junction of the A35 and A351. Signposted.
3.2 hectares (8 acres). Level, grassy, sheltered.
78 touring pitches

36	£6.50—£8.00
6	£5.50—£7.00
36	£6.50—£8.00
3	

42 units not for hire
Open March–October

Pear Tree Caravan Park

✓✓✓✓✓
Member BH&HPA
Organford Road, Organford, Poole BH16 6LA
☎ Lytchett Minster (01202) 622434
Between A351 and A35. Turn right off A351 (Wareham Road) at Holton Heath, signposted Organford, the park entrance is half a mile on the left. Signposted.
3 hectares (7.5 acres). Level, sloping, grassy, hard, sheltered.
125 touring pitches

76	£6.50—£8.50
66	£6.50—£8.50
49	£6.50—£8.50

Open April–October

Rockley Park

✓✓✓✓ Rose Award
Member BH&HPA/NCC
Hamworthy, Poole BH15 4LZ
☎ Reservations/free brochure (01442) 248668
Fax (01442) 232459
Leave M27 and follow signs for Poole town centre, then signs for Rockley Park. Signposted.
29.6 hectares (74 acres). Level, sloping, grassy.
74 touring pitches

70	£7.70—£19.25
70	£7.70—£19.25
10	£7.70—£16.00
504	£142.00—£588.00

500 units not for hire
Open March–October
Cards accepted: Access, Visa, Switch/Delta

Ad See display advertisement inside front cover

Sandford Holiday Park

✓✓✓✓✓
Member BH&HPA
Holton Heath, Poole BH16 6JZ
☎ Lytchett Minster (01202) 631600 & Bookings (01392) 447447
Fax (01202) 625678
Between Bournemouth and Swanage on A351. Signposted.
24 hectares (60 acres). Level, grassy, sheltered.
447 touring pitches

447	£7.80
447	£7.80
447	£7.80
210	£99.00—£571.00

19 units not for hire
Open April–October
Cards accepted: Access, Visa, Switch/Delta

RINGWOOD

Hampshire
Map ref 3B3

Market town by the River Avon comprising old cottages, many of them thatched. Although just outside the New Forest, there is heath and woodland nearby and it is a good centre for horse-riding and walking.

Red Shoot Camping Park ⚠
⊖✓✓✓✓
Linwood, Ringwood BH24 3QT
☎ (01425) 473789 & 478940
Fax (01425) 471558
2 miles north of Ringwood on A338 and follow signs to Linwood or off M27 exit 1, follow signs for Linwood. Signposted.
1.6 hectares (4 acres). Level, grassy.
100 touring pitches

30	🚐	£7.50—£10.00
70	🚏	£7.50—£10.00
70	▲	£7.50—£10.00

Open March–October
♣P🖪⚙🛉🏕♨⊙🛒🛢✦🔲☉
⚠ ♿
Ad See display advertisement on this page

> A key to symbols can be found inside the back cover flap.

> All accommodation in this guide has been graded, or is awaiting a grading, by a trained Tourist Board inspector.

SANDOWN

Isle of Wight
Map ref 3C3

The 6-mile sweep of Sandown Bay is one of the island's finest stretches, with excellent sands. The pier has a pavilion and sun terrace; the esplanade has amusements, bars, eating-places and gardens.
Tourist Information Centre ☎ (01983) 403886

Adgestone Camping Park ⚠
⊖✓✓✓✓
Member BH&HPA
Lower Road, Adgestone, Sandown
PO36 0HL
☎ Isle of Wight (01983) 403432 & 403989
Fax (01983) 404955
A3055 between Sandown and Shanklin, turn off at Manor House Pub, Lake. Past golf club to T Junction, turn right. Park 200yds on right. Signposted.
6.3 hectares (15.75 acres). Level, grassy.
200 touring pitches

100	🚐	£6.40—£9.90
50	🚏	£6.40—£9.90
50	▲	£6.40—£9.90

Open April–September
Cards accepted: Access, Visa
P🖪⚙🛉🏕♨⊙🛒🛢✦🔲☉
🔍⚠🔭🎣🏴♿

> Please check prices and other details at the time of booking.

> The ⚠ symbol after an establishment name indicates that it is a Regional Tourist Board member.

STANDLAKE

Oxfordshire
Map ref 3C1

13th C church with an octagonal tower and spire standing beside the Windrush. The interior of the church is rich in woodwork.

Hardwick Parks ⚠
⊖✓✓✓
Member BH&HPA
Downs Road, Standlake, Witney
OX8 7PZ
☎ Oxford (01865) 300501
Fax (01865) 300037
From Witney, take A415 signposted to Abingdon. Signposted.
72 hectares (180 acres). Level, grassy.
250 touring pitches

100	🚐	£7.25—£9.25
100	🚏	£7.25—£9.25
50	▲	£7.25—£9.25

115 units not for hire
Open April–October
Cards accepted: Access, Visa, Switch/Delta
🖪⚙🛉🏕♨⊙🛒✕🍴🔲🛢✦🔲☉
⚠🔭🎣🛶♨🏴♿
Ad See display advertisement on this page

Lincoln Farm Park ⚠
⊖✓✓✓✓
Member BH&HPA
High Street, Standlake, Witney
OX8 7RH
☎ Oxford (01865) 300239
From Witney, take the A415 south-east for five and a half miles. Turn left into the High Street. Signposted.
2.4 hectares (6 acres). Level, grassy, hard.
60 touring pitches

48	🚐	£10.00—£12.00
6	🚏	£10.00—£12.00
6	▲	£10.00—£12.00

Continued ▶

STANDLAKE

Continued

18 units not for hire
Open March–October
Cards accepted: Access, Visa

🔥⚓🅿️🎿🏕️🍴💧🐟☕🍺📞📺🌀⚡
🛒☺️⚠️🎾🚣🪁

SWANAGE

Dorset
Map ref 3B3

Began life as an Anglo-Saxon port, then a quarrying centre of Purbeck marble. Now the safe, sandy beach set in a sweeping bay and flanked by downs is good walking country, making it an ideal resort.
Tourist Information Centre ☎ (01929) 422885

Ulwell Cottage Caravan Park ⚠

⊖✓✓✓✓✓ Rose Award
Member BH&HPA
Ulwell, Swanage BH19 3DG
☎ (01929) 422823
Studland Road, one and a half miles on left. On Swanage to Studland Road. Signposted.
5.2 hectares (13 acres). Level, sloping, grassy, hard, sheltered.

---

77 touring pitches

	🚐	£10.00—£17.00
	�"	£10.00—£17.00
	🅰	£10.00—£17.00
80	🛖	£145.00—£455.00

60 units not for hire
Open January, March–December
Cards accepted: Access, Visa, Amex

🔥🚐🎿🏕️💧🐟☕🛒🍴✕🍺📞📺🌀⚡🛒
☺️⚠️🎾🪁◎
Ad See display advertisement on this page

Ulwell Farm Caravan Park ⚠
⊖✓✓✓✓
Member BH&HPA
Ulwell, Swanage BH19 3DG
☎ (01929) 422825
From Swanage Road signposted Studland and Bournemouth, site approximately one and a quarter miles. Park entrance on the right. Signposted.
1 hectares (2.5 acres). Sloping, grassy, sheltered.
5 touring pitches

> All accommodation in this guide has been graded, or is awaiting a grading, by a trained Tourist Board inspector.

5	🚐	£7.50—£12.00
1	🚚	£6.00—£10.50
1	🅰	£6.00—£10.50
24	🛖	£70.00—£290.00

21 units not for hire
Open April–September

⚓🅿️🚐🎿🏕️🍴💧🐟☕🍺📞📺🌀⚡🛒🚉☺️
⚠️🪁🇹

WAREHAM

Dorset
Map ref 3B3

This site has been occupied since pre-Roman times and has a turbulent history. In 1762 fire destroyed much of the town, so the buildings now are mostly Georgian.
Tourist Information Centre ☎ (01929) 552740

Birchwood Tourist Park
Member BH&HPA
Bere Road, North Trigon, Wareham
BH20 7PA
☎ (01929) 554763
From Dorchester, follow A35 to Bere Regis, then follow signs to Wareham. Birchwood Park is second touring park on the left. Signposted.
20 hectares (50 acres). Level, grassy, sheltered.
175 touring pitches

Sandy Beaches

Indoor Pool ~ Shop

Ulwell **C**ottage
ROSE AWARD CARAVAN HOLIDAY PARK
CARAVAN PARK
Swanage BH19 3DG

For Brochure
Telephone 01929 422823

Scenic Walks

Village Inn

BRITISH GRADED HOLIDAY PARKS
EXCELLENT

Nestling in the beautiful Isle of Purbeck

175	🚐	£6.00—£9.50
175	🚏	£6.00—£9.50
175	▲	£6.00—£9.50

Open March–October

🅿️🚐🅿️🔥🏕️🛝🅟🏪🛒✕🛒🗑️⚡🎣
☺️🔍🎣⛰️∪🎣👣🧗

Ⓐ See display advertisement on page 158

The Lookout Caravan Park 🏕️
🌐✓✓✓✓✓ Rose Award
Member BH&HPA
Stoborough, Wareham BH20 5AZ
☎ Swanage (01929) 552546
From Wareham take the A351 for one and a quarter miles towards Corfe Castle. Site on on left hand side. Signposted.
6 hectares (15 acres). Level, grassy, hard, sheltered.
150 touring pitches

150	🚐	£8.50—£10.50
150	🚏	
100	▲	
45	🏠	£90.00—£350.00

45 units not for hire
Open February–November

🅿️🚐🔥🏕️🛝🅟🛒🗑️⚡🎣☺️🔍
⛰️👣🧗

Ⓐ See display advertisement on this page

Wareham Forest Tourist Park 🏕️
🌐✓✓✓✓✓
Member BH&HPA/NCC
North Trigon, Wareham BH20 7NZ
☎ (01929) 551393
From Bere Regis, take the A35 east for one and a half miles, then turn right signposted Wareham. Signposted.
17.4 hectares (43.5 acres). Level, grassy, stony, hard, sheltered.
200 touring pitches

200	🚐	£6.60—£10.40
200	🚏	£6.60—£10.40
200	▲	£6.60—£10.40

🅿️🚐🅿️🔥🏕️🛝🅟🏪🛒✕🛒🗑️⚡🎣
☺️🔍⛰️🧗👣

Ⓐ See display advertisement on this page

Map references apply to the colour maps at the back of this guide.

For ideas on places to visit refer to the introduction at the beginning of this section.

Durdle Door Caravan Park 🏕️
🌐✓✓✓
Member BH&HPA
West Lulworth, Wareham
BH20 5PU
☎ (01929) 400200
Fax (01929) 400563
Signposted from West Lulworth village on the road going west.
18 hectares (45 acres). Level, sloping, grassy, sheltered.
175 touring pitches

32	🚐	£9.00—£12.00
25	🚏	£8.00—£9.00
150	▲	£8.00—£9.00
25	🏠	£100.00—£300.00

390 units not for hire
Open March–October
Cards accepted: Access, Visa

🅿️🅿️🔥🏕️🛝🅟🛒⚡🎣🗑️⚡🎣☺️
🔍⛰️🧗

Ⓐ See display advertisement on page 158

WIMBORNE MINSTER

Dorset
Map ref 3B3

Market town centred on the twin-towered Minster Church of St Cuthberga which gave the town the second part of its name. Good touring base for the surrounding countryside, depicted in the writings of Thomas Hardy.
Tourist Information Centre ☎ *(01202) 886116*

Charris Camping & Caravan Park ⚠
⊖✓✓✓✓
Member BH&HPA
Candy's Lane, Corfe Mullen,
Wimborne Minster BH21 3EF
☎ Wimborne (01202) 885970
2 miles west of Wimborne on the A31. Signposted.
1.2 hectares (3 acres). Level, sloping, grassy, sheltered.
45 touring pitches

45	🚐	£5.25—£6.25
22	🚏	£5.25—£6.25
22	⛺	£5.25—£6.25

Open March—October
⚓P🔥🔆🔧🍴⊙🛒📶📦🚰🚿⊙ ▶🔥

Merley Court Touring Park ⚠
⊖✓✓✓✓✓
Member BH&HPA
Merley, Wimborne Minster
BH21 3AA
☎ Wimborne (01202) 881488
Fax (01202) 881484
Wimborne one and a half miles. Off Wimborne bypass A31 junction A349

Poole road and follow signs for Merley Bird Gardens. Signposted.
6.2 hectares (15.5 acres). Level, grassy, hard, sheltered.
160 touring pitches

160	🚐	£6.00—£11.30
160	🚏	£6.00—£11.30
80	⛺	£6.00—£11.30

Open March—December
⚓📶🔥🔆🔧🍴⊙🛒❌🍴📺📶📦🚰
🔥⊙🔆🔧🚻🔧🔔🔥

Ad See display advertisement on page 159

Springfield Touring Park ⚠
⊖✓✓✓✓✓
Member BH&HPA
Candys Lane, Corfe Mullen,
Wimborne Minster BH21 3EF
☎ Bournemouth (01202) 881719
Close to main A31 trunk road, one and a half miles west of Wimborne. Signposted.
1.4 hectares (3.5 acres). Level, sloping, grassy, hard.
45 touring pitches

45	🚐	£6.00—£8.00
45	🚏	£6.00—£8.00
45	⛺	£5.00—£8.00

Open March—October
⚓🚐🔥🔆🔧🍴⊙🛒📦🚰🔥🚰⊙
🚻🔥

Wilksworth Farm Caravan Park ⚠
⊖✓✓✓✓✓
Member BH&HPA
Cranborne Road, Wimborne
Minster BH21 4HW
☎ Bournemouth (01202) 885467
Fax (01202) 885467

1 mile north of Wimborne and A31 on B3078 to Cranborne Signposted.
4.4 hectares (11 acres). Level, grassy, hard, sheltered.
85 touring pitches

60	🚐	£6.00—£11.00
60	🚏	£6.00—£11.00
25	⛺	£6.00—£11.00
2	🛖	£100.00—£280.00

75 units not for hire
Open March—October
⚓P🚐🔥🔆🔧🍴⊙🛒📦🚰🔥🔆
⊙🔥🚻🔧🔔🔥🚻🔔◎

WOKINGHAM

Berkshire
Map ref 3C2

Pleasant town which grew up around the silk trade and has some half-timbered and Georgian houses.
Tourist Information Centre ☎ *(01734) 774722*

California Chalet & Touring Park ⚠
⊖✓✓✓✓
Member BH&HPA
Nine Mile Ride, Finchampstead,
Wokingham RG40 4HU
☎ Eversley (01734) 733928
Take the A321 from Wokingham and turn right. Travel along the B3016 for 1 mile and turn right. The site is situated three quarters of a mile on the right. Signposted.
2.2 hectares (5.5 acres). Level, grassy, hard, sheltered.
35 touring pitches

29	🚐	£9.00—£10.50
29	🚏	£9.00—£10.50
6	⛺	£5.00—£9.00

2 units not for hire
Open March–October
🔌🏠🅿️📮🍴🎣🛝💧🚿🛒🔟🔌📞☺️
🛟🎾🎣🔥

WOOL

Dorset
Map ref 3B3

On the River Frome with a mainline station. Woolbridge Manor is of interest and occupies a prominent position.

Whitemead Caravan Park
⊖✓✓✓✓
East Burton Road, Wool, Wareham BH20 6HG
☎ Bindon Abbey (01929) 462241
On A352 from Wareham turn right before Wool level crossing 350 yards. Signposted.
2 hectares (5 acres). Level, grassy, hard, sheltered.
90 touring pitches

90	🚐	£6.00—£9.50
90	🚏	£6.00—£9.50
90	⛺	£6.00—£9.50

Open April–October
🔌🏠🍴🎣🛝💧🚿🛒📮🔟🔌📞
☺️⚠️🔥

YARMOUTH

Isle of Wight
Map ref 3C3

Small, historic port on the Solent in the west of the island. A good, central starting-point for exploring the island.
Tourist Information Centre ☎ (01983) 760015

The Orchards Holiday Caravan Park ⚠️
⊖✓✓✓✓✓ Rose Award
Member BH&HPA
Newbridge, Yarmouth PO41 0TS
☎ Isle of Wight (01983) 531331
Fax (01983) 531666
6 miles west of Newport, 4 miles east of Yarmouth on B3401. Signposted.
6 hectares (15 acres). Level, sloping, grassy, hard, sheltered.
179 touring pitches

129	🚐	£6.90—£9.90
25	🚏	£6.90—£9.90
25	⛺	£6.90—£9.90
57	🏠	£95.00—£495.00

4 units not for hire
Open April–October
Cards accepted: Access, Visa
🅿️📮🎣🛝💧🚿🛒📺🔟📞☺️
🍴⚠️🎾🎣🛟🎣🔥🔳

COUNTRY CODE

Always follow the Country Code 🌿 Enjoy the countryside and respect its life and work 🌿 Guard against all risk of fire 🌿 Fasten all gates 🌿 Keep your dogs under close control 🌿 Keep to public paths across farmland 🌿 Use gates and stiles to cross fences, hedges and walls 🌿 Leave livestock, crops and machinery alone 🌿 Take your litter home 🌿 Help to keep all water clean 🌿 Protect wildlife, plants and trees 🌿 Take special care on country roads 🌿 Make no unnecessary noise

USE YOUR *i*'s

There are more than 550 Tourist Information Centres throughout England offering friendly help with accommodation and holiday ideas as well as suggestions of places to visit and things to do. There may well be a centre in your home town which can help you before you set out. You'll find the address of your nearest Tourist Information Centre in your local Phone Book.

AT-A-GLANCE SYMBOLS

Symbols at the end of each accommodation entry give useful information about services and facilities. A key to symbols can be found inside the back cover flap.

Keep this open for easy reference.

CHECK THE MAPS

The colour maps at the back of this guide show all the cities, towns and villages for which you will find accommodation entries.

Refer to the town index to find the page on which it is listed.

SOUTH EAST ENGLAND

South East England conjures up images of cricket on the village green, traditional village pubs and Sussex cream teas with lashings of home-made jam!

The beauty is, the fantasy is reality. South East England truly is unspoilt.

Visit Kent, the Garden of England, with its oasthouses, abundant vineyards, fruitful orchards and pretty weatherboard cottages.

Wander across the glorious South Downs, the heathland of Surrey, or head for Dover's white cliffs or the buzz of Regency Brighton.

Explore the medieval Cinque Ports and the region's churches, castles, manor houses and gardens. It's all here. As it has been for centuries.

FOR MORE INFORMATION CONTACT:
South East England Tourist Board,
The Old Brew House, Warwick Park,
Tunbridge Wells, Kent TN2 5TU
Tel: (01892) 540766 **Fax:** (01892) 511008

Where to Go in South East England -
see pages 162-165
Where to Stay in South East England -
see pages 166-172

SOUTH EAST ENGLAND

Where to Go and What to See

You will find hundreds of interesting places to visit during your stay in South East England, just some of which are listed in these pages. The number against each name will help you locate it on the map (page 165). Contact any Tourist Information Centre in the region for more ideas on days out in South East England.

1 Royal Engineers Museum
Prince Arthur Road,
Gillingham,
Kent ME4 4UG
Tel: (01634) 406397
The characters, lives and work of Britain's soldier-engineers 1066-1945. Medals, uniforms, scientific and technical equipement. Collection of ethnography and decorative arts.

2 The Historic Dockyard
Chatham, Kent ME4 4TE
Tel: (01634) 812551
Historic 18thC 80 acre dockyard. Museum with seven major attractions including the award-winning 'Wooden Walls' gallery, sail and colour loft, working ropery.

3 Brogdale Horticultural Trust
Brogdale Farm,
Brogdale Road,
Faversham, Kent ME13 8XZ
Tel: (01795) 535286
National Fruit Collection with 4,000
varieties of fruit in 30 acres of orchards: apples, pears, cherries, plums, currants, quinces, medlars and other fruits.

4 Belmont
Belmont Park,
Throwley,
Kent ME13 0HH
Tel: (01795) 890202
Late 18thC country mansion designed by Samuel Wyatt, seat of the Harris family since 1801. Harris clock collection, mementos of connections with India. Gardens and pinetum.

5 Leeds Castle
Leeds, Maidstone,
Kent ME17 1PL
Tel: (01622) 765400
Castle on two islands in lake dating from 12thC. Furniture, tapestries, art treasures. Dog Collar Museum. Gardens, parkland, duckery, aviaries, maze, grotto, small vineyard, greenhouses.

6 The Royal Horticultural Society's Garden
Wisley, Surrey GU23 6QB
Tel: (01483) 224234
World famous RHS garden covering 250 acres of vegetable, fruit and ornamental gardening. Trial grounds, glasshouses, rock garden, ponds. Rose, model and specialist gardens.

7 Guildford Boat House River Trips
Millbrook, Guildford,
Surrey GU1 3XJ
Tel: (01483) 504494
Regular trips from Guildford to St. Catherine's Lock and Farncombe along River Wey. Also 'Alfred Leroy' cruising restaurant. Rowing boats and canoes.

8 Guildford Cathedral
Stag Hill, Guildford,
Surrey GU2 5UP
Tel: (01483) 565287
New Anglican cathedral, foundation

stone laid 1936 and consecrated 1961. Notable glass engravings, embroidered kneelers. Modern furnishings. Brass Rubbing Centre.

9 Loseley House and Park Farm
Loseley Park,
Guildford,
Surrey GU3 1HS
Tel: (01483) 304440
Elizabethan mansion with decorated ceilings, unusual chalk fireplace, period furniture and paintings. Parkland and farm with famous Jersey cows, rare breeds and trailer tours.

10 Denbies Wine Estate
London Road, Dorking,
Surrey RH5 6AA
Tel: (01306) 876616
England's largest wine estate, 250 acres in beautiful countryside. Winery and visitor centre featuring 3-D time-lapse film of vine growing. Viewing and picture galleries.

11 Birdworld and Underwaterworld
Holt Pound, Farnham,
Surrey GU10 4LD
Tel: (01420) 22140
20 acres of garden and parkland with ostriches, flamingoes, hornbills, parrots, emus, pelicans etc. Penguin island, tropical and marine fish. Plant area, seashore walk.

12 Hever Castle and Gardens
Hever, Edenbridge,
Kent TN8 7NG
Tel: (01732) 865224
Moated castle, family home of Anne Boleyn. Restored by Astor family. Fine interior, furniture, paintings and panelling. Gardens, lake, topiary, maze, minature model houses exhibition.

13 Headcorn Flower Centre and Vineyard
Grigg Lane, Headcorn,
Ashford, Kent TN27 9LX
Tel: (01622) 890250
Walk around 6 acres of vines. Reservoir with wildlife. Weekend and group tours visit flowerhouses with chrysanthemums and orchid lilies flowering all year.

14 Dover Castle and Hellfire Corner
Dover, Kent CT16 1HU
Tel: (01304) 201628
One of the most powerful medieval fortresses in Western Europe. St Mary-in-Castro Saxon church. Roman lighthouse, Hellfire Corner, 'All The Queen's Men' exhibition.

15 Groombridge Place Gardens
Groombridge,
Royal Tunbridge Wells,
Kent TN3 9QG
Tel: (01892) 863999

Grade I listed 17thC restored walled gardens. Drunken topiary garden, oriental and sculpture gardens, ancient and mystical woodland with spring-fed pools.

16 Bedgebury National Pinetum
Goudhurst, Kent TN17 2SL
Tel: (01580) 211044
The Forestry Commission's superb collection of specimen conifers in 150 acres with lake and streams. Plus many rhododendrons and azaleas.

17 Leonardslee Gardens
Lower Beeding,
West Sussex RH13 6PP
Tel: (01403) 891212
Rhododendrons and azaleas in a peaceful 240-acre valley garden with seven beautiful lakes. Rock garden, Bonsai exhibition and wallabies.

18 The Bluebell Railway
Sheffield Park,
East Sussex TN22 3QL
Tel: (01825) 722370
9 miles of vintage steam and train railway from Sheffield Park to Horsted Keynes and extension to Kingscote. Largest collection of engines in the south. Victorian stations and museum.

19 Brickwall House and Gardens
Northiam,
East Sussex TN31 6NL
Tel: (01797) 223329
Formal gardens with terracotta entrance gates, 18thC bowling alley, sunken topiary garden, yew hedges, chess garden, arboretum. Jacobean house with 17thC plaster ceilings.

20 Great Dixter House and Gardens
Northiam,
East Sussex TN31 6PH
Tel: (01797) 253107
Fine example of 15thC manor house with antique furniture and needlework. Unique great hall restored by Lutyens who also designed garden – topiary, meadow garden, flower beds.

21 Buckleys Yesterday's World
89-90 High Street, Battle,
East Sussex TN33 0AQ
Tel: (01424) 775378
Over 100,000 exhibits in a Wealden hall house recall shopping and domestic life from 1850 to 1950 with smells and commentaries. Railway station, play village, garden.

22 A Smugglers Adventure At St. Clements Caves
West Hill, Hastings,
East Sussex TN34 3HY
Tel: (01424) 422964
An extensive exhibition of 18thC smuggling, housed in 2000 sq m of caves. Exhibition, museum, video theatre, extensive Adventure Walk incorporating dramatic special effects.

23 Brighton Sea Life Centre
Marine Parade,
Brighton,
East Sussex BN2 1TB
Tel: (01273) 604234
Discover the thrilling world beneath the waves as the Brighton Sea Life Centre takes you on an unforgettable voyage of discovery.

24 Foredown Tower Countryside Centre
Foredown Road, Portslade,
East Sussex BN41 2EW
Tel: (01273) 422540
Water tower housing a camera obscura, an unusual viewing device used by artists and astronomers since the 17thC. Popular entertainment in Victorian times.

25 Charleston Farmhouse
Firle, Lewes, East Sussex BN8 6LL
Tel: (01323) 811265
A 17-18thC farmhouse, home of Vanessa and Clive Bell and Duncan Grant. House and contents decorated by the artists. Restored garden room. Traditional flint-walled garden.

26 Amberley Museum
Houghton Bridge, Amberley,
Arundel, West Sussex BN18 9LT
Tel: (01798) 831370
Open-air industrial history centre in chalk quarry. Working craftsmen, narrow gauge railway, early buses, working machines and many other exhibits. Nature trail and visitor centre.

27 The Wildfowl and Wetlands Centre
Mill Road, Arundel,
West Sussex BN18 9PB
Tel: (01903) 883355
Reserve in 60 acres of watermeadows. Tame swans, ducks, geese and many wild birds. Film theatre and visitor centre with gallery.

28 Weald and Downland Open Air Museum
Singleton,
West Sussex PO18 0EU
Tel: (01243) 811348
Open-air museum of rescued historic buildings from South East England reconstructed on downland. 35 buildings include medieval farmstead and watermill.

29 Pallant House
9 North Pallant, Chichester,
West Sussex PO19 1TJ
Tel: (01243) 774557
Queen Anne townhouse with important works by British and European masters of the 20thC. Antiques include the world's greatest collection of Bow porcelain.

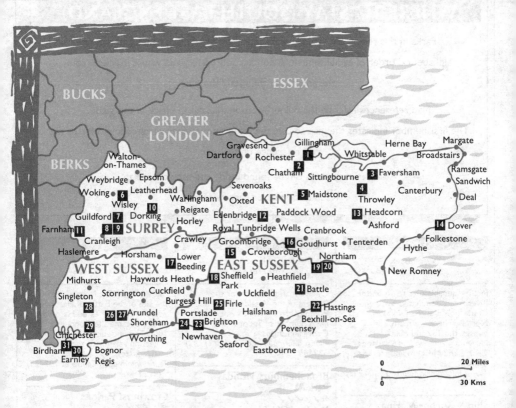

BUCKS

ESSEX

GREATER
LONDON

BERKS

Walton-
on-Thames
Weybridge • Epsom
Woking • Leatherhead **6**
Wisley **10**
Guildford **7** Dorking
Farnham **11** **8 9** SURREY
Cranleigh Horley
Haslemere Horsham • Lower
WEST SUSSEX **17** Beeding
Midhurst Haywards Heath
Singleton Storrington Cuckfield
28 Burgess Hill
26 27 Arundel Portslade
29 Shoreham **24 23** Brighton
Chichester Worthing Newhaven
Birdham **31 30** Bognor Seaford
Earnley Regis Eastbourne

Gravesend Gillingham Herne Bay Margate
Dartford • Rochester **1** Whitstable Broadstairs
Chatham **2** Ramsgate
Sittingbourne **3** Faversham Sandwich
Sevenoaks **4** Canterbury Deal
Oxted KENT **5** Maidstone Throwley
Warlingham Paddock Wood **13** Headcorn
Reigate Edenbridge **12** Ashford
Royal Tunbridge Wells Cranbrook **14** Dover
Crawley Groombridge **16** Goudhurst • Tenterden Folkestone
Groombridge • Crowborough Hythe
15 Northiam
EAST SUSSEX **19 20** New Romney
Sheffield • Heathfield
18 Park
Uckfield **21** Battle
25 Firle
Hailsham **22** Hastings
Bexhill-on-Sea
Pevensey

0   20 Miles
0   30 Kms

30 Earnley Butterflies and
Gardens
133 Almodington Lane, Earnley,
West Sussex PO20 7JR
Tel: (01243) 512637
*Ornamental butterfly house,
covered theme gardens from
around the world, exotic bird
garden, children's play area, small
animal farm and pottery.*

31 Sussex Falconry Centre
Locksacre Aquatic Nursery,
Wophams Lane, Birdham,
West Sussex PO20 7BS
Tel: (01243) 512472
*Aviaries containing birds of prey
including hawks, falcons and owls.
Flying displays of birds throughout
the day, weather permitting.*

FIND OUT MORE
Further information about
holidays and attractions in South
East England is available from:
**South East England
Tourist Board,**
The Old Brew House,
Warwick Park,
Tunbridge Wells,
Kent TN2 5TU.
Tel: (01892) 540766

These publications are available
free from the South East England
Tourist Board:
■ **Great Escapes**
■ **Accommodation Guide**
■ **Events South East**
■ **Bed and Breakfast Touring
Map**

■ **Outstanding Churches and
Cathedrals**

Also available is (price includes
postage and packaging):
■ **South East England Leisure
Map** £4
■ **Hundreds of Place to Visit
in the South East** £2.80
■ **Villages to Visit** £2.50

WHERE TO STAY (SOUTH EAST ENGLAND)

Parks in this region are listed in alphabetical order of place name, and then in alphabetical order of establishment. A contact address is given where it differs from the address of the establishment.

Map references refer to the colour location maps at the back of this guide. The first number indicates the map to use; the letter and number which follow refer to the grid reference on the map.

At-a-glance symbols can be found inside the back cover flap.

Keep this open for easy reference.

ARUNDEL

West Sussex
Map ref 3D3

Picturesque, historic town on the River Arun, dominated by Arundel Castle, home of the Dukes of Norfolk. There are many 18th C houses, the Toy and Military Museum, Wildfowl and Wetlands Centre and Museum and Heritage Centre.
Tourist Information Centre ☎ *(01903) 882268*

Ship & Anchor Marina
⊖✓✓✓✓
Member NCC
Heywood & Bryett Ltd, Ford, Arundel BN18 0BJ
☎ Yapton (01243) 551262
Fax (01243) 555256
2 m. S. of Arundel on Ford Rd. 2.25 m. N. of Littlehampton. Signposted.
4.8 hectares (12 acres). Level, grassy.
160 touring pitches

160	🚐	£8.50—£8.50
160	🚃	£8.50—£8.50
160	⛺	£8.50—£8.50

Open March–October
Cards accepted: Access, Visa
🚗🅿🗄🔌🌙🛆🔥⚡🔉⚡✕🍴🏕🗑
⊙🔍⛏🏊

COLOUR MAPS
Colour maps at the back of this guide pinpoint all places in which you will find accommodation listed.

ASHFORD

Kent
Map ref 4B4

Once a market centre for the farmers of the Weald of Kent and Romney Marsh. The town centre has a number of Tudor and Georgian houses.
Tourist Information Centre ☎ *(01233) 629165*

Broadhembury Holiday Park Ⓜ
⊖✓✓✓✓✓
Member BH&HPA
Steeds Lane, Kingsnorth, Ashford TN26 1NQ
☎ (01233) 620859
Fax (01233) 620859
From junction 10 on M20 take A2070 for 2 miles, then follow signs for Kingsnorth. Turn left at second crossroads in Kingsnorth. Signposted.
2 hectares (5 acres). Level, grassy, sheltered.
60 touring pitches

30	🚐	£8.00—£11.00
30	🚃	£8.00—£11.00
30	⛺	£8.00—£11.00
5	🏠	£80.00—£280.00

20 units not for hire
Cards accepted: Access, Visa
🚗🅿🗄🔌🌙🛆🔥⚡🔉⚡📺🏕🗑✎
🏠⊙🔍⛏✈🔥🌐

All accommodation in this guide has been graded, or is awaiting a grading, by a trained Tourist Board inspector.

BATTLE

East Sussex
Map ref 4B4

The Abbey at Battle was built on the site of the Battle of Hastings, when William defeated Harold II and so became the Conqueror in 1066. The museum has a fine collection relating to the Sussex iron industry.
Tourist Information Centre ☎ *(01424) 773721*

Crowhurst Park Ⓜ
⊖✓✓✓✓
Member BH&HPA/NCC
Crowhurst Park, Telham, Battle TN33 0SL
☎ Hastings (01424) 773344
Fax (01424) 775727
2 miles South from Battle Abbey on A2100 to Hastings. Signposted.
12.4 hectares (31 acres). Level, sloping, grassy.
40 touring pitches

40	🚐	£9.00
40	🚃	£9.00

275 units not for hire
Open March–December
Cards accepted: Access, Visa, Switch/Delta
🗄🚗🅿🗄🔌🌙🛆🔥⚡🔉⚡✕🍴🏕🗑✎
🏠⊙🔍⛲🏊🔥✈🎵🏀⚘⊛

The Ⓜ symbol after an establishment name indicates that it is a Regional Tourist Board member.

BEXHILL-ON-SEA

East Sussex
Map ref 4B4

Popular resort with beach of shingle and firm sand at low tide. The De la Warr Pavilion has good entertainment facilities.
Tourist Information Centre ☎ (01424) 212023 or 732208

Cobbs Hill Farm Caravan and Camping Park
☻✓✓✓✓
Member BH&HPA
Watermill Lane, Sidley, Bexhill-on-Sea TN39 5JA
☎ (01424) 213460
Bexhill take A269 turn R. to Watermill Lane, site 1m Left. Signposted.
2.8 hectares (7 acres). Level, grassy, sheltered.
45 touring pitches

45	🚐	£4.10—£4.50
45	🚕	£3.90—£4.30
45	▲	£4.10—£4.50
2	🏠	£80.00—£200.00

8 units not for hire
Open April–October
⚡P🖂🚐🏕▲♿🅿🛒🍴📻🎦⊙◖♨

CAMBER

East Sussex
Map ref 4B4

Well-known for fine sand dunes and safe bathing.

Camber Sands Leisure Park
☻✓✓✓✓
Member BH&HPA/NCC
New Lydd Road, Camber, Rye TN31 7RT
☎ Rye (01797) 225555
Fax (01797) 225756
Take A21 from London to Flimwell, left on to A268 for Rye, A259 east for 1 mile then turn right for Camber. The park is located at the far end of the village on the left. Signposted.
34 hectares (85 acres). Level, grassy.
68 touring pitches

	🚐	£15.00—£20.00
	🚕	£15.00—£20.00
125	🏠	£75.00—£325.00

586 units not for hire
Open March–October and Christmas

Cards accepted: Access, Visa, Switch/Delta
⚡🖂P📻🗑🎦♿🅿⊙🛒✕🍴📻🎦⊙
⊙◖🎿🎣♨⛵🏊🎾🏹🎽🎦🎲📻◉
Ad See display advertisement on this page

CANTERBURY

Kent
Map ref 4B3

Place of pilgrimage since the martyrdom of Becket in 1170 and the site of Canterbury Cathedral. Visit St Augustine's Abbey, St Martin's (the oldest church in England), Royal Museum and Art Gallery and the Canterbury Tales. Nearby is Howletts Wild Animal Park. Good shopping centre.
Tourist Information Centre ☎ (01227) 766567

Yew Tree Caravan Park
☻✓✓✓✓
Member BH&HPA
Stone Street, Petham, Canterbury CT4 5TL
☎ Petham (01227) 700306
On B2068 4 miles from Canterbury and 7 miles junction 11 of M20. Signposted.
1.6 hectares (4 acres). Level, sloping, grassy, sheltered.
45 touring pitches

15	🚐	£7.50—£11.00
5	🚕	£7.00—£10.00
25	▲	£6.50—£8.50
6	🏠	£140.00—£325.00

7 units not for hire
Open April–October
⚡🎦◖🗑♿🅿🛒🎦🍴♨🎦⊙🎿🎣
🏹♨

A key to symbols can be found inside the back cover flap.

All accommodation in this guide has been graded, or is awaiting a grading, by a trained Tourist Board inspector.

CHICHESTER

West Sussex
Map ref 3C3

The county town of West Sussex with a beautiful Norman cathedral. Noted for its Georgian architecture but also has modern buildings like the Festival Theatre. Surrounded by places of interest, including Fishbourne Roman Palace and Weald and Downland Open-Air Museum.
Tourist Information Centre ☎ (01243) 775888

Bell Caravan Park 🏍
☻✓✓
Member BH&HPA
Bell Lane, Birdham, Chichester PO20 7HY
☎ (01243) 512264
Take A286 S. from Chichester for 5m turn left into Bell La. Signposted.
2.8 hectares (7 acres). Level, grassy, sheltered.
15 touring pitches

15	🚐	£7.50—£8.00
15	🚕	£7.50—£8.00

60 units not for hire
Open March–October
⚡P🖂🗑◖♿🅿🛒🍴📻🎦⊙🏍♨

Wicks Farm Caravan & Camping Park 🏍
☻✓✓✓✓✓
Member BH&HPA
Redlands Lane, West Wittering, Chichester PO20 8QD
☎ Birdham (01243) 513116
Fax (01243) 511296
A286 from Chichester follow B2179 sign posted West Wittering. Redlands Lane is on the right off the B2179 one mile before West Wittering centre Signposted.
5.6 hectares (14 acres). Level, grassy.
40 touring pitches

40	🚕	£6.00—£9.00
40	▲	£6.00—£9.00

72 units not for hire
Open March–October
🗑◖🗑♿🅿🛒🎦🍴📻🎦⊙🏍♨🍴
♨◉

Kent
Map ref 4C4

A Cinque Port and busiest passenger port in the world. Still a historic town and seaside resort beside the famous White Cliffs. The White Cliffs Experience attraction traces the town's history through the Roman, Saxon, Norman and Victorian periods.
Tourist Information Centre ☎ *(01304) 205108*

Hawthorn Farm Caravan & Camping Park ⚠
θ✓✓✓✓✓
Member BH&HPA/NCC
Station Road, Martin Mill, Dover
CT15 5LA
☎ (01304) 852658 & 852914
Fax (01227) 740585
Take A258 from Dover in direction of Deal. Third turn on the left at Martin Mill. Signposted.
10.8 hectares (27 acres). Grassy, sheltered.
230 touring pitches

| 87 | ⛺ | £5.50—£10.50 |
| 143 | ⛺ | £5.50—£10.50 |

176 units not for hire
Open March–November
Cards accepted: Access, Visa
🚗🔌🔧📷🛁♿☕🛒🎮🔳🍴🧺💈📱☺
🔥🕹

Kent
Map ref 4B4

For centuries the headquarters of the Lords of the Level, the local government of this area. Probably best known today because of the fame of its fictional parson, the notorious Dr Syn, who has inspired a regular festival.

Dymchurch Caravan Park
θ✓✓✓✓
Member NCC
St Mary's Road, Dymchurch,
Romney Marsh TN29 0PW
☎ (01303) 872303
Fax (01303) 875179
St Mary's Rd. turning off A259
5.6 hectares (14 acres). Level, grassy.

| 13 | 🚐 | £120.00—£200.00 |

257 units not for hire
Open April–October
🚗🔧🛁☕🛒🎮🔳🍴🧺☺🎢🎯♿

New Beach Holiday Village

⊖✓✓✓✓
Member NCC
Hythe Road, Dymchurch, Romney
Marsh TN29 OJX
☎ (01303) 872233 (holiday homes)
or 872234 (touring pitches)
Fax (01303) 872939
M20 jct 11 then coast road A259
between Hythe and Dymchurch.
Signposted.
18 hectares (45 acres). Level, grassy.
200 touring pitches

	⊞	£10.00—£15.00
	🚐	£10.00—£15.00
	⛺	£10.00—£15.00
31	⊞	£75.00—£150.00

400 units not for hire
Open March–December
Cards accepted: Access, Visa

🔌P🖥📞🚿🛁♨♿🚻✕🍴📺🛒🛢
🚮🏪⚕🎣♬⚓Ⓣ
🅰 See display advertisement on
page 168

EASTCHURCH

Kent
Map ref 4B3

Village on the Isle of Sheppey, once
an important centre of aviation. The
Short brothers built England's first
aircraft factory here and there is a
stone memorial to C S Rolls and C
S Grace - pioneers of flying -
opposite the church.

Warden Springs Caravan Park Ltd ⚠

⊖✓✓✓✓
Member BH&HPA/NCC
Warden Point, Eastchurch,
Sheerness ME12 4HF
☎ (01795) 880 216 & 880217
Fax (01795) 880218
M2 junction 5 A249 Sheerness, M20
junction 7 A249 Sheerness. B2231 to
Eastchurch, left at church, first right to
end of lane. Signposted.
7.2 hectares (18 acres). Level,
sloping, grassy.
48 touring pitches

48	⊞	£8.50—£12.50
48	🚐	£8.50—£12.50
8	⛺	£8.00—£12.50

250 units not for hire
Open March–October
Cards accepted: Visa

📞🛁♨♿🚻🍴📺🛒🛢🚮🛢☺📞
🏪⚓🎯♬⚓

FARNHAM

Surrey
Map ref 3C2

Town noted for its Georgian houses.
Willmer House (now a museum)
has a facade of cut and moulded
brick with fine carving and panelling
in the interior. The 12th C castle has
been occupied by Bishops of both
Winchester and Guildford.
Tourist Information Centre ☎ *(01252)*
715109

Tilford Touring ⚠

Tilford, Farnham GU10 2DF
☎ Frensham (0125279) 3296
Fax (0125279) 3597
Head S from Farnham railway, take R
fork over crossing, 3 miles to Tilford
Village down lane beside Duke of
Cambridge Pub. Signposted.
1.6 hectares (4 acres). Level, grassy,
hard, sheltered.
80 touring pitches

60	⊞	£6.00—£6.00
10	🚐	£6.00—£6.00
10	⛺	£5.00—£5.00

Cards accepted: Access, Visa

⚓P🖥🚿📞🛁♨✕🍴☺⚓Ⓤ🎣Ⓣ

FOLKESTONE

Kent
Map ref 4C4

Popular resort and important
cross-channel port. The town has a
fine promenade, the Leas, from
where orchestral concerts and
other entertainments are presented.
Horse-racing at Westenhanger
Racecourse nearby.
Tourist Information Centre ☎ *(01303)*
258594

Black Horse Farm Caravan and Camping Park ⚠

⊖✓✓✓✓
Member BH&HPA
385 Canterbury Road, Densole,
Folkestone CT18 7BG
☎ Hawkinge (01303) 892665
On A260 to Canterbury , 2 miles from
junction with A20, site on left.
Signposted.
2.8 hectares (7 acres). Level, sloping,
grassy, stony, hard, sheltered.
70 touring pitches

⊞	£7.80—£9.00
🚐	£7.80—£9.00
⛺	£7.80—£9.00

🚙🖥📞🚿🛁♨♿🚻🍴🛒🛢🚮🛢☺⚓
♨

HASTINGS

East Sussex
Map ref 4B4

Ancient town which became famous
as the base from which William the
Conqueror set out to fight the
Battle of Hastings. Later became one
of the Cinque Ports, now a leading
resort. Castle, Hastings Embroidery
inspired by the Bayeux Tapestry and
Sea Life Centre.
Tourist Information Centre ☎ *(01424)*
781111

Shear Barn Holiday Park ⚠

⊖✓✓✓✓
Member BH&HPA/NCC
Barley Lane, Hastings TN35 5DX
☎ (01424) 423583
Fax (01424) 718740
From Hastings old town take A259 to
Rye/Folkestone.
13.6 hectares (34 acres). Level,
sloping, grassy.
450 touring pitches

150	⊞	£6.00—£13.00
150	🚐	£5.50—£12.00
300	⛺	£5.00—£13.00
20	⊞	£150.00—£390.00

197 units not for hire
Open March–December
Cards accepted: Access, Visa,
Switch/Delta

🚙🖥📞🚿🛁♨♿🚻🍴🛒🛢🚮🛢
☺🔍🏪♬⚓

HENFIELD

West Sussex
Map ref 3D3

Ancient village with many old
houses and good shopping facilities,
on a ridge of high ground
overlooking the Adur Valley. Views
to the South Downs.

Downsview Caravan Park

⊖✓✓✓✓
Member BH&HPA
Bramlands Lane, Woodmancote,
Henfield BN5 9TG
☎ Brighton (01273) 492801
Fax (01273) 495214
Signed from A281 in village of
Woodmancote 2.5m Brighton side of
Henfield. Also just north of Small Dole
on A2037. Signposted.
1.8 hectares (4.5 acres). Level, grassy,
hard, sheltered.
27 touring pitches

12	⊞	£9.00—£9.75
12	🚐	£9.00—£9.75
15	⛺	£8.00—£8.75
1	⊞	£100.00—£265.00

Continued ▶

HENFIELD

Continued

28 units not for hire
Open February–November
Cards accepted: Access, Visa
🅰🛆🗙🛆🛒🔥⛽(🍴⊡⚡🚿🛜⊙∪🎳
♨

HOLLINGBOURNE

Kent
Map ref 4B3

Pleasant village near romantic Leeds
Castle in the heart of orchard
country at the foot of the North
Downs. Some fine half-timbered
houses and a flint and ragstone
church.

Pine Lodge Touring Park
⊖✓✓✓✓
Member BH&HPA
A20 Ashford Road, Hollingbourne,
Maidstone ME17 1XH
☎ Maidstone (01622) 730018
Fax (01622) 734498
*M20 Jun 8 onto A20 r/bt. Turn off
towards Bearsted/Maidstone Park 1
mile signposted from r/bt. Signposted.*
2.8 hectares (7 acres). Level, sloping,
grassy, hard, sheltered.
100 touring pitches

60	🚐	£7.50—£8.50
20	🚚	£7.50—£8.50
20	⛺	£3.00—£7.50

🅰🗃🍴🛆🗙🛆🔥⛽(🍴⊡⚡🚿⊙∆
🎳♨

HORAM

East Sussex
Map ref 3D3

Horam Manor Touring
Park 🏕
⊖✓✓✓✓
Member BH&HPA/NCC
Horam, Heathfield TN21 0YD
☎ (01435) 813662 & Mobile 0973
848896
*Entrance on the A267, south of Horam
Village. Signposted.*
2.8 hectares (7 acres). Sloping,
grassy, sheltered.
90 touring pitches

90	🚐	£10.00—£11.00
90	🚚	£10.00—£11.00
90	⛺	£10.00—£11.00

Open March–October
🅰🅿⊡🍴🛆🗙🛆🔥🚿⛽⊙∪🚶➤
♨

LINGFIELD

Surrey
Map ref 3D2

Wealden village with many buildings
dating back to the 15th C. Nearby
there is year-round horse racing at
Lingfield Park.

Long Acres Caravan &
Camping Park 🏕
⊖✓✓✓✓
Member BH&HPA
Newchapel Road, Lingfield RH7 6LE
☎ (01342) 833205
Fax (01342) 834307
*From M25 leave at jct 6 onto A22
South towards East Grinstead, at
Newchapel roundabout turn left onto
B2028 towards Lingfield, site 700 yards
on right. Signposted.*
16 hectares (40 acres). Level, sloping,
grassy, hard, sheltered.
60 touring pitches

60	🚐	£7.50—£7.50
60	🚚	£7.50—£7.50
60	⛺	£7.50—£7.50

🅿⊡🗃🍴🛆🛆🔥⛽(🍴⊡⚡🚿⊙⊙∆
🚶🗙♨

LITTLEHAMPTON

West Sussex
Map ref 3D3

Ancient port at the mouth of the
River Arun, now a popular holiday
resort, offering flat, sandy beaches,
sailing, fishing and boat trips. The
Sussex Downs are a short walk
inland.

White Rose Touring Park 🏕
Member BH&HPA/NCC
Mill Lane, Wick, Littlehampton
BN17 7PH
☎ (01903) 716176
Fax (01903) 732671
*1.5 miles south of A27 on the A284
Littlehampton road. Signposted.*
2.8 hectares (7 acres). Level, grassy.
127 touring pitches

127	🚐	£10.70—£14.80
127	🚚	£7.25—£14.80
127	⛺	£7.25—£14.80

14 units not for hire
Open March–December
Cards accepted: Access, Visa,
Switch/Delta
🅰🅿⊡🗃🍴🛆🛆⛽🔥(🍴⊡⚡🚿🔥⛽
⊙∆♨

MARDEN

Kent
Map ref 4B4

The village is believed to date back
to Saxon times, though today more
modern homes surround the 13th
C church.

Tanner Farm Touring Caravan
& Camping Park 🏕
⊖✓✓✓✓
Member BH&HPA
Goudhurst Road, Marden, Tonbridge
TN12 9ND
☎ Maidstone (01622) 832399
Fax (01622) 832472
*From A21 or A229 onto B2079
midway between Marden and
Goudhurst. Signposted.*
60 hectares (150 acres). Level,
grassy, hard, sheltered.
100 touring pitches

	🚐	£6.00—£10.00
	🚚	£6.00—£10.00
	⛺	£5.00—£10.00

Cards accepted: Access, Visa,
Switch/Delta
🅿⊡🗃🍴🛆🛆⛽🔥(🍴⊡⚡🚿🔥⛽⊙
∆🚶♨

MONKTON

Kent
Map ref 4C3

The Foxhunter Park 🏕
⊖✓✓✓✓✓ Rose Award
Member BH&HPA/NCC
Monkton, Ramsgate CT12 4JG
☎ Ramsgate (01843) 821311 &
821587
Fax (01843) 821458
*A2, M2 straight over seven
roundabouts on A299. Signposted.*
12 hectares (30 acres). Level, grassy,
sheltered.

60	🛏	£90.00—£400.00

280 units not for hire
Open March–October
Cards accepted: Access, Visa
🅰🅿⊡🍴🛆🛆⚡🗙🍽📺(🍴⊡🔥⛽
⊙🔍∆🥂∪🔍🚶➤🎵♨

Map references apply to
the colour maps at the
back of this guide.

For ideas on places to visit
refer to the introduction at
the beginning of this section.

PAGHAM

West Sussex
Map ref 3C3

Around Pagham Harbour is a coastal nature reserve established by the Sussex Naturalists' Trust.

Church Farm Holiday Village ⚠

⊖✓✓✓✓✓ Rose Award
Member BH&HPA/NCC
Pagham, Bognor Regis PO21 4NR
☎ Reservations/free brochure
(01442) 248668
Fax (01442) 232459
A27, Pagham exit from Bognor roundabout. Signs to Pagham. Signposted.
24.8 hectares (62 acres). Level, grassy, sheltered.

170	🚐	£120.00—£522.00

750 units not for hire
Open March–October
Cards accepted: Access, Visa,
Switch/Delta
🚗🐾🛁♨🅿⛽🛒✕🍴🏕🖥⚡💧🚙☺
🔍🏔⛵🚲🔌🎵🎣🎡

Ad See display advertisement inside front cover

PEVENSEY BAY

East Sussex
Map ref 4B4

Small but popular resort, with spacious beach, near the village of Pevensey.

Bay View Caravan & Camping Park ⚠

⊖✓✓✓✓
Old Martello Road, Pevensey Bay
BN24 6DX
☎ Eastbourne (01323) 768688
On the coastal side of the A259 between Pevensey Bay and Eastbourne. Signposted.
1.4 hectares (3.5 acres). Level, grassy, hard.
49 touring pitches

49	🚐	£7.15—£7.80
49	🚛	£7.15—£7.80
49	⛺	£6.65—£7.25
5	🚐	£105.00—£225.00

Open April–October
🚗🅿🏕🐾🛁♨🅿🛒⛽🖥⚡💧🚙☺
🏔⛵

A key to symbols can be found inside the back cover flap.

RAMSGATE

Kent
Map ref 4C3

Popular holiday resort with good sandy beaches. At Pegwell Bay is replica of a Viking longship. Terminal for car-ferry service to Dunkirk and Ostend.
Tourist Information Centre ☎ (01843) 583333

Manston Caravan & Camping Park

⊖✓✓✓✓
Member BH&HPA
Manston Court Road, Manston,
Ramsgate CT12 5AU
☎ (01843) 823442
From M2, A299 to r'bout. A253 to Minster r'bout. Follow signs for RAF Manston and Kent International Airport and Ramsgate. First left past airport. Signposted.
2.8 hectares (7 acres). Level, grassy.
100 touring pitches

60	🚐	£7.00—£9.50
60	🚛	£7.00—£9.00
40	⛺	£4.50—£10.50

36 units not for hire
Open April–October
🚗🔌🏕🛁♨🅿🛒🖥⚡💧🚙☺🏔
♨

ROCHESTER

Kent
Map ref 4B3

Ancient cathedral city on the River Medway. Has many places of interest connected with Charles Dickens (who lived nearby) including the fascinating Dickens Centre. Also massive castle overlooking the river and Guildhall Museum.
Tourist Information Centre ☎ (01634) 843666

Allhallows Leisure Park ⚠

⊖✓✓✓✓
Member BH&HPA/NCC
Allhallows-on-Sea, Rochester
ME3 9QD
☎ Reservations/free brochure
(01442) 248668
Fax (01442) 232459
From Rochester follow A228 direct to Allhallows. Signposted.
64 hectares (160 acres). Sloping, grassy.

140	🚐	£98.00—£499.00

1138 units not for hire
Open March–November

Cards accepted: Access, Visa,
Switch/Delta
🚗🐾✕🍴🖥⚡💧🚙☺🔍🏔⛵🎣U
♨🎵🔌🅃☺

Ad See display advertisement inside front cover

Sheppey Industries Ltd Woolmans Wood Tourist Caravan Park ⚠

⊖✓✓✓
Rochester/Maidstone Road,
Bridgewood, Rochester ME5 9SB
☎ Medway (01634) 867685
Leave M2 at exit 3 onto the A229. In half a mile turn left at roundabout. Signposted.
1.6 hectares (4 acres). Grassy, hard.
60 touring pitches

60	🚐	£9.00—£10.50
40	🚛	£9.00—£10.50
20	⛺	£4.00

🚗🅿🖥🏔♨🛁♨🐾🛒✕🍴☺🎡

ST NICHOLAS AT WADE

Kent
Map ref 4C3

Village in the Isle of Thanet with ancient church built of knapped flint.

Frost Farm Thanet Way Caravan Co

⊖✓✓✓
Member BH&HPA
Thanet Way, St Nicholas at Wade,
Birchington CT7 0NA
☎ Thanet (01843) 847219
Take M2 - 17 miles on 299 Thanet Way to St. Nicholas roundabout turn back on 299 site quarter mile. Follow signs on 299. Signposted.
1 hectares (2.5 acres). Level, sloping, grassy.
12 touring pitches

12	🚛	£6.00—£8.00

48 units not for hire
Open March–October
🚗🔌🏔🛁♨🅿☺🏔

The map references refer to the colour maps towards the end of the guide.
The first figure is the map number; the letter and figure which follow indicate the grid reference on the map.

SELSEY

West Sussex
Map ref 3C3

Almost surrounded by water, with the English Channel on two sides and an inland lake, once Pagham Harbour, and the Brook on the other two. Ideal for yachting, swimming, fishing and wildlife.

Green Lawns Caravan Park

Θ✓✓✓✓ Rose Award
Paddock Lane, Selsey, Chichester
PO20 9EJ
☎ Chichester (01243) 604121
Fax (01243) 602355
B2145 to Selsey turn R into School Lane first R off School lane into Paddock Lane, straight off for White Horses and Green Lawns. Signposted.
10 hectares (25 acres). Level, grassy, sheltered.

| 19 | 🏕 | £140.00—£395.00 |

270 units not for hire
Open March–October
Cards accepted: Access, Visa, Amex, Switch/Delta

Warners Farm Touring Park ⚠

Θ✓✓✓✓✓
Member NCC
Warner Lane, Selsey, Chichester
PO20 9EL
☎ Chichester (01243) 604121
Fax (01243) 602355
B2145 into Selsey turn right into School Lane first right off School Lane first left proceed until you see sign for touring caravans. Signposted.
4.2 hectares (10.5 acres). Level, grassy, sheltered.
250 touring pitches

| 250 | 🚐 | £5.50—£20.50 |
| 250 | 🚚 | £5.50—£20.50 |

Open March–October
Cards accepted: Access, Visa, Switch/Delta

West Sands Caravan Park

Θ✓✓✓✓
Member NCC
Mill Lane, Selsey, Chichester
PO20 9BH
☎ Chichester (01243) 606080
Fax (01243) 606068
B2145 to Selsey through village, first right after predestrian crossing. Signposted.
60 hectares (150 acres). Level, grassy, stony, hard.

| 300 | 🏕 | £140.00—£395.00 |

1301 units not for hire
Open April–October
Cards accepted: Access, Visa, Amex

White Horse Caravan Co Ltd ⚠

Θ✓✓✓ Rose Award
Member NCC
Paddock Lane, Selsey, Chichester
PO20 9EJ
☎ Chichester (01243) 604121
Fax (01243) 602355
B2145 into Selsey, turn right into School Lane, first right off School Lane into Paddock Lane, straight on for White Horse Reception. Signposted.
16 hectares (40 acres). Level, grassy, sheltered.

| 13 | 🏕 | £140.00—£395.00 |

344 units not for hire
Open March–October
Cards accepted: Access, Visa, Amex, Switch/Delta

SOUTHWATER

West Sussex
Map ref 3D3

Raylands Park

Θ✓✓✓✓✓
Member BH&HPA
Jackrells Lane, Southwater, Horsham
RH13 7DH
☎ (01403) 730218 & 731822
Fax (01403) 732828
Horsham A24 turn L. past Hen & Chicken Pub foll. Caravan S. Signposted.
2 hectares (5 acres). Level, grassy.
80 touring pitches

40	🚐	£8.50—£8.50
40	🚚	£8.50—£8.50
40	⛺	£8.50—£8.50

65 units not for hire
Open March–October

UCKFIELD

East Sussex
Map ref 3D3

Once a medieval market town and centre of the iron industry, Uckfield is now a busy country town on the edge of the Ashdown Forest.

Honeys Green Farm Caravan Park

Θ✓✓✓
Member BH&HPA
Easons Green, Framfield, Uckfield
TN22 5RE
☎ Halland (01825) 840334
Turn off A22 at Halland roundabout B2192 (sp Heathfield). Site quarter of a mile on left. Signposted.
0.8 hectares (2 acres). Level, grassy, sheltered.
22 touring pitches

18	🚐	£6.50—£9.00
4	🚚	£6.50—£9.00
4	🏕	£125.00—£190.00

4 units not for hire
Open April–October

WASHINGTON

West Sussex
Map ref 3D3

Near the village is the famous Chanctonbury Ring, an Iron Age camp on a rise nearly 800 ft above sea-level.

Washington Caravan and Camping Park ⚠

Θ✓✓✓✓
London Road, Washington, Pulborough RH20 4AT
☎ Worthing (01903) 892869
Fax (01903) 893252
A24 - A283 Signposted.
1.8 hectares (4.5 acres). Hard.
60 touring pitches

20	🚐	£8.00—£8.00
20	🚚	£8.00—£8.00
40	⛺	£8.50—£8.50

Cards accepted: Access, Visa

NORTHERN IRELAND

Northern Ireland is a land of six counties. Dotted with clear lakes and loughs, it is traversed by rivers and canals, branching out towards a spectacular coastline. A land of rolling hills, forest parks and wooded valleys, it is also a place of legend and mysticism. The Giant Cuchillain built the Giant's Causeway here. In ancient Downpatrick you can discover the grave of St Patrick, Ireland's patron saint. From the Glens of Antrim to the Mountains of Mourne and on to bustling Belfast you'll find much to explore - with good roads, plenty of parks and the legendary Irish welcome wherever you venture!

NORTHERN IRELAND
For more information on Northern Ireland, contact:
Northern Ireland Tourist Board
St Anne's Court, North Street,
Belfast BT1 1NB
Tel: (01232) 231221 **Fax:** (01232) 240960

Where to Go in Northern Ireland –
see pages 174-176
Where to Stay in Northern Ireland –
see page 177

NORTHERN IRELAND

Where to Go and What to See

You will find hundreds of interesting places to visit during your stay in Northern Ireland, just some of which are listed in these pages. The number against each name will help you locate it on the map (page 176). Contact any Tourist Information Centre in the region for more ideas on days out in Northern Ireland.

1 Giant's Causeway and Causeway Visitor Centre
44 Causeway Road,
Bushmills,
County Antrim BT57 8SU
Tel: (012657) 31159/31855
A World Heritage Site. Over 40,000 many-sided stone columns. Wreck site of Armada treasure ship Girona is nearby.

2 Old Bushmills Distillery
2 Distillery Road, Bushmills,
County Antrim BT57 8XH
Tel: (012657) 31521
Oldest whiskey distillery in the world, established in 1608. Visitor centre.

3 Carrick-a-Rede Rope Bridge
Coast Road,
Ballintoy, Ballycastle,
County Antrim
Tel: (012657) 31169/41474
Swinging rope bridge spans an 18-metre (60ft)-wide chasm between Carrick-a-Rede island and the mainland. Salmon fishery.

4 Carrickfergus Castle
Marine Highway,
Carrickfergus,
County Antrim BT38 7BG
Tel: (01960) 351273
Started in 1180 by John de Courcy, conqueror of east Ulster, and garrisoned until 1928. Exhibition on castle's history.

5 Ulster - American Folk Park
Mellon Road,
Castletown, Omagh,
County Tyrone BT78 5QY
Tel: (01662) 243292
The story of 200 years of emigration. Ancestral homes of Mellons of Pitsburgh and of Robert Campbell, Rocky Mountains pioneer.

6 Belfast Zoo
Antrim Road,
Belfast BT36 7PN
Tel: (01232) 776277
In a picturesque mountain park. Underwater viewing of sea lions and penguins.

7 City Hall
Donegall Square,
Belfast BT1 5GS
Tel: (01232) 320202
Built in Portland stone, completed in 1906. Fine interiors.

8 Ulster Museum
Botanic Gardens,
Belfast BT9 5AB
Tel: (012657) 383000
Noted for its Irish antiquities, art collections and natural sciences. Treasures from Armada shipwreck, Girona.

9 Ulster Folk & Transport Museum
153 Bangor Road,
Cultra,
Holywood,
County Down BT18 0EU
Tel: (01232) 428428
New road transport galleries. Original farmhouses, watermills, village with church and shops. Irish Railway Collection, including Old Maeve.

10 **Belleek Pottery**
Belleek,
County Fermanagh BT93 3FY
Tel: (013656) 58501
*See craftsmen create, glaze and
decorate this world-famous
porcelain and watch the intricate
'basket weaving'.*

11 **Tyrone Crystal**
Killybrackey,
Coalisland Road, Dungannon,
County Tyrone BT71 6TT
Tel: (01868) 725335
*Blowing, marking, cutting and
finishing stages of this fine crystal.*

12 **Mount Stewart House &
Gardens**
Newtownards,
County Down BT22 2AD
Tel: (012477) 88387/88487
*Boyhood home of Robert Stewart,
Lord Castlereagh. Gardens are
among the finest in Europe. Temple
of the Winds overlooks Strangford
Lough.*

13 **Oxford Island Nature
Reserve & Lough Neagh
Discovery Centre**
Oxford Island,
Craigavon,
County Armagh BT66 6NJ
Tel: (01762) 322205
The wildlife, history and
*management of Lough Neagh and
Oxford Island are interpreted at the
Discovery Centre. Interactive
exhibitions.*

14 **Armagh Planetarium**
College Hill,
Armagh BT61 9DB
Tel: (01861) 523689
*Explore the universe with hands-on
computers. Outside Astropark
features a model solar system.
Eartharium displays place of Earth
in the universe.*

15 **Navan Centre**
Navan Centre,
81 Killylea Road,
Armagh BT60 4LD
Tel: (01861) 525550
*Centre presents the history of the
nearby famous hill fort, Navan
(Emain Macha), capital of the Kings
of Ulster from 600BC.*

16 **St Patrick's Trian**
40 English Street,
Armagh BT61 7BA
Tel: (01861) 521801
*The Armagh Story and the Land of
Lilliput (adapted from Swift's
Gulliver's Travels). Exhibition on
St Patrick.*

17 **Exploris Aquarium**
The Rope Walk,
Castle Street,
Portaferry,
County Down BT22 1NZ
Tel: (012477) 28062
*A showcase for the rich diversity of
life in the Irish Sea and Strangford
Lough.*

18 **Marble Arch Caves**
Marlbank Scenic Loop,
Florencecourt,
County Fermanagh BT92 1EW
Tel: (01365) 348855
*Underground boat trip past
stalactites and stalagmites.
Geology exhibition.*

19 **Tollymore Forest Park**
Tullybrannigan Road,
Newcastle,
County Down BT33 0PW
Tel: (013967) 22428
*Numerous stone follies and bridges,
and a 30-metre (100ft) sequoia
tree in the arboretum. Wildlife and
forestry exhibits.*

20 **Silent Valley**
Ballymartin, Kilkeel,
County Down
Tel: (01232) 746581
*Silent Valley and Ben Crom
reservoirs supply 30 million gallons
of water a day to Belfast and Co.
Down. Beautiful parkland before
the dams.*

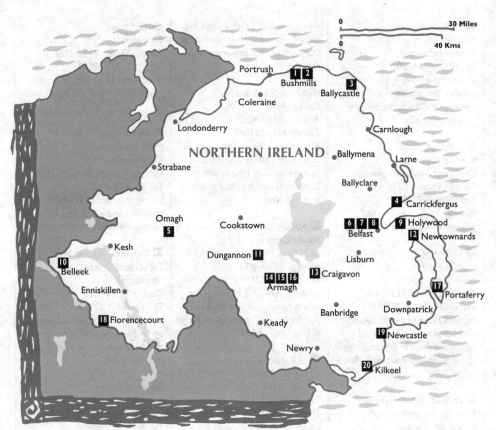

NORTHERN IRELAND

Portrush
Bushmills **1** **2**
Coleraine
Ballycastle **3**

Londonderry

Carnlough

Strabane

Ballymena

Larne

Ballyclare

Omagh
5

Cookstown

Carrickfergus **4**

Kesh

Dungannon **11**

Belfast **6** **7** **8**

Holywood **9**

Newtownards **12**

Belleek **10**

Lisburn

Enniskillen

Armagh **14** **15** **16**

Craigavon **13**

Portaferry **17**

Florencecourt **18**

Keady

Banbridge

Downpatrick

Newcastle **19**

Newry

Kilkeel **20**

0   30 Miles

0   40 Kms

FIND OUT MORE

Further information about
holidays and attractions in
Northern Ireland is available
from:
**Northern Ireland Tourist
Board,**
St Anne's Court,
North Street,
Belfast BT1 1NB
Tel: (01232) 231221
Fax: (01232) 240960

WHERE TO STAY (NORTHERN IRELAND)

Parks in Northern Ireland are listed in alphabetical order of place name, and then in alphabetical order of establishment. A contact address is given where it differs from the address of the establishment.

Map references refer to the colour location maps at the back of this guide.

The first number indicates the map to use; the letter and number which follow refer to the grid reference on the map.

At-a-glance symbols can be found inside the back cover flap.

Keep this open for easy reference.

BALLYMONEY

County Antrim
Map ref 9B1

Drumaheglis Marina & Caravan Park

⊖✓✓✓✓✓

36 Glenstall Road, Ballymoney
BT53 7QN
☎ (012656) 66466
Fax (012656) 67659
On the A26 between Ballymoney and Coleraine, turn off at Seacon Crossroads and follow signposts for Drumaheglis Marina. Site well signposted from A26.
6 hectares (15 acres). Level, hard, sheltered.
40 touring pitches

40	🚐	£9.00—£10.00
40	🚎	£9.00—£10.00
15	⛺	£8.00—£9.00

Open April–September

🏕️P🔌🔋📻🏕️❄️🛁☎♿🍴📮🖥️⚡☀️⛰️
🛒✂️⛱️🅿️

ROSTREVOR

County Down
Map ref 9C2

Kilbroney Park

⊖✓✓✓✓✓

Shore Road, Rostrevor, Newry
☎ (016937) 38134
Take A2 from Rostrevor to Kilkeel and turn off main road to left after one mile (2km) into Kilbroney Park. Signposted.
40 hectares (100 acres). Stony, hard, sheltered.
39 touring pitches

24	🚐	£7.40—£8.40
24	🚎	£7.40—£8.40
25	⛺	£5.00—£5.00

Open March–December

🏕️P🔌🔋📻🏕️❄️🛁☎✖️🍴🖥️⚡📮☀️⛰️
⛱️🛒🅿️⚓
Ad See display advertisement on this page

KILBRONEY PARK

Shore Road, Rostrevor, Newry, Co. Down. Tel: (016937) 38134

100-acre park on outskirts of Rostrevor, by Carlingford Lough. West-facing slope with well-spaced caravan pitches on concrete hard standing, each with electric hook-up and drain. Toilets, showers, launderette, payphone, cafe. Forest drive, walking routes, tennis courts, children's play area.

USE YOUR *i*'s

There are more than 550 Tourist Information Centres throughout England offering friendly help with accommodation and holiday ideas as well as suggestions of places to visit and things to do. There may well be a centre in your home town which can help you before you set out. You'll find the address of your nearest Tourist Information Centre in your local Phone Book.

AT-A-GLANCE SYMBOLS

Symbols at the end of each accommodation entry give useful information about services and facilities. A key to symbols can be found inside the back cover flap.

Keep this open for easy reference.

COUNTRY CODE

Always follow the Country Code ⚘ Enjoy the countryside and respect its life and work ⚘ Guard against all risk of fire ⚘ Fasten all gates ⚘ Keep your dogs under close control ⚘ Keep to public paths across farmland ⚘ Use gates and stiles to cross fences, hedges and walls ⚘ Leave livestock, crops and machinery alone ⚘ Take your litter home ⚘ Help to keep all water clean ⚘ Protect wildlife, plants and trees ⚘ Take special care on country roads ⚘ Make no unnecessary noise

SCOTLAND

The majestic beauty of Scotland comes as a surprise, even to experienced travellers. Mountains and glens, sparkling lochs and wild, romantic islands form a breathtaking backdrop to a country steeped in history and culture. A paradise for golfers, fishermen and ramblers, it is also home to the Highland Games, the Edinburgh Festival and the finest whisky in the world! Come in spring or autumn when the scenery's most spectacular.

Explore the Highlands and discover the Islands. Britain's ancient kingdom of the north is unforgettable; starkly beautiful in parts, yet with a warmth and vibrance that cannot be equalled.

SCOTLAND
For more information on Scotland, contact:
Scottish Tourist Board
23 Ravelston Terrace,
Edinburgh EH4 3EU
Tel: (0131) 332 2433 **Fax:** (0131) 343 1513

Where to Go in Scotland – see pages 180-185
Where to Stay in Scotland – see pages 186-200

SCOTLAND

Where to Go and What to See

You will find hundreds of interesting places to visit during your stay in Scotland, just some of which are listed in these pages. The number against each name will help you locate it on the map (page 185). Contact any Tourist Information Centre in the region for more ideas on days out in Scotland.

1 The Official Loch Ness Monster Exhibition Centre
Loch Ness Centre,
Drumnadrochit,
Highland IV3 6TU
Tel: (01456) 450573
The fascinating story of the search for the Loch Ness Monster told in a multi-media presentation.

2 Landmark Highland Heritage and Adventure Park
Carrbridge, Highland PH23 3AJ
Tel: (014798) 41614
A 3-D slide show telling the story of the Great Wood of Caledon and dramatic permanent exhibition depicting the main events of turbulent Highland history. Scottish Forestry Heritage Park with operational steam powered sawmill and 75-foot viewing tower.

3 Strathspey Steam Railway
Dalfaber Road,
Aviemore, Highland PH22 1PY
Tel: (01479) 810725
Part of the former main line between Perth and Inverness, it was re-opened in 1978. Trains run from Aviemore to Boat of Garten.

4 Highland Wildlife Park
Kincraig, Kingussie,
Highland PH21 1NL
Tel: (01540) 651270
Breeding groups of Scottish mammals and birds of past and present. Drive through the reserve and see red deer, bison, Highland cattle and more. Walkaround area, visitor centre and picnic area.

5 Grampian Transport Museum
Alford, Grampian AB33 8AD
Tel: (019755) 62292
An extensive collection of historic road vehicles. Also driving simulator, video bus featuring motor sport and road transport history.

6 Clan Donald Visitor Centre
Armadale,
Isle of Skye IV45 8RS
Tel: (01471) 844305
Award-winning Visitor Centre with Museum of the Isles, exhibition, ancestral research service, woodland gardens.

7 Aberdeen Art Gallery and Museum
Schoolhill,
Aberdeen AB10 1FQ
Tel: (01224) 646333
Permanent collection of 18th, 19th and 20thC art with emphasis on contemporary works. Music, dance, poetry, events, films, special exhibitions, reference library and print room.

8 Hazlehead Park
Groats Road,
Hazlehead Avenue,
Aberdeen,
Grampian AB1 8BE
Large park with extensive woodland, trees, including a 150-year-old sequoia, and shrubs, rose heather and azalea gardens. North Sea Memorial Garden (including Piper Alpha Memorial).

9 Satrosphere, The Discovery Place
19 Justice Mill Lane,
Off Union Street,
Aberdeen AB1 2EQ
Tel: (01224) 213232
Exciting hands-on science and technology centre with 70-100 experiments, exploring sound, light, energy and the environment.

10 Storybook Glen
Maryculter,
by Aberdeen AB12 5ST
Tel: (01224) 732941
Twenty-eight scenic acres with attractions specially geared to children: Old Woman's Shoe and Three Bears' House.

11 Mull and West Highland Narrow Gauge Railway
Craignure (Old Pier) Station,
Craignure, Isle of Mull PA65 6AY
Tel: (01680) 812494 (summer)
300389 (winter)
Ten and a quarter-inch gauge railway operating a scheduled service to Torosay Castle and Gardens from Craignure (Old Pier) Station. Steam and diesel-hauled trains.

12 Oban Sealife Centre
Barcaldine, Oban,
Strathclyde PA37 1SE
Tel: (01631) 720386
Explore life under the sea. A unique display of native marine life from sinister conger eel to lovable seals, in a delightful setting.

13 Camperdown Wildlife Centre
Camperdown Country Park,
Coupar Angus Road,
Dundee DD2 4TF
Tel: (01382) 432689
Indigenous wildlife: deer, wildcats, pinemartins, European brown bear, lynx, wolves, arctic foxes, pheasants, golden eagles and buzzards, plus wildlife ponds, bantams and domestic stock.

14 Discovery Point
Discovery Quay,
Dundee,
Tayside DD1 4XA
Tel: (01382) 201245
Centre portraying the 'Discovery's' construction, its launch in Dundee in 1901 and Scott's voyage to Antarctica.

15 Frigate 'Unicorn'
Victoria Dock,
Dundee,
Tayside DD1 3JA
Tel: (01382) 200900
The 'Unicorn' is a 46-gun wooden warship launched at Chatham in 1824. She is the oldest British-built warship and the third oldest ship afloat. See the guns, models and displays.

16 Scone Palace
By Perth,
Tayside PH2 6BD
Tel: (01738) 552300
Impressive palace with notable grounds and a pinetum. Collections of porcelain, furniture, ivories, clocks and needlework.

17 Glenturret Distillery
Crieff,
Tayside PH7 4HA
Tel: (01764) 656565
Scotland's oldest distillery offers guided tours, free tasting, an award-winning visitors centre, audio-visual presentation, 3-D exhibition museum and whisky-tasting bar.

18 St Andrew's Sealife Centre
The Scores,
St Andrews,
Fife KY16 9AS
Tel: (01334) 474786
Hundreds of sea creatures in re-creations of their natural environments while multi-level viewing gives the chance to come face to face with them.

19 The Scottish Deer Centre
Bow of Fife, By Cupar,
Fife KY15 4NQ
Tel: (01337) 810391
A unique opportunity to see many species of deer at close hand. Visitors can feed, stroke and photograph the animals. Outdoor adventure land, treetop canopy walk, maze and craft centre.

20 Doune Motor Museum
Doune,
Central FK16 6HD
Tel: (01786) 841203
View the Earl of Moray's exciting collection of vintage and post-vintage cars.

21 Inveraray Jail
Inveraray,
Argyll,
Strathclyde PA32 8TX
Tel: (01499) 302381
A living 19thC prison. Costumed 'prisoners' and 'warders' and life-like figures. See trials in progress in the 1820 courtroom.

22 Scotland's Safari and Leisure Park
Blair Drummond,
Nr Stirling FK9 4UR
Tel: (01786) 841456
Wild game reserves with Siberian tigers, lions, zebras, camels, young elephants and monkeys, plus amusements galore.

**23 Deep Sea World
The National Aquarium of Scotland**
North Queensferry,
Fife KY11 1JR
Tel: (01383) 411411
Visitors have a diver's eye view of thousands of fish as they travel along transparent tunnels on an underwater safari beneath the Firth of Forth. Wet and dry interactive exhibits in this, the largest single fish display in the northern hemisphere.

24 Stirling Castle
Stirling FK8 1EJ
Tel: (01786) 244 3101
Standing on a 250-foot rock, the castle has been rebuilt over the centuries, but the James IV towers, the fine 16thC hall, the James V Renaissance palace and the Chapel Royal of 1594 remain.

25 Palacerigg Country Park
Palacerigg Road,
Cumbernauld,
Strathclyde G67 3HU
Tel: (01236) 720047
Scottish and European wildlife collection includes bison, wildcat, lynx, owls and rare breeds. Also a deer park. Golf course.

26 Art Gallery and Museum, Glasgow
Kelvingrove, Argyll Street,
Glasgow G3 8AG
Tel: (0141) 331 1854
Collections of French Barbizon, Impressionist, post-Impressionist works and a good range of Old Master and British pictures. Also furniture, silver, pottery, glass, porcelain, arms and armour, natural history and archeological material.

27 Burrell Collection
Pollok Country Park,
2060 Pollokshaws Road,
Glasgow G43 1AT
Tel: (0141) 649 7151
A world-famous collection of textiles, furniture, ceramics, stained glass, art objects and pictures (especially 19thC French) donated to Glasgow by Sir William and Lady Burrell.

28 David Livingstone Centre
165 Station Road, Blantyre,
Glasgow G72 9BT
Tel: (01698) 823140
Birthplace of the famous explorer. Historic building, museum of African Exploration, Blantyre Story exhibition, Children's Environmental Display. Jungle Garden.

29 Glasgow Zoo Park
Calderpark, Uddingston,
Glasgow G71 1RZ
Tel: (0141) 771 1185/6
See many rare animals, most of them breeding pairs. The zoo's specialities are cats and reptiles.

30 Museum of Transport
Kelvin Hall, 1 Bunhouse Road,
Glasgow G3 8DP
Tel: (0141) 287 2720
A museum covering the history of transport, including a reproduction of a typical 1938 Glasgow street. Other features are a large display of shops' models and a walk-in motor car showroom with cars from the 1930s onwards.

31 Bo'ness and Kinneil Railway
Scottish Railway Preservation Society,
Bo'ness Station, Union Street,
Bo'ness, Lothian EH51 9AQ
Tel: (01506) 822298
Working steam railway system with historic locomotives and rolling stock. Visitor trail and shop. Special event days throughout the year.

32 Edinburgh Castle
Castle Hill, Edinburgh EH1 2YT
Tel: (0131) 225 9846
The castle stands on a rock - a fortress since time immemorial. 12thC chapel dedicated to St Margaret. Great Hall built by James IV, Old Palace housing the regalia of Scotland.

33 Edinburgh Zoo
Corstorphine Road,
Edinburgh EH12 6TS
Tel: (0131) 334 9171
With over one thousand rare and beautiful mammals, birds and reptiles, this is one of Britain's leading zoos. It is famous for its penguin colony and is now home to the world's biggest penguin house. New evolution maze.

34 Museum of Antiquities
Queen Street, Edinburgh EH2 1JD
Tel: (0131) 225 7534
'Dynasty' - the Royal House of Stewart exhibition traces 300 years of Stewart rule in Scotland through portraits and objects from the Scottish National Collection.

35 Museum of Childhood
42 High Street,
Royal Mile, Edinburgh EH1 1TG
Tel: (0131) 529 4142
This museum has a fine collection of toys, dolls and dolls' houses, costumes and nursery equipment. Two of its five galleries are in a former Georgian theatre. It also has a programme of temporary exhibitions and activities.

36 Royal Museum of Scotland
Chambers Street,
Edinburgh EH1 1JF
Tel: (0131) 225 7534
Part of the National Museums of Scotland in a fine Victorian building. Houses the national collections of decorative arts of the world, ethnography, natural history, geology, technology and science.

37 Myreton Motor Museum
Aberlady,
East Lothian EH32 0PZ
Tel: (01875) 870288
A varied collection of road transport from 1897, including motor cars, cycles, motorcycles, commercials, World War II military vehicles and automobilia.

38 Museum of Flight
East Fortune Airfield,
Nr Haddington,
Lothian EH39 5LF
Tel: (01620) 880308
A massive collection of aircraft are on display at Scotland's National Museum of Aviation. See a supersonic Lightning Fighter, a Comet 4, a Spitfire, a 1930 Puss Moth and many more.

39 Scottish Mining Museum
Lady Victoria Colliery,
Newtongrange,
Lothian EH22 4QN
Tel: (0131) 663 7519
*Renovated Victorian collieries. Take
a tour of the pithead and see a
Grant Richie steam winding
machine. The visitor centre contains
a display describing life in a
Victorian pit village.*

**40 Edinburgh Butterfly and
Insect World**
Melville Nurseries,
Lasswade,
Lothian EH18 1AZ
Tel: (0131) 663 4932
*Explore a rainforest landscaped
with tropical plants and waterfalls -
a perfect setting for butterflies and
insects from all over the world.*

41 Purves Puppets
Biggar Little Theatre,
Broughton Road, Biggar,
Strathclyde ML12 6HA
Tel: (018992) 20521
*Complete Victorian puppet
theatre in miniature, seating 100.*

42 Kelburn Country Centre
Nr Largs, Strathclyde KA29 0BE
Tel: (01475) 568865
*The historic estate of the Earls of
Glasgow, famous for its gardens,
rare trees and the Kelburn Glen.
Also craft shops, exhibitions, pets'
corner, children's play areas, assault
course and pony trekking.*

43 Magnum Leisure Centre
Harbour Street, Irvine,
Strathclyde KA12 8PP
Tel: (01294) 278381
*Exciting leisure-centre attractions,
including water park, indoor
bowling, sports hall, ice rink,
theatre, cinema, children's
superbounce area (summer),
squash courts, sauna and fitness
centre.*

44 Scottish Maritime Museum
Harbourside, Irvine,
Ayrshire KA12 8QE
Tel: (01294) 278283
*Visit the special exhibition 'There's a
Cow in my Cabin' (yes really!). See
historic vessels and pontoon
moorings. Stroll around the wharf
and harbour and see the restored
Edwardian ship worker's flat.*

**45 Dean Castle
and Country Park**
Dean Road, Off Glasgow Road,
Kilmarnock,
Strathclyde KA3 1XB
Tel: (01563) 534580
*14thC keep with dungeon and
battlements and 15thC palace.
Country park has 200 acres of
woodland, nature trails, children's
corner and riding centre.*

**46 Robert Smail's Printing
Works**
7/9 High Street,
Innerleithen,
Tweeddale EH44 6HA
Tel: (01896) 830206
*Victorian offices containing many
historic items. Visitors may watch
the printer at work.*

47 Traquair House
Innerleithen,
Borders EH44 6PW
Tel: (01896) 830323
*This is said to be the oldest
continuously occupied house in
Scotland. Attractions include craft
workshops, art gallery, brewery,
woodland and River Tweed walks
and maze.*

48 Abbotsford House
Nr Melrose,
Borders TD6 9BQ
Tel: (01896) 752043
*Sir Walter Scott's mansion
built in 1817-22. It contains the
many historical relics he collected,
armouries, the library and his study.*

**49 Bowhill House and
Country Park**
Bowhill, Selkirk,
Borders TD7 5ET
Tel: (01750) 22204
*The Border home of the Scotts of
Buccleuch for many generations.
Outstanding collection of pictures by
famous artists. Adventure woodland
play area, riding centre, garden and
nature trails, mountain bicycle hire,
Victorian kitchen.*

50 Butlin's Wonderwest World
Dunure Road, Ayr,
Strathclyde KA7 4LB
Tel: (01292) 265141
*Scotland's largest theme park
featuring 'Wondersplash'
sub-tropical waterworld, over 20
funfair rides and a host of family
entertainment.*

**51 Culzean Castle and Country
Park**
Maybole,
Ayrshire KA19 8LE
Tel: (01655) 760274
*One of Robert Adam's most notable
creations built for David, 10th Earl
of Cassillis. Special features include
the round drawing room, fine
plaster ceilings and an oval
staircase.*

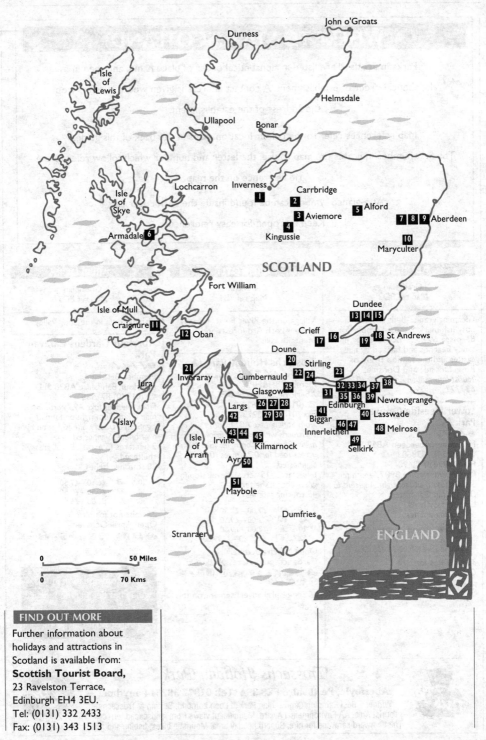

Durness

John o'Groats

Isle of Lewis

Helmsdale

Ullapool

Bonar

Lochcarron

Inverness

Carrbridge

1

2

Isle of Skye

3 Aviemore

5 Alford

7 **8** **9** Aberdeen

Armadale **6**

4

Kingussie

10

Maryculter

SCOTLAND

Fort William

Isle of Mull

Craignure **11**

Dundee

13 **14** **15**

12 Oban

Crieff

17 **16**

19 **18** St Andrews

Doune

20

21

Inveraray

Stirling

22 **24**

23

Jura

Cumbernauld

25

32 **33** **34** **37** **38**

Glasgow

31 **35** **36** **39**

Newtongrange

Islay

Largs

26 **27** **28**

Edinburgh

41

40 Lasswade

42

29 **30**

Biggar

Isle of Arran

43 **44**

Irvine

45

46 **47**

Innerleithen

48 Melrose

Kilmarnock

49

Selkirk

Ayr **50**

51

Maybole

Dumfries

ENGLAND

0   50 Miles

0   70 Kms

FIND OUT MORE

Further information about holidays and attractions in Scotland is available from:
Scottish Tourist Board,
23 Ravelston Terrace,
Edinburgh EH4 3EU.
Tel: (0131) 332 2433
Fax: (0131) 343 1513

185

WHERE TO STAY (SCOTLAND)

Parks in Scotland are listed in alphabetical order of place name, and then in alphabetical order of establishment. A contact address is given where it differs from the address of the establishment.

Map references refer to the colour location maps at the back of this guide.

The first number indicates the map to use; the letter and number which follow refer to the grid reference on the map.

At-a-glance symbols can be found inside the back cover flap.

Keep this open for easy reference.

ABERDEEN

Grampian
Map ref 8D3

Gleaming granite-built city with a busy fish market and a harbour for deep-sea trawlers. Bordered by fine sandy beaches and backed by hills, castles and the salmon rivers of Royal Deeside and Donside.
Tourist Information Centre ☎ (01224) 632727

Lower Deeside Caravan Park ⋀
⊖✓✓✓✓
Maryculter, Aberdeen AB12 5FX
☎ (01224) 733860
Fax (01224) 732490
From Aberdeen take B9077 south for 5 miles (8km) site on right. Adjacent to Old Mill Inn. Signposted.
Level, grassy, hard.
45 touring pitches

30	🚐	£8.50—£10.00
15	⛺	
6	🚙	£150.00—£235.00

30 units not for hire
Cards accepted: Access, Visa
🔌🚿🕹☕🍴♨🚻🛁🚾📺🎱🔥🛒⚡🏪☀️🍺⛰🎣♿

ABERFOYLE

Central
Map ref 7B1

Village on the River Forth. Nearby are the Loch Ard forests and Menteith Hills.

Trossachs Holiday Park ⋀
⊖✓✓✓✓✓ Thistle Award
Member BH&HPA
Aberfoyle, Stirling FK8 3SA
☎ (01877) 382614
Fax (01877) 382732
From Stirling take A811. Turn right at crossroads with A81 and follow for 5 miles (8km). Park on right. Take farm access road for 0.25 miles (0.5km). Signposted.
6 hectares (15 acres). Level, sloping, grassy, hard, sheltered.
45 touring pitches

45	🚐	£7.00—£9.50
45	🚙	£7.00—£9.50
20	⛺	£7.00—£9.50
12	🚙	£125.00—£399.00

Open March—October
Cards accepted: Access, Visa
🔌🚿🕹☕🍴♨🚻🛁🚾📺🎱🔥🛒⚡🏪☀️🍺⛰♿🎡

Ad See display advertisement on this page

ABERLOUR

Grampian
Map ref 8C3

Fishing town in the Spey Valley.

Aberlour Gardens Caravan Park
⊖✓✓✓✓
Member BH&HPA
Aberlour, Banffshire AB38 9LD
☎ (01340) 871586
From Aberlour take A95 north for 1 mile (2km). Turn right on to road signposted Quarry. Site is first on right over bridge. Signposted.
2 hectares (5 acres). Level, grassy, sheltered.
20 touring pitches

20	🚐	£6.50—£7.50
20	🚙	£6.50—£7.50
20	⛺	£5.50—£6.50

26 units not for hire
Open April—October
🚿🔌🕹☕♨🚻🛁🚾🛒⚡🏪☀️⛰♿

ALYTH

Tayside
Map ref 7C1

Small holiday centre in the
Grampian foothills overlooking
Strathmore. Popular destination for
trout fishing.

Nether Craig Caravan Park
⊖✓✓✓✓✓
Member BH&HPA
Alyth, Blairgowrie, Perthshire
PH11 8HN
☎ Lintrathen (01575) 560204
Fax (01575) 560315
*South of Alyth, join B954, signposted
Glenisla. After 4 miles (5km) turn right
onto unclassified road, signposted
Nether Craig Caravan Park. Park is 0.5
miles (1km) on left.*
1.6 hectares (4 acres). Level, grassy,
hard, sheltered.
40 touring pitches

40	🚐	£7.00—£9.00
40	🚎	£7.00—£9.00
40	⛺	£5.00—£5.00

Open mid-March–October
Cards accepted: Access

🅿️ 🔌 ♨ 🚰 🔥 🛒 ⚡ 🧺 📻 📺 ✳ 🛢 ☉
🏔 ⚓

ARDLUI

Strathclyde
Map ref 7B1

Small resort at the head of Loch
Lomond. Magnificent Highland
scenery.

Ardlui Hotel, Marina and Holiday Home Park
⊖✓✓✓✓
Member BH&HPA
Loch Lomond, Ardlui,
Dunbartonshire G83 7EB
☎ Inveruglas (01301) 704243
Fax (013014) 268
*Hotel and caravan park on the main
A82 road north. Signposted.*
6 hectares (15 acres). Level, sloping,
grassy, stony, hard.
32 touring pitches

12	🚐	£8.50—£9.00
12	🚎	£8.50—£9.00
20	⛺	£6.50—£8.50
6	🏠	£220.00—£270.00

---

80 units not for hire
🅿️ 🔌 ♨ 🚰 🔥 🛒 ⚡ 🧺 📻 📺 🎮 📻 🖥
🧺 🛢 ☉ 🔍 🏔 ♨ ⚓ 🚶 🅿️ ⚓

ARROCHAR

Strathclyde
Map ref 7B1

Ardgartan Campsite
⊖✓✓✓
Member BH&HPA
Forest Enterprise, Arrochar,
Dunbartonshire G83 7AR
☎ (01301) 702293 & 702360
Fax (01369) 840617
*Take the A82 from Glasgow then the
A83 at Tarbet. Signposted.*
6.8 hectares (17 acres). Level, grassy,
hard.
160 touring pitches

160	🚐	£7.00

Open March–October
Cards accepted: Access, Visa
🔌 🔥 🚰 ♨ 🚰 🛒 📻 🖥 ⚡ ☉ 🏔 ⚓

AUCHENBOWIE

Central
Map ref 7C2

Auchenbowie Caravan Site
⊖✓✓✓
Auchenbowie, Stirling FK7 8HE
☎ Denny (01324) 822141
*Junction 9 off M9/M80, take A872
towards Denny for 0.5 miles and turn
right. Signposted.*
1.4 hectares (3.5 acres). Level,
sloping, grassy, hard, sheltered.
60 touring pitches

60	🚐	£7.00—£7.00
60	🚎	£7.00—£7.00
60	⛺	£7.00—£7.00
7	🏠	£155.00—£205.00

Open April–October
Cards accepted: Access, Visa
🔌 🔥 🚰 ♨ 🚰 🛒 📻 ⚡ 🛢 ☉ 🏔
Ad See display advertisement on this
page

┌──────────────────────────┐
│ The 🅜 symbol after an │
│ establishment name indicates │
│ that it is a Regional │
│ Tourist Board member. │
└──────────────────────────┘

AUCHENMALG

Dumfries and Galloway
Map ref 7B3

Cock Inn Caravan Park
⊖✓✓✓✓ Thistle Award
Member BH&HPA
Auchenmalg, Newton Stewart,
Wigtownshire DG8 0JT
☎ (01581) 500227
*On the A747 Glenluce to Port William
road, 5 miles (8km) from the A75
Newton Stewart to Stranraer road.
Signposted.*
2.8 hectares (7 acres). Level, sloping,
grassy, hard.
30 touring pitches

30	🚐	£7.00—£8.00
30	🚎	£7.00—£8.00
30	⛺	£6.00—£6.00
5	🏠	£120.00—£230.00

70 units not for hire
Open March–October
🔥 🅿️ 🔌 ♨ 🚰 🔥 🛒 ⚡ 🧺 📻 🖥 ✳ 🛢 🖥
🧺 🛢 ☉ 🔍 🏔 ⚓ 🚶 🅿️ ⚓

AVIEMORE

Highland
Map ref 8C3

Popular centre for exploring
Speyside and the Cairngorms.
Winter sports, fishing, walking and
climbing.
*Tourist Information Centre ☎ (01479)
810363*

Campgrounds of Scotland
⊖✓✓✓✓✓✓ Thistle Award
Member BH&HPA/NCC
Coylumbridge, Aviemore,
Inverness-shire PH22 1QU
☎ (01479) 810120
Fax (01479) 810120
*Take B970 (ski road) from Aviemore
for 1.5 miles. Park is on the right.
Signposted.*
3.6 hectares (9 acres). Level, sloping,
grassy, stony, hard, sheltered.
47 touring pitches

17	🚐	£7.50
17	🚎	£7.50
30	⛺	£5.50
15	🏠	£180.00

Cards accepted: Access
🅿️ 🔌 🔥 🚰 ♨ 🚰 🛒 📻 🖥 ⚡ 🧺 🛢 ☉ 🏔 ⚓

187

AYR

Strathclyde
Map ref 7B2

One of Scotland's brightest seaside resorts. Also a Royal Burgh and noted centre for the manufacture of carpets and fabrics. Many associations with the poet Robert Burns. Faces the Isle of Arran across the Firth of Clyde.
Tourist Information Centre ☎ (01292) 288688

Heads of Ayr Caravan Park
☺✓✓✓✓
Member BH&HPA/NCC
Dunure Road, Ayr KA7 4LD
☎ Alloway (01292) 442269
Fax (01292) 500298
5miles (8km) south of Ayr on A719. Site overlooking Arran and the Firth of Clyde. Signposted.
3.6 hectares (9 acres). Level, sloping, grassy.
50 touring pitches

20	🚐	£8.50—£11.00
20	🚛	£7.50—£9.50
10	⛺	£7.50—£9.50

100 units not for hire
Open March—October
🅿🎏🔌🍴♿🚿🔥☕⚡✕🍴📺🏧◎✳🔵🔍⛰🚶♨

BALLOCH

Strathclyde
Map ref 7B2

Situated at the southern end of Loch Lomond, an ideal starting place for touring the loch.

Tullichewan Holiday Park
☺✓✓✓✓ Thistle Award
Member BH&HPA
Old Luss Road, Balloch, Alexandria, Dunbartonshire G83 8QP
☎ Alexandria (01389) 759475
Fax (01389) 755563
0.25 mile from junction of A82 and A811, 17 miles north-west of Glasgow. Signposted.
6 hectares (15 acres). Level, grassy, hard, sheltered.
120 touring pitches

120	🚐	£7.50—£11.50
120	🚛	£7.50—£11.50
40	⛺	£7.50—£11.50
6	🏠	£175.00—£395.00

23 units not for hire
Cards accepted: Access, Visa, Switch
🔌🍴🅿🔵⚙♿🚿⚡☕⚡📺📶◎✳🔵🔍⛰🚶🔑
🅃

🆎 See display advertisement on this page

BALMACARA

Highland
Map ref 8B3

Small village on the north shore of Loch Alsh with views towards the south of Sleat and Skye.

Reraig Caravan Site ⛰
☺✓✓✓✓
Balmacara, Kyle of Lochalsh, Ross-shire IV40 8DH
☎ (01599) 566215
1.75 miles (3km) west of junction of A87 and A890 behind Balamacara Hotel. Signposted.
1 hectare (2.25 acres). Level, grassy.
45 touring pitches

40	🚐	£6.50
40	🚛	£6.50
5	⛺	£6.50

Open May—September
Cards accepted: Access, Visa
🔌🍴🅿🔍♿🚿☕⚡◎

BANCHORY

Grampian
Map ref 8D3

Pleasant resort on lower Deeside, rich in wood and river scenery.
Tourist Information Centre ☎ (01330) 822000

Feughside Caravan Park
☺✓✓✓✓✓ Thistle Award
Member BH&HPA
Strachan, Banchory, Kincardineshire AB31 6NT
☎ Feughside (01330) 850669
25 miles (40kms) west of Aberdeen. From Banchory, take B974 to Strachan; road number changes to B976 for Aboyne. Park is 2 miles west of Strachan. Turn right after Feughside Inn. Signposted.

2 hectares (5 acres). Level, grassy, sheltered.
20 touring pitches

20	🚐	£8.00—£8.50
20	🚛	£8.00—£8.50
20	⛺	£6.50—£8.00
2	🏠	£130.00—£270.00

48 units not for hire
Open April—October
🅿🔍🍴♿🚿☕⚡📶◎✳🔌🍴⊙🔍⛰
🚶♨

BIGGAR

Strathclyde
Map ref 7C2

Atractive town and good centre for the Scottish Lowlands.

Biggar Caravan Site
☺✓✓✓
Biggar Park, Biggar, Lanarkshire ML12 6JS
☎ (01899) 20319
Off Broughton road to north east of Biggar for about 200 yards (217m) and turn on to unclassified road for park .Signposted.
Level, grassy, stony.
60 touring pitches

40	🚐	£7.00—£9.00
20	🚛	

Open April—September
🅿🔍♿🚿✕🍴📶◎🔌🍴⊙⛰🚶♨
🔍🅿🎵♨

BLAIR ATHOLL

Tayside
Map ref 7C1

Highland village at the foot of the Grampian mountains.

Blair Castle Caravan Park
☺✓✓✓✓✓✓ Thistle Award
Member BH&HPA/NCC
Blair Atholl, Perthshire PH18 5SR
☎ Pitlochry (01796) 481263
Fax (01796) 481587
Take A9 north from Pitlochry. Turn off for Blair Atholl after 6 miles. Signposted.
12.8 hectares (32 acres). Level, sloping, grassy, hard, sheltered.
241 touring pitches

tullichewan – LOCH LOMOND HIGHLY COMMENDED
* PREMIER TOURING PARK FOR LOCH LOMOND AND GLASGOW
* PINE LODGES AND THISTLE AWARD CARAVANS FOR HIRE
* LEISURE SUITE WITH SAUNA, JACUZZI AND SUN BED
* GAMES ROOM AND T.V. LOUNGE * FREE COLOUR BROCHURE
BALLOCH, LOCH LOMOND G83 8QP
Tel: Alexandria (01389) 759475 Fax: (01389) 755563
The Best of British Thistle

140	🚐	£7.50—£9.00
15	🚏	£7.50—£9.00
82	⛺	£6.50—£9.00
27	🏠	£150.00—£315.00

74 units not for hire
Open April–October
Cards accepted: Access, Visa

⚓🅿🔌🍴🚰🔥🛟🚿✕ TV ⛽◻ ≈
☺🛝⚠🕖🅿🛉🛎

[Ad] See display advertisement on this page

BLAIRGOWRIE

Tayside
Map ref 7C1

Bracing inland resort overlooking the fertile valley of Strathmore.
Tourist Information Centre ☎ *(01250) 872960 or 873701*

Blairgowrie Holiday Park
⊖✓✓✓✓✓ Thistle Award
Member BH&HPA
Rattray, Blairgowrie, Perthshire
PH10 7AL
☎ (01250) 872941
Fax (01250) 874535
From Perth take A93 to Blairgowrie, over river and follow signs for caravan park.
6 hectares (15 acres). Level, sloping, grassy, sheltered.
25 touring pitches

25	🚐	£7.50—£10.00
25	🚏	£7.50—£10.00
25	⛺	£7.50—£10.00
15	🏠	£175.00—£350.00

130 units not for hire
Cards accepted: Access, Visa, Switch

🔥⚓🅿🔌🍴🚰🔥🛟⛽◻ ≈ 🚿 ≈
☺⚠🕖🅿🛉🛎

BLAIRLOGIE

Central
Map ref 7C1

Village 3 miles north-east of Stirling.

Witches Craig Caravan Park ᛗ
⊖✓✓✓✓✓
Member BH&HPA
Blairlogie, Stirling FK9 5PX
☎ Stirling (01786) 474947
Leave Stirling on St Andrews road, A91. Site 3 miles (5km) east of Stirling. Signposted.

2 hectares (5 acres). Level, grassy, hard, sheltered.
60 touring pitches

60	🚐	£10.00—£13.00
60	🚏	£10.00—£13.00
60	⛺	£10.00—£13.00

Open April–October

⚓🅿🔌🍴🚰🔥🛟🛎⛽◻ ≈ 🚿 ≈ 🚮☺
⚠🛝🕖

CAIRNRYAN

Dumfries and Galloway
Map ref 7B3

Cairnryan Caravan and Chalet Park
⊖✓✓✓✓ Thistle Award
Member BH&HPA
Cairnryan, Stranraer, Wigtownshire
DG9 8QX
☎ (01581) 200231
Fax (01581) 200207
On the side of the A77. Village of Cairnryan directly opposite P&O ferry terminal. Signposted.
Sloping, grassy, sheltered.
15 touring pitches

15	🚐	£8.00
15	🚏	£8.00
10	⛺	£4.00
4	🏠	£100.00—£250.00

78 units not for hire
Open April–October
Cards accepted: Access

🔥⚓🅿🔌🍴🚰🔥🛟🛎⛽◻ ≈ 🚮🚿 ≈ 🚮
⚠🕖🅿🛎 ᛗ

CONTIN

Highland
Map ref 8C3

Hamlet near Strathpeffer with an interesting church.

Riverside Chalets and Caravan Park
⊖✓✓
Contin, Strathpeffer, Ross-shire
IV14 9ES
☎ Strathpeffer (01997) 421351
In Contin Village, on A835 between Inverness and Ullapool at Strathpeffer junction. Signposted.
0.8 hectares (2 acres). Sloping, grassy, sheltered.
30 touring pitches

15	🚐	£5.00—£5.00
15	🚏	£5.00—£5.00
15	⛺	£5.00—£5.00
1	🏠	£100.00

🔥⚓🅿🔌🍴🚰🔥🛟🛎⛽✕◻◻ ≈
☺🛝🕖

CRIEFF

Tayside
Map ref 7C1

Attractive resort on the edge of the Perthshire Highlands.
Tourist Information Centre ☎ *(01764) 652578*

Crieff Holiday Village
⊖✓✓✓✓ Thistle Award
Member BH&HPA/NCC
Turret Bank, Crieff, Perthshire
PH7 4JN
☎ (01764) 653513
Fax (01764) 655028
Turn left off the A85, 0.5 miles west of Crieff. We are 300 yards on the left. Signposted.
1.8 hectares (4.5 acres). Level, grassy, hard, sheltered.
45 touring pitches

45	🚐	£7.00—£8.50
45	🚏	£7.00—£8.50
10	⛺	£6.50—£8.00
5	🏠	£140.00—£260.00

47 units not for hire
Cards accepted: Access, Visa

🔥⚓🅿🔌🍴🚰🔥🛟🛎⛽◻ TV ⛽◻
≈ 🚿 ≈ 🚮⚠🕖🅿🛉🛎

CROCKETFORD

Dumfries and Galloway
Map ref 7C3

Small village in the valley of the River Urr.

Park of Brandedleys ᛗ
⊖✓✓✓✓✓ Thistle Award
Member BH&HPA/NCC
Crocketford, Dumfries DG2 8RG
☎ (01556) 690250
Fax (01556) 690681
Turn south from A75, at west end of Crocketford village, for 150 yards. Signposted.
9.6 hectares (24 acres). Level, sloping, grassy, hard, sheltered.
80 touring pitches

Continued ▶

CROCKETFORD

Continued

80	🚐	£9.00—£13.00
80	🚚	£9.00—£13.00
80	⛺	£9.00—£13.00
12	🏚	£140.00—£480.00

15 units not for hire
Open March–October
Cards accepted: Access, Visa

🛁🔥⚡🅿️🗑🔌🐕👜🚿♿🎱✕📻📺
🛢🚲⚓🛒🏧🔺🔗�" ℹ️⊙
Ad See display advertisement on this page

DALKEITH

Lothian
Map ref 7C2

Tourist Information Centre ☎ *(0131)
6606818 or 6632083*

Fordell Caravan and Camping Park
⊖✓✓✓✓
Lauder Road, Dalkeith, Midlothian
EH22 2PH
☎ office 9-5 (0131) 660 3921 &
Booking Office 24 hours 663 3046
Fax (0131) 663 8891
*2 miles (3km) south of Dalkeith on
A68. 9 miles (15.5km) south of
Edinburgh. Signposted.*
Level, grassy, hard, sheltered.
105 touring pitches

35	🚐	£8.00—£10.75
25	🚚	
45	⛺	£6.50—£8.00

Open March–October
Cards accepted: Access, Visa, Diners,
Amex, Switch/Delta
🅿️🔌🐕👜🚿♿🎱✕📻📺🛢🚲⚓⊙
🛒🔗🔺

The map references refer
to the colour maps towards
the end of the guide.
The first figure is the
map number; the letter and
figure which follow indicate
the grid reference
on the map.

DUMFRIES

Dumfries and Galloway
Map ref 7C3

Fascinating town with old
five-arched bridge spanning the
River Nith. County capital and Royal
Burgh with associations with Robert
Burns, James Barrie and Robert
Bruce. Burns died here and the
house he occupied contains
interesting personal relics. His tomb
is in St Michaels.
Tourist Information Centre ☎ *(01387)
253862*

Barnsoul Farm and Wild Life Area
⊖✓✓✓
Member BH&HPA
Shawhead, Dumfries DG2 9SQ
☎ (01387) 730249
Fax (01387) 730249
*Off A75 at sign for Shawhead and
Barnsoul. At Shawhead take right, then
within 50 metres bear left. After 1.5
miles Barnsoul is on left. Signposted.*
100 hectares (250 acres). Level,
sloping, grassy, hard, sheltered.
20 touring pitches

20	🚐	£6.00—£8.00
20	🚚	£6.00—£8.00
20	⛺	£5.00—£7.00
4	🏚	£150.00—£250.00

Open April, October
🛁🔥🅿️🗑🔌🐕👜🚿♿🛢🚲⚓⊙
🏧🔺🔗

DUNKELD

Tayside
Map ref 7C1

Picturesque cathedral town
beautifully situated in the richly
wooded valley of the River Tay on
the edge of the Perthshire
Highlands. Salmon and trout fishing.

Inver Mill Farm Caravan Site 🏔
⊖✓✓✓
Inver, Dunkeld, Perthshire PH8 0JR
☎ (01350) 727477
Fax (01350) 727477
*Turn off the A9 onto the A822
(signposted Crieff). Immediately turn
right following the sign to Inver for 0.5
miles past the static site and cross the*

*bridge. We are the first on the left.
Signposted.*
4 hectares (10 acres). Level, grassy,
sheltered.
50 touring pitches

50	🚐	£7.00
50	🚚	£7.00
50	⛺	£7.00
1	🏚	

Open April–October
Cards accepted: Access
🛁🔥⚓🐕👜🚿♿🎱🛢🚲⚓⊙♿
🔗🔺🔺⚓

DURNESS

Highland
Map ref 8B1

Sango Sands Caravan Camping Site
⊖✓✓✓
Durness, Sutherland IV27 4PP
☎ (01971) 511262 & 511222
Fax (01971) 511205
*Site in centre of Durness village
adjacent to A838. Overlooking Sango
Bay. Signposted.*
5 hectares (12.5 acres). Level, grassy,
hard.
82 touring pitches

82	🚐	£6.50—£6.50
82	🚚	£6.50—£6.50
82	⛺	£6.50—£6.50

Open April–mid-October
Cards accepted: Access
🛁🔥⚓🐕👜🚿♿🎱✕📻🛢🚲⚓
⊙🏧🔗🔺⚓

EDINBURGH

Lothian
Map ref 7C2

Scotland's capital and international
festival city. Dominated by its
ancient fortress, the city is
surrounded by hills, woodlands and
rivers. Good shopping on Princes
Street.
Tourist Information Centre ☎ *(0131)
557 1700 or 333 2167*

Mortonhall Caravan Park
⊖✓✓✓✓ Thistle Award
Member BH&HPA/NCC
38 Mortonhall Gate, Frogston Road
East, Edinburgh EH16 6TJ
☎ (0131) 664 1533 & 664 2104
Fax (0131) 664 5387

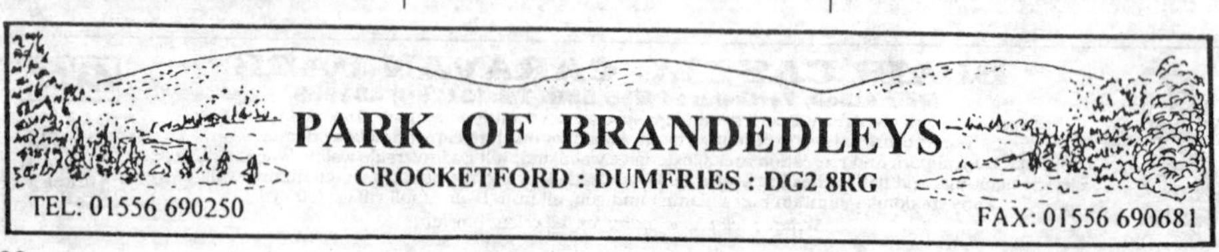

From the city bypass at Lothianburn junction, follow signs for Mortonhall. From city centre take the east or west ends of Princes Street. Signposted.
10 hectares (25 acres). Level, sloping, grassy, hard, sheltered.
250 touring pitches

150	🚐	£7.75—£12.00
150	🚍	£7.75—£12.00
100	▲	£7.75—£12.00
14	🏠	£145.00—£380.00

Open March–October
Cards accepted: Access, Visa, Amex, Switch/Delta

🚐🚩🚿🛉🐕🏧☎🐾✕♨📺🗑📶
🍽🚬☺🔍🛡🚶🏧♨
[Ad] See display advertisement on this page

EVANTON
Highland
Map ref 8C3

Black Rock Caravan Park
⊖✓✓✓✓✓ Thistle Award
Member BH&HPA
Balconie Street, Evanton, Ross-shire
IV16 9UN
☎ (01349) 830917
Fax (01349) 830321
From Inverness take A9 north for 12 miles (19km), turn left for Evanton on B817. Park is 0.75 miles (1km) further on. Signposted.
1.8 hectares (4.5 acres). Level, grassy, sheltered.
55 touring pitches

45	🚐	£8.00—£10.00
45	🚍	£8.00—£10.00
10	▲	£6.00—£8.00
6	🏠	£220.00—£280.00

14 units not for hire
Open April–October
Cards accepted: Access

🚐🚩🛉🏧☎🐾📶🗑🍽🚬🚶☺🔍🏧🚶🛡

FINTRY
Central
Map ref 7C2

Balgair Castle Caravan Park 🏕
⊖✓✓✓✓✓✓ Thistle Award
Member BH&HPA
Overglinns, Fintry, Glasgow G63 0LP
☎ (01360) 860283
Fax (01360) 860300

On B822 between Fintry and Kippen. 1.5 miles (3km) north of Fintry. Signposted.
15.2 hectares (38 acres). Level, sloping, grassy, sheltered.
63 touring pitches

	🚐	£7.95—£8.95
	🚍	£7.95—£8.95
	▲	£7.95—£8.75
5	🏠	£150.00—£260.00

Open March–October
Cards accepted: Access

🚐🅿🚩🛉🐕🛉🏧☎♨✕♨📺🗑📶
🚬🚶☺🔍🍽🎵🏧♨

FORT WILLIAM
Highland
Map ref 7B1

One of the finest touring centres in the Western Highlands. A busy holiday town set on the shores of Loch Linnhe at the western end of the Great Glen almost in the shadow of Ben Nevis, the highest mountain in the British Isles. Nearby are fishing, climbing, walking and steamer trips to the islands.
Tourist Information Centre ☎ (01397) 703781

Corran Caravans
⊖✓✓✓✓✓
Moss Cottage, Onich, Fort William, Inverness-shire PH33 6SE
☎ Onich (018553) 208
8 miles south of Fort William take first right after Corran Ferry, signposted Bunree. Follow single track road to T-junction and turn right. Signposted.
2.8 hectares (7 acres). Level, grassy, hard.
15 touring pitches

10	🚐	£5.00—£7.50
5	🚍	£5.00—£7.50
5	▲	
10	🏠	£100.00—£250.00

Open February–October

🚐🅿🚩🛉🐕🛉🏧☎🐾📶🗑🚬☺🔍🛡🚶🛡

Linnhe Caravan and Chalet Park 🏕
⊖✓✓✓✓✓✓ Thistle Award
Member BH&HPA/NCC
Corpach, Fort William, Inverness-shire PH33 7NL
☎ Corpach (01397) 772376
Fax (01397) 772007

On A830 1.5 miles (3km) west of Corpach village. Terraced to the shores of Loch Eil. Signposted.
5.4 hectares (13.5 acres). Level, hard, sheltered.
77 touring pitches

75	🚐	£8.50—£12.00
75	🚍	£8.50—£12.00
15	▲	£6.50—£7.50
75	🏠	£160.00—£405.00

18 units not for hire
Open January–October, December
Cards accepted: Access, Visa

🚐🅿🚩🛉🐕🛉🏧☎🐾📶🗑🍽🚬
☺🏧🚶🛡🚶♨🏧T
[Ad] See display advertisement on page 192

GAIRLOCH
Highland
Map ref 8B2

Scattered village at the head of Loch Gairloch with superb beaches and glorious scenery.
Tourist Information Centre ☎ (01445) 712130

Gairloch Holiday Park
⊖✓✓✓
Strath, Gairloch, Ross-shire
☎ (01445) 712373
Follow A832 to Gairloch. At Gairloch take B8021 to Strath (for 1/2 mile), site in village. Signposted.
2.4 hectares (6 acres). Level, grassy.
50 touring pitches

30	🚐	£6.00—£8.00
20	🚍	£5.00—£7.00
30	▲	£4.50—£7.00

Open April–October
🚐🚩🛉🐕🛉🏧☎📺🗑📶🚬🍽☺🔍🚶🛡

Sands Holiday Centre
⊖✓✓✓✓ Thistle Award
Member NCC
Gairloch, Ross-shire IV21 2DL
☎ (01445) 712152
From village of Gairloch, take B8021 Melvaig road for 3 miles (5km). Through village over two cattle grids and on past youth hostel from first view of sandy beach Signposted.
Level, sloping, grassy.
360 touring pitches

Continued ▶

GAIRLOCH

Continued

120	🚐	£7.00—£8.30
40	🚏	£7.00—£7.70
200	▲	£7.00—£8.30
5	🏕	£208.00—£346.00

15 units not for hire
Open April–October
Cards accepted: Access, Visa, Switch/Delta

🛶🅿️🔌🔥📻♨️🚰🚻🛒🏪🛍📺🗑🚿🚮🔋☀️🎡
🏇🏼🐾🎣✚

GLEN NEVIS

Highland
Map ref 7B1

Glen Nevis Caravan and Camping Park

⊖✓✓✓✓✓
Member BH&HPA
Glen Nevis, Fort William,
Inverness-shire PH33 6SX
☎ Fort William (01397) 702 191
Fax (01397) 703 904
Follow A82 to mini roundabout on northern outskirts of Fort William. Exit Glen Nevis and park 2.5 miles on right. Start of ascent of Ben Nevis 0.25 miles (0.5km) from park. Signposted.
11.6 hectares (29 acres). Level, sloping, grassy, stony, hard, sheltered.
380 touring pitches

250	🚐	£7.80—£10.40
250	🚏	£7.50—£10.00
130	▲	£7.50—£10.00

Open March–October
Cards accepted: Access, Visa, Switch/Delta

🔌🔥📻♨️🚰🚻🛒🛍✕🍴📺🗑🚿🔋☀️
🏇🐾🅣
Ad See display advertisement on page 193

GLENCOE

Highland
Map ref 7B1

Village at the foot of Glen Coe, a deep and rugged defile enclosed by towering mountains. Scene of massacre of MacDonalds of Glencoe by the Campbells of Glen Lyon in 1692. A valley of haunting beauty offering winter sports.

Invercoe Caravans

⊖✓✓✓✓✓ Thistle Award
Member BH&HPA
Invercoe, Glencoe, Argyll PA39 4HP
☎ Ballachulish (01855) 811210
Fax (01855) 811210
0.25 miles from Glencoe crossroads (A82) on the Kinlochleven road B863. Signposted.
2 hectares (5 acres). Level, grassy, hard.
55 touring pitches

55	🚐	£8.00—£14.00
55	▲	£8.00—£14.00
55	▲	£8.00—£10.00
5	🏕	£165.00—£300.00

Open March–October

🛶🅿️🔌🔥📻♨️🚰🚻🛒🛍📺🗑🚿🚮🔋☀️
🎡

GRANTOWN-ON-SPEY

Highland
Map ref 8C3

Popular resort in the wooded valley of the Spey, with fine views of The Cairngorms. Golf, salmon and trout fishing and water sports.

Grantown-on-Spey Caravan Park

⊖✓✓✓✓✓ Thistle Award
Member BH&HPA
Seafield Avenue, Grantown-on-Spey, Morayshire PH26 3JQ
☎ (01479) 872474
Fax (01479) 873696
From town centre, turn north at Bank of Scotland and park is straight ahead in 0.25 mile. Signposted.
8 hectares (20 acres). Level, grassy, hard, sheltered.
100 touring pitches

100	🚐	£7.00—£13.00
100	🚏	£7.00—£11.00
50	▲	£5.50—£7.50
3	🏕	£130.00—£280.00

40 units not for hire
Open April–September
Cards accepted: Access, Visa, Switch/Delta

🛶🅿️🔌🔥📻♨️🚰🚻🛒🛍📺🗑🚿🔋☀️
🚮🎡🐾🎣✚

GRETNA

Dumfries and Galloway
Map ref 7C3

Gretna, the first settlement in Scotland, was renowned for its many "marriage booths", including a blacksmith's shop. It still has an air of romance today.

The Braids Caravan Park

⊖✓✓✓✓
Annan Road, Gretna, Carlisle DG16 5DQ
☎ (01461) 337409
Off A74/A75 on B721. 0.25miles (0.5km) West of Gretna. Signposted.
Level, grassy, hard, sheltered.
80 touring pitches

65	🚐	£6.25—£7.00
65	🚏	£6.25—£7.00
15	▲	£5.00—£7.00

4 units not for hire

🅿️🔌🔥📻♨️🚰🚻🛒🛍📺🗑🚿🔋☀️🐾🎣♨️

HADDINGTON

Lothian
Map ref 7C2

County capital and birthplace of John Knox, the religious reformer. Well situated on the River Tyne with old houses and 14th C church.

The Monks' Muir

⊖✓✓✓✓✓ Thistle Award
Member BH&HPA/NCC
Haddington, East Lothian EH41 3SB
☎ East Linton (01620) 860340
Fax (01620) 860340
Site entrance on A1, 2.5 miles (4km) east of Haddington. Signposted.
2.8 hectares (7 acres). Level, sloping, grassy, hard, sheltered.
70 touring pitches

70	🚐	£10.40
70	🚏	£10.40
70	⛺	£8.00
6	🏠	£110.00—£365.00

15 units not for hire

� P 🖧 🅿 🛁 🚻 🔥 🛒 ⚓ ⊙ 🚿 ✕ ⛾ ▥ ◉ ✦
🛶 ⊙ ⛰ ⋃ 🅿 ☎ ⊤

Strathclyde
Map ref 7B1

Inverbeg Holiday Park

⊖✓✓✓✓ Thistle Award
Member BH&HPA
Inverbeg, Luss, Dunbartonshire
G83 8PD
☎ Luss (01436) 860267
Fax (01436) 860266
4 miles north of Luss on A82.
Signposted.
6 hectares (15 acres). Level, grassy,
hard, sheltered.
35 touring pitches

35	🚐	£6.75—£8.75
35	🚏	£6.75—£8.75
10	⛺	£6.75—£8.75
12	🏠	£150.00—£420.00

100 units not for hire
Open March—October

🔥 🛏 P 🖧 🔌 🚻 🔥 🅿 ⊙ 🛒 ▥ ◉ ⛾
✦ 🛶 ⊙ ⚓ ⛰ ⋌ ↔ ⋃ ⋃ 🎵 ✦ ⊤

Highland
Map ref 8B3

Highland centre for fishing and
deer-stalking. Beautiful scenery.

Faichem Park ⚠

⊖✓✓✓✓✓
Member BH&HPA
Ardgarry Farm, Faichem, Invergarry,
Inverness-shire PH35 4HG
☎ (01809) 501226
From A82 at Invergarry, take A87.
Continue 1 mile and turn right at
Faichem sign. First up hill on right.
Signposted.

4 hectares (10 acres). Level, sloping,
grassy, sheltered.
30 touring pitches

15	🚐	£6.00—£6.50
15	🚏	£6.00—£6.50
15	⛺	£6.00—£6.50

Open April—October

🔥 🛏 🅿 🔌 🚻 🔥 🅿 ⊙ 🛒 ▥ ⊙ ⋃ 🛁

Highland
Map ref 8C3

Town at the mouth of the River
Ness at entrance to Beauly Firth.
Once the capital of the ancient
Kingdom of the Picts, it is now a
favourite centre for touring the
Highlands.
Tourist Information Centre ☎ *(01463)*
234353

Auchnahillin Caravan and Camping Centre

⊖✓✓✓✓
Member BH&HPA
Daviot East, Inverness IV1 2XQ
☎ Daviot (01463) 772286
Fax (01463) 772286
Off A9 7 miles south of Inverness. Take
B9154 off A9 to the east. Well
signposted from A9.
4 hectares (10 acres). Level, grassy,
sheltered.
65 touring pitches

65	🚐	£7.50—£9.00
65	🚏	£7.50—£9.00
35	⛺	£5.50—£7.50
25	🏠	£85.00—£275.00

4 units not for hire
Open March—October

🔥 🛏 🅿 P 🔌 🚻 🔥 🅿 ⊙ 🛒 ✕ ⛾ ▥ ◉ ✦
🛶 ⊙ ⚓ ⛰ ⋃ 🎵 🎻 🏠 🔥 ☎ ⊤
Ad See display advertisement on
page 194

Strathclyde
Map ref 7B1

Loch Lomond Holiday Park (Self-Catering)

⊖✓✓✓✓✓ Thistle Award
Member NCC
Inveruglas, Tarbet, Dunbartonshire
G83 7DW
☎ Inveruglas (01301) 704224
Fax (01301) 704206
From Glasgow A82 north 30 miles
(48km) to Tarbet Hotel. Turn right on
A82 Oban Road for 3 miles (5km) and
park on right. Signposted.
5.2 hectares (13 acres). Sloping,
grassy, stony, hard, sheltered.
18 touring pitches

18	🚐	£6.50—£12.00
18	🚏	
12	🏠	£130.00—£450.00

46 units not for hire
Open January, March—October,
December
Cards accepted: Access, Visa

🔥 🛏 🅿 🔌 🚻 🔥 🅿 ⊙ 🛒 ▥ ◉ ✦ 🛶
⊙ ⚓ ⛰ ⋃ ⋃ 🎻 ✦ ⊤

Grampian
Map ref 8D3

Hillhead Caravan Park ⚠

⊖✓✓✓✓ Thistle Award
Member BH&HPA
Kintore, Inverurie, Aberdeenshire
AB51 0YX
☎ (01467) 632809
Fax (01467) 633173
A96 from Aberdeen. Turn left in centre
of Kintore, sign for Ratch-hill. After 0.5
miles (1km) take left turn, sign for
Blairs. Continue 0.5 miles (1km). Park
on left. Signposted.
0.6 hectares (1.5 acres). Level, grassy,
sheltered.
24 touring pitches

Continued ▶

193

KINTORE

Continued

24	🚐	£5.75—£7.30
24	🚍	£5.75—£7.30
24	⛺	£5.75—£7.30
5	🏠	£100.00—£245.00

Open April–October
Cards accepted: Access, Visa
🅰️🅿️⊖🛎️🔥♨️🔌⊙♨️🛒📶📺⚡💈🔌⊙
⚠️♨️◉

KIPPFORD

Dumfries and Galloway
Map ref 7C3

Village on the east side of Urr
Water Estuary.

Kippford Caravan Park 🅰

⊖✓✓✓✓✓ Thistle Award
Member BH&HPA/NCC
Kippford, Dalbeattie,
Kirkcudbrightshire DG5 4LF
☎ (01556) 620636
Fax (01556) 620636
*From A711 Dalbeattie take Solway
Coast Road A710. After 3.5 miles
continue straight ahead at junction with
Kippford Road. Entrance to park is 300
yards on right. Signposted.*
6 hectares (15 acres). Level, sloping,
grassy, hard, sheltered.
45 touring pitches

30	🚐	£9.00—£12.00
5	🚍	£9.00—£12.00
10	⛺	£6.00—£12.00
10	🏠	£120.00—£325.00

105 units not for hire
Open March–October
⚡🅰️⊕🛎️🔥♨️🔌⊙📶📺🔌⊙⚠️
♨️

Please check prices and other
details at the time of booking.

The 🅰 symbol after an
establishment name indicates
that it is a Regional
Tourist Board member.

KIRKCUDBRIGHT

Dumfries and Galloway
Map ref 7C3

Delightful old town at the head of
Kirkcudbright Bay, much frequented
by painters.

Brighouse Bay Holiday Park

⊖✓✓✓✓✓ Thistle Award
Member BH&HPA/NCC
Borgue Road, Kirkcudbright
DG6 4TT
☎ Borgue (015577) 267
Fax (01557) 7319
*From Kirkcudbright take A755 west for
0.5 miles. Turn left on to B727
signposted Borgue. After 4 miles, turn
left at Brighouse Bay signpost. Park is
on right after 2 miles. Signposted.*
280 hectares (700 acres). Level,
sloping, grassy, hard, sheltered.
120 touring pitches

120	🚐	£8.50—£11.25
120	🚍	£8.50—£11.25
120	⛺	£8.50—£11.25
24	🏠	£150.00—£365.00

92 units not for hire
⚡🅰️⊕📶🔥♨️🔌⊙📶🛒✖️🍴📶📺⚡💈
⊙🔍⚠️♨️➰🍴♨️⊙🔌☂️T
Ad See display advertisement on
page 195

LAURENCEKIRK

Grampian
Map ref 7D1

Dovecot Caravan Park 🅰

⊖✓✓✓✓
Member BH&HPA
North Water Bridge, Laurencekirk,
Kincardineshire AB30 1QL
☎ Northwaterbridge (01674)
840630
*Off A90 Dundee-Aberdeen Rd. Turn off
Northwater Bridge at R.A.F. Base Edzell
sign. Signposted.*
2.4 hectares (6 acres). Level, grassy,
sheltered.
25 touring pitches

25	🚐	£6.75—£7.75
25	🚍	£6.75—£7.75
25	⛺	£6.75—£7.75
2	🏠	£150.00—£180.00

44 units not for hire
Open April–October
🅰️⊕🔥♨️🔌⊙📶📺📶🔌⊙
⊙⚠️♨️◉

LESWALT

Dumfries and Galloway
Map ref 7B3

Drumlochart Caravan Park

⊖✓✓✓✓✓ Thistle Award
Member BH&HPA
Lochnaw, Leswalt, Stranraer,
Wigtownshire DG9 0RN
☎ (0177687) 232
Fax (0177687) 276
*From Stranraer take A718 to Leswalt.
In Leswalt turn left by church on
B7043, site on right in 1.7 miles (3km).
Signposted.*
8.8 hectares (22 acres). Level,
sloping, grassy, hard, sheltered.
30 touring pitches

30	🚐	£7.50—£10.00
30	🚍	£7.50—£10.00
8	🏠	£150.00—£300.00

72 units not for hire
Open March–October
⚡🅰️🅿️🔥♨️🔌⊙🛒🍴📶📺⚡💈🔌⊙
⚡⚠️➰🍴♨️

LINLITHGOW

Lothian
Map ref 7C2

Historic town west of Edinburgh
whose industries include electronics,
distilling and manufacturing. Close
by stand the ruins of Linlithgow
Palace, birthplace of Mary Queen of
Scots.
*Tourist Information Centre ☎ (01506)
844600*

Beecraigs Caravan Park

⊖✓✓✓✓✓
Linlithgow, West Lothian EH49 6PL
☎ (01506) 844516
Fax (01506) 847824
*From Linlithgow, follow Beecraigs
country park or international caravan
park signposts. Park is 2 miles south of
Linlithgow. From M8, follow B792.
Signposted.*
400 hectares (1000 acres). Level,
grassy, hard, sheltered.
56 touring pitches

36	🚐	£8.00—£9.00
36	🚍	£8.00—£9.00
20	⛺	£7.00—£8.00

🅿️⊕🔥♨️🔌⊙✖️🍴📺📶🔌⊙🔌⊙☂️
➰🍴✖️♨️

LOCHGILPHEAD

Strathclyde
Map ref 7B2

Harbour town at the head of Loch Gilphead.

Lochgilphead Caravan Park ⚐
⊖✓✓✓✓✓ Thistle Award
Member BH&HPA
Bank Park, Lochgilphead, Argyll
PA31 8NE
☎ (01546) 602003
Fax (01546) 603699
Adjacent to junction of A83/A816 within town of Lochgilphead. Signposted.
2.8 hectares (7 acres). Level, grassy, hard, sheltered.
40 touring pitches

30	⊞	£7.00—£9.00
30	⇞	£7.00—£9.00
10	▲	£7.00—£9.00
15	⊞	£120.00—£350.00

15 units not for hire
Open April—October
🚗🔲🅿🍴📶🛁🏕🔥📶🔌🅿🔥
⛰⛺🔌♿
🅰 See display advertisement on page 196

LOCHWINNOCH

Strathclyde
Map ref 7B2

Barnbrock Camping Site
⊖✓✓✓
Barnbrock Farm Kilbarchan, Lochwinnoch, Renfrewshire
PA10 2PZ
☎ Bridge-of-Weir (01505) 614791
M8 to A737 to A760 to B786. Approximately 4 miles on the B786 turn right at sign for Barnbrock Camping Site.
0.8 hectares (2 acres). Level, grassy, sheltered.
15 touring pitches

15	▲	£2.50

Open March—October
🅿🔥⚠🛁✖

> Map references apply to the colour maps at the back of this guide.

LOCKERBIE

Dumfries and Galloway
Map ref 7C3

Market town in the beautiful Valley of Annandale.

Hoddom Castle Caravan Park ⚐
⊖✓✓✓✓✓
Hoddom, Lockerbie, Dumfriesshire DG11 1BE
☎ Ecclefechan (01576) 300251
From A74 turn off at Ecclefechan. At church in village turn west onto B725 to Dalton. Entrance to site at Hoddom Bridge. 200 yards (182 m) from River Annan. Signposted.
11.2 hectares (28 acres). Level, sloping, grassy, hard, sheltered.
150 touring pitches

150	⊞	£6.50—£10.00
150	⇞	£6.50—£10.00
150	▲	£6.50—£10.00

Open April—October
🚗🔲🅿🔥🛁⚠🔌🅿🔌🍴✖🍴📶🔥
⛰⛺⛰⛰🔍🎣🏕🍴⛺
🅰 See display advertisement on page 196

LOSSIEMOUTH

Grampian
Map ref 8C3

Fishing port and holiday resort with good sands and excellent golf course.

Silver Sands Leisure Park
⊖✓✓✓✓ Thistle Award
Member BH&HPA/NCC
Covesea West Beach, Lossiemouth, Morayshire IV31 6SP
☎ (01343) 813262
Fax (01343) 815205
A941 from Elgin to Lossiemouth. Turn left on the B9135 past the RAF camp, then take the B9040 towards Hopeman. The caravan park is situated beside the lighthouse. Signposted.
22.8 hectares (57 acres). Level, grassy.
140 touring pitches

140	⊞	£7.50—£10.75
140	⇞	£7.50—£10.75
140	▲	£7.50—£10.75
50	⊞	£95.00—£440.00

130 units not for hire
Open April—October
🚗🔲🅿🔥🛁⚠🔌🅿🔌🍴✖🍴📺📶🔥
⛰☉🔍⛰🎣🎵♫☎

LUNDIN LINKS

Fife
Map ref 7C1

Golfing resort with good sands.

Woodland Gardens Caravan and Camping Site ⚐
⊖✓✓✓
Member BH&HPA
Lundin Links KY8 5QG
☎ Upper Largo (01333) 360319
Turn north off the A915 at the east end of Lundin Links (0.5 miles). Signposted on the A915 by international camping/caravanning signs.
0.4 hectares (1 acres). Level, grassy, hard, sheltered.
20 touring pitches

20	⊞	£6.60—£6.60
20	⇞	£6.60—£6.60
10	▲	£6.60—£6.60
4	⊞	£95.00—£240.00

Open March—October
🚗🅿🅿🔥🛁⚠🔌🅿🔌📺📶🔥🚗
☉🔍⛰🏕

MUSSELBURGH

Lothian
Map ref 7C2

Drum Mohr Caravan Park ⚐
⊖✓✓✓✓✓✓
Member BH&HPA/NCC
Levenhall, Musselburgh, Edinburgh EH21 8JS
☎ (0131) 665 6867
Fax (0131) 653 6859
From south on A1, take A199 Musselburgh, then B1361. Follow park signs. From the west on the A1, come off at Wallyford slip road and follow Caravan Park and Mining Museum signs.
4 hectares (10 acres). Level, grassy, hard, sheltered.
120 touring pitches

120	⊞	£8.00—£9.00
40	⇞	£8.00—£9.00
60	▲	£8.00—£9.00

Continued ▶

MUSSELBURGH

Continued

Open March–October

🚐 🎪 ⊙ ʀ ♨ ⚑ ⚙ ᗢ ⚡ 🛒 📶 🚫 🛒 ⊙
⚠ ⚐
Ad See display advertisement on this page

NAIRN

Highland
Map ref 8C3

Royal Burgh, county town and popular holiday resort on the southern shore of the Moray Firth and at the mouth of the River Nairn.

Spindrift Caravan & Camping Park M

⊙✓✓✓✓✓
Member BH&HPA
Little Kildrummie, Nairn,
Invernesshire IV12 5QU
☎ (01667) 453992
From Nairn take B9090 south for 1.5 miles. Turn right at sharp left hand bend signposted Little Kildrummie, onto unclassified road, site is 400 yards on the left. Signposted.
1.2 hectares (3 acres). Level, grassy, sheltered.
40 touring pitches

40	🚐	£5.50—£7.50
40	🚏	£5.50—£7.50
40	⛺	£5.50—£7.50

Open April–October

🚐 ⊙ ʀ ♨ ⚑ ⚙ ᗢ 📶 🚫 🛒 ⊙ ∪ ⊚

NORTH BERWICK

Lothian
Map ref 7D2

Holiday resort on the Firth of Forth with sandy beaches, golf and a picturesque harbour.
Tourist Information Centre ☎ *(01620) 892197*

Tantallon Caravan Park

⊙✓✓✓✓✓ Thistle Award
Member BH&HPA
Dunbar Road, North Berwick, East Lothian EH39 5NJ
☎ (01620) 893348
Fax (01620) 895623
From North Berwick take A198 towards Dunbar. Situated on east side of town overlooking golf course and Firth of Forth. From A1 turn onto A198 3 miles west of Dunbar. Signposted.
Level, sloping, grassy.
200 touring pitches

140	🚐	£6.50—£10.00
140	🚏	£6.50—£10.00
140	⛺	£6.50—£10.00
7	🏠	£125.00—£360.00

15 units not for hire
Open March–December
Cards accepted: Access, Visa
🚐 🎪 ʀ ♨ ⚑ ⚙ ᗢ ⚡ 🛒 📺 📶 🚫 🛒 ⊙
🔍 ⚠ 🏊 ⚑ 🛒
Ad See display advertisement on page 197

> Please check prices and other details at the time of booking.

OBAN

Strathclyde
Map ref 7B1

The leading resort on the Highland coast, situated on a sheltered bay which is almost landlocked by the Isle of Kerrera. Comparatively modern town dominated by McCaig's Folly. Centre for touring by land and sea and the starting point for many steamer cruises to the Western Isles.
Tourist Information Centre ☎ *(01631) 563122*

Oban Caravan & Camping Park

⊙✓✓✓✓
Gallanachmore Farm, Gallanach Road, Oban, Argyll PA34 4QH
☎ (01631) 562425
Fax (01631) 566624
Follow signs to Gallanach from Oban town centre roundabout. Park situated beside the sea 2.5 miles (4km) from Oban, 300 yards past Oban Marine Centre on left. Signposted.
2.44 hectares (6.09 acres). Level, sloping, grassy, hard, sheltered.
200 touring pitches

30	🚐	£7.00—£8.00
20	🚏	£7.00—£8.00
150	⛺	£7.00—£8.00
10	🏠	£150.00—£290.00

Open April–September

🚐 🎪 ʀ ♨ ⚑ ⚙ ᗢ 🛒 📶 🚫 🛒 ⊙ ⊙ 🔍
⚠ 🏊 🛒

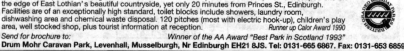

PEEBLES

Borders
Map ref 7C2

County capital and market town in the Tweed Valley. A favourite holiday centre popular with anglers.

Rosetta Caravan and Camping Park
⊖✓✓✓✓✓
Member NCC
Rosetta Road, Peebles EH45 8PG
☎ (01721) 720770
Travelling west from centre of Peebles on A72, turn right in town onto unclassified road signposted Rosetta. Site 0.5 miles (1km) on left. Signposted.
10.8 hectares (27 acres). Grassy.
130 touring pitches

100	🚐	£8.25—£9.00
100	🚏	£8.25—£9.00
30	⛺	£6.00—£7.00
5	🏠	£130.00—£190.00

Open April—October

🔲🪑🛱🔥🛁♿🚻🍴📞🏪🎣🚿 🚌☺️🔍⛰️ 🚽🅿️

PITLOCHRY

Tayside
Map ref 7C1

A favourite holiday resort and touring centre in the valley of the Tummel. Points of interest are Pitlochry Dam and Salmon Ladder.
Tourist Information Centre ☎ (01796) 472215 or 472751

Milton of Fonab Caravan Site
⊖✓✓✓✓ Thistle Award
Member BH&HPA
Pitlochry, Perthshire PH16 5NA
☎ (01796) 472882
Fax (01796) 474363
Off A9 0.5 miles (1km) south of Pitlochry opposite distillery. Signposted.
6 hectares (15 acres). Level, grassy, sheltered.
154 touring pitches

114	🚐	£8.50—£9.00
15	🚏	£8.50—£9.00
25	⛺	£8.50—£9.00
36	🏠	£240.00—£340.00

Open March—October

🚗🔌🪑🛱🔥🛁♿🚻🍴📞🏪🚿 🚌☺️♪ 🛁

PORT SETON

Lothian
Map ref 7C2

Seton Sands Holiday Village 🏕
⊖✓✓✓✓ Thistle Award
Member BH&HPA/NCC
Longniddry, East Lothian EH32 0QF
☎ Reservations/free brochure
(01442) 248668
Fax (01442) 232459
Turn off A1 at Tranent roundabout onto B6371 for Cockenzie, then right onto B1348. The park is 1 mile along on the right. Signposted.
Level, grassy.
60 touring pitches

60	🚐	£7.15—£17.60
60	🚏	£7.15—£17.60
	🏠	£99.00—£439.00

Open March—October
Cards accepted: Access, Visa, Switch/Delta

🚗🅿️🔌🪑🔥🛁♿🚻🍴📞🏪🚿🍴📺📞🍴 🛒☺️⛰️🔄🍴🎣📵
[Ad] See display advertisement inside front cover

PORTPATRICK

Dumfries and Galloway
Map ref 7B3

Summer resort with a picturesque harbour, fine sands and striking cliff scenery.

Galloway Point Holiday Park
⊖✓✓✓✓ Thistle Award
Member BH&HPA/NCC
Portpatrick, Stranraer, Wigtownshire DG9 9AA
☎ (01776) 810 561
Fax (01776) 810 561
A77 from north, A75 from Gretna. First left after war memorial for 0.5 miles. Park is on the right. Signposted.
7.2 hectares (18 acres). Level, sloping, grassy, hard, sheltered.
40 touring pitches

40	🚐	£9.00—£12.00
10	🚏	£9.00—£12.00
40	⛺	£7.00—£12.00
5	🏠	£175.00—£290.00

60 units not for hire
Open March—October

🚗🔌🪑🛱🔥🛁♿🚻🍴📞🏪✕🍴📺📞🛁 ☺️🍴🚽🅿️

ST ANDREWS

Fife
Map ref 7C1

Historic university city known to golfers world-wide as the home of the Royal and Ancient Club. Old harbour, priory and 13th C castle.
Tourist Information Centre ☎ (01334) 472021

Craigtoun Meadows Holiday Park 🏕
⊖✓✓✓✓✓ Thistle Award
Member BH&HPA
Mount Melville, St Andrews KY16 8PQ
☎ St Andrews (01334) 475959
Fax (01334) 476424
From M90 junction 8 take A91 to St Andrews. Turn right 436 yards (400m) after Guardbridge, sign Strathkinness. Turn left at second crossroads after Strathkinness. Signposted.
12.8 hectares (32 acres). Level, sloping, grassy, hard, sheltered.
98 touring pitches

98	🚐	£11.75—£17.75
98	🚏	£11.75—£17.75
98	⛺	£9.50—£12.75
30	🏠	£145.00—£395.00

111 units not for hire
Open March—October
Cards accepted: Access, Visa, Switch/Delta

🛢️🚗🅿️🔌🪑🔥🛁♿🚻🍴✕🍴📺📞🛁 ☺️🔍⛰️🔄🍴

ST CYRUS

Grampian
Map ref 7D1

East Bowstrips Caravan Park 🏕
⊖✓✓✓✓✓
Member BH&HPA
St Cyrus, Montrose, Kincardineshire DD10 0DE
☎ St Cyrus (01674) 850328
Enter St Cyrus village on A92. From south: pass St Cyrus Hotel, first left, second right. From north: enter St Cyrus, first right, second right. Signposted.
1.6 hectares (4 acres). Level, sloping, grassy, hard, sheltered.
30 touring pitches

Continued ▶

ST CYRUS

Continued

30	🚐	£6.50—£7.50	
30	🚎	£6.50—£7.50	
20	⛺	£3.50—£7.50	
3	🏚	£199.00	

16 units not for hire
Open April–October

🚐P🔲🅿💧📶🔥♨️🚰🛒🧺📶🗑️ ⚡ 🔌
☺⚠♨

SANDHEAD

Dumfries and Galloway
Map ref 7B3

Sands of Luce Caravan Park
⊖✓✓✓✓
Member BH&HPA
Sandhead, Stranraer, Wigtownshire
DG9 9JR
☎ (01776) 830456
*From Stranraer take A77 to the A716
for 7 miles (11km) entrance to site off
A716, 1 mile past village of Stoneykirk.
Signposted.*
4.8 hectares (12 acres). Level,
sloping, grassy.
46 touring pitches

26	🚐	£6.50—£8.00	
10	🚎	£6.00—£7.50	
10	⛺	£6.50—£8.00	
8	🏚	£125.00—£260.00	

26 units not for hire
Open March–October

🚐🔲🅿💧📶🔥♨️🚰🛒🧺📶🗑️ ⚡ 🔌☺⚠
♨

SANDYHILLS

Dumfries and Galloway
Map ref 7C3

Location on Sandyhills Bay with easy
access to Castle Douglas.

Sandyhills Bay Leisure Park
⊖✓✓✓✓✓ Thistle Award
Member BH&HPA/NCC
Sandyhills, Dalbeattie,
Kirkcudbrightshire
☎ Southwick (01387) 780257
*From Dalbeattie, take A710 to
Sandyhills (approx. 6 miles). Park is on
the right hand side just past the golf
course. Signposted.*
Level, grassy, sheltered.
30 touring pitches

30	🚐	£6.75—£9.95	
30	🚎	£6.75—£9.95	
30	⛺	£6.75—£9.95	
12	🏚	£120.00—£305.00	

18 units not for hire
Open April–October

🚐🔲🅿💧📶🔥♨️🚰🛒🧺📶🗑️ ⚡ 🔌☺⚠
▸⚠🗂️

SELKIRK

Borders
Map ref 7C2

County capital and Royal Burgh set
in the heart of Scott country. An
ideal centre for exploring the
border country.

Angecroft Caravan Park
⊖✓✓✓✓
Member BH&HPA
Ettrick Valley, Selkirk TD7 5HY
☎ Ettrick Valley (01750) 62251 &
Peebles (01721) 730657
*From M6 junction 44 at Carlisle, take
A7 to Langholm and then B709 to
caravan park. From Selkirk, take B7009
then B709 to caravan park.*
2 hectares (5 acres). Level, grassy,
sheltered.
4 touring pitches

4	🚐	£7.00—£8.55	
4	🚎	£7.00—£8.55	
4	⛺	£4.00—£8.55	
4	🏚	£95.00—£215.00	

39 units not for hire
Open March–October

🚐🅿🔲💧📶🔥♨️🚰🛒🧺📶🗑️ ⚡ 🔌☺
🔌🏊♨🗂️

SHIELBRIDGE

Highland
Map ref 8B3

Morvich Caravan Club Site
⊖✓✓✓✓✓
Shielbridge, Kyle of Lochalsh,
Ross-shire IV40 8HQ
☎ Glenshiel (01599) 511354
*From Loch Duich take A87 then turn
into unclassified road signposted
Morvich. After 1 mile turn into side
road. Signposted.*
2 hectares (5 acres). Level, grassy,
hard.
106 touring pitches

82	🚐	£9.50—£11.50	
82	🚎	£7.20—£8.70	
24	⛺		

Open March–October
Cards accepted: Access, Visa

🔲📶💧📶🔥♨️📺📶🗑️ ⚡ 🔌☺🔌🏊
♨

The symbols in each entry
give information about
services and facilities.
A 'key' to these symbols
appears at the back
of this guide.

SKELMORLIE

Strathclyde
Map ref 7B2

Firth of Clyde resort opposite Bute.

Mains Caravan Park
⊖✓✓
Skelmorlie Mains, Skelmorlie,
Ayrshire PA17 5EU
☎ Wemyss Bay (01475) 520794
Fax (01475) 520794
*Off A78, 4 miles north of Largs.
Signposted.*
96 hectares (240 acres). Level,
sloping, grassy, stony, hard, sheltered.
96 touring pitches

26	🚐	£7.00—£8.00	
26	🚎	£6.00—£7.00	
70	⛺	£6.00—£7.00	
10	🏚	£175.00—£300.00	

72 units not for hire
Open March–October

🔥🚐P🔲🅿💧📶🔥♨️🚰🛒🧺📺📶🗑️
☺🔌🥤♨

SOUTHERNESS

Dumfries and Galloway
Map ref 7C3

Southerness Holiday Village
⊖✓✓✓✓
Member BH&HPA/NCC
Southerness, Dumfries DG2 8AZ
☎ Kirkbean (0138788) 256 &
281/278
*From Dumfries take A710 for 15 miles
(24km) towards Southerness. Park just
after village of Kirkbean. Signposted.*
24 hectares (60 acres). Level, grassy.
250 touring pitches

250	🚐	£6.00—£7.50	
50	🏚	£70.00—£225.00	

250 units not for hire
Open March–October

🚐🔲🅿💧📶🔥♨️🚰🛒🧺❌🍽️📶🗑️ ⚡ 🔌☺
🥤⚠🔔🎵♨

SPEY BAY

Grampian
Map ref 8D3

Spey Bay Caravan Park
⊖✓✓✓✓
Fochabers, Spey Bay, Fochabers,
Morayshire IV32 7PJ
☎ Fochabers (01343) 820424
*At Fochabers turn off A96 to Spey Bay
then follow road to sea front, site
adjoins hotel grounds. Signposted.*
1.2 hectares (3 acres). Level, grassy.
30 touring pitches

20	🚐	£6.50—£6.50	
5	🚎		
5	⛺		

5 units not for hire
Open April–October
Cards accepted: Access, Visa

P 🏪 🛉 ⚴ ⚲ ⚡ ✕ ⚑ 📺 🚽 🖼 ⏚ 🔥 ☺ 🔍
⚠ ◔ ₱

Grampian
Map ref 8D3

Drummie Hill Caravan Park

⊖✓✓✓✓

Tarland, Aboyne, Aberdeenshire
AB34 4UP
☎ (013398) 81388 & 81264
Enter Tarland on B9119. Turn left at
bridge. Continue for 600 yards,
signposted park on left.
3.2 hectares (8 acres). Level, grassy,
hard.
30 touring pitches

30	🚐	£8.00—£8.00
30	🚃	£8.00—£8.00
15	⛺	£4.00—£8.00
6	🏠	£120.00—£180.00

57 units not for hire
Open April–October

🔌 P 🖼 ⚑ 🏪 🛉 ⚴ ⚡ ⚲ 🖼 🚽 ⏚ 🔥 ☺ 🔍 ⚠ ∪ 🔥

Highland
Map ref 8B2

Picturesque fishing village and
holiday resort on a promontory in
sheltered Loch Broom. Glorious
scenery, angling and boating.

Ardmair Point Caravan Park

⊖✓✓✓✓

Member BH&HPA
Ardmair Point, Ullapool, Ross-shire
IV26 2TN
☎ (01854) 612054
Fax (01854) 612757
From south turn right at the entrance
of Ullapool. Proceed north on the A835
for 3 miles and enter site at telephone
kiosk. Signposted.
2 hectares (5 acres). Level, grassy.
45 touring pitches

45	🚐	£6.50—£8.00
45	🚃	£6.50—£8.00
45	⛺	£6.50—£8.00

Open April, June–September

🔌 🔌 🏪 🛉 ⚴ ⚡ ⚲ ✕ 🖼 🚽 🔥 🔥 ☺
✶

Broomfield Holiday Park

⊖✓✓✓

Member BH&HPA
Shore Street, Ullapool, Ross-shire
IV26 2SX
☎ (01854) 612020
In Ullapool, turn 2nd right past
Harbour. Signposted.
4.4 hectares (11 acres). Level, grassy.
140 touring pitches

140	🚐	£8.00—£9.50
140	🚃	£7.50—£9.00
140	⛺	£4.00—£9.50

Open April–September and
Christmas

🖼 🏪 🛉 ⚴ ⚡ ⚲ 🔥 🔥 ⏚ ☺ ⚠
[Ad] See display advertisement on this
page

Strathclyde
Map ref 7B2

Wemyss Bay Holiday Park ⚠

⊖✓✓✓✓ Thistle Award
Member BH&HPA/NCC
Wemyss Bay, Renfrewshire
☎ Reservations/free brochure
(01442) 248668
Fax (01442) 232459
From Glasgow follow the M8 to
Greenock and take the A78 to Wemyss
Bay. Entrance opposite railway station
and Wemyss Bay Ferry terminal.
Signposted.
Steep, terraced, hillside.

60	🏠	£109.00—£455.00

480 units not for hire
Open March–October
Cards accepted: Access, Visa,
Switch/Delta

P ⚲ ✕ ⚑ 🖼 🚽 🔥 🔥 ⚠ 🎵 ♫ ₱ ⚴ T
[Ad] See display advertisement inside
front cover

USE YOUR *i*'s

There are more than 550
Tourist Information Centres
throughout England offering friendly
help with accommodation and
holiday ideas as well as
suggestions of places to visit
and things to do. There may well be
a centre in your home town which
can help you before you set out.
You'll find the address of your
nearest Tourist Information Centre
in your local Phone Book.

AT-A-GLANCE SYMBOLS

Symbols at the end of each accommodation entry
give useful information about services
and facilities. A key to symbols can be found
inside the back cover flap.

Keep this open for easy reference.

CHECK THE MAPS

The colour maps at the back of this guide show
all the cities, towns and villages for which you will
find accommodation entries.

Refer to the town index to find the page
on which it is listed.

WALES

The poignant sound of a Welsh male voice choir bears eloquent testimony to the beauty of Wales. A land of myth and music, rugged coastline and towering mountains, this proud country is most famous for its castles - from Harlech Castle to the historic Caernarfon, built more than 600 years ago. Rich in culture and craft, Wales has many Areas of Outstanding Natural Beauty while the legacy of Britain's Industrial Revolution is still clearly visible in mill and pit alike. Road conditions for towing are good, and the road network comprehensive. There are many parks on the coast, and some in the National Parks themselves.

WALES
For more information on Wales, contact:
Wales Tourist Board
Brunel House, 2 Fitzalan Road,
Cardiff CF2 1UY
Tel: (01222) 499909 Fax: (01222) 485031

Where to Go in Wales – see pages 202-207
Where to Stay in Wales – see pages 208-217

WALES

Where to Go and What to See

You will find hundreds of interesting places to visit during your stay in Wales, just some of which are listed in these pages. The number against each name will help you locate it on the map (page 207). Contact any Tourist Information Centre in the region for more ideas on days out in Wales.

1 Anglesey Sea Zoo
Brynsiencyn, Isle of Anglesey,
Gwynedd LL61 6TQ
Tel: (01248) 430411
Countless fish and other sea creatures swim above, alongside and below you. See the Wave and Touch Tanks and the Kelp Forest exhibition. Free adventure playground.

2 Plas Newydd
Llanfairpwll,
Isle of Anglesey,
Gwynedd LL61 6EQ
Tel: (01248) 714795
An elegant 18thC mansion in lovely grounds. Military museum. Rex Whistler exhibition, including his largest wall painting.

3 Pili Palas/Butterfly and Bird Palace
Ffordd Penmynydd,
Menai Bridge,
Isle of Anglesey,
Gwynedd LL59 5RP
Tel: (01248) 712474
Step into a steamy, tropical jungle full of exotic butterflies from all over the world. Also see the collections of birds, snakes and lizards.

4 Beaumaris Castle
Beaumaris,
Isle of Anglesey,
Gwynedd LL58 8AP
Tel: (01248) 810361
Begun in 1295 but never completed, Beaumaris was the last of the castles built by Edward I to control the Welsh.

5 Museum of Childhood
1 Castle Street,
Beaumaris,
Isle of Anglesey,
Gwynedd LL58 8AP
Tel: (01248) 712498
Displays include teddy bears and nursery furniture, money boxes, clockwork toys, bicycles, an art gallery of pictures of children at work and play and educational toys. Audio-visual room.

6 Conwy Castle
Conwy,
Gwynedd LL32 8AY
Tel: (01492) 592358
A masterpiece of medieval architecture, Conwy Castle was built between 1283 and 1289. See the perfect scale model of the castle and town as it may have appeared in 1312.

7 Welsh Mountain Zoo
Colwyn Bay LL28 5UY
Tel: (01492) 532938
The Welsh Mountain Zoo stands in a 37-acre estate. Enjoy the Jungle Adventureland and Tarzan Trail activity area. Chimpanzee World with unique Chimp Encounter.

8 Penrhyn Castle
Nr Bangor,
Gwynedd LL57 4HN
Tel: (01248) 353084
An impressive neo-Norman castle by Thomas Hopper, who also designed the magnificent interior decoration and much of the

furniture. See the important collection of old master pictures. Industrial railway museum.

9 Caernarfon Air Museum
Caernarfon Airport,
Dinas Dinlle, Caernarfon,
Gwynedd LL54 5TP
Tel: (01286) 830800
Climb into the cockpits of planes and helicopters and take the controls of a flight simulator. Continuous film plus exhibitions.

10 Caernarfon Castle
Caernarfon, Gwynedd LL55 2AY
Tel: (01286) 677617
Attractions include the Royal Welch Fusiliers Museum and the Prince of Wales Exhibition.

11 Llanberis Lake Railway
Padarn Country Park,
Llanberis, Gwynedd LL55 4TY
Tel: (01286) 870549
This historic narrow-gauge line runs for two miles along the shores of beautiful Llyn Padarn in the heart of Snowdonia.

12 Snowdon Mountain Railway
Llanberis,
Gwynedd LL55 4TY
Tel: (01286) 870223
Opened in 1896, the railway runs on the north-west slope of the highest mountain in England and

Wales. The upper terminus is over 1,000 metres above sea level giving spectacular views.

13 Erddig Hall
Nr Wrexham LL13 0YT
Tel: (01978) 355314
17thC house with a splendid collection of 18thC furniture, ceramics and textiles. Visit the joiner's shop, smithy, stables, vintage cars, bakehouse, laundry, kitchen, housekeeper's room, servants' hall and the walled gardens.

14 Gloddfa Ganol Slate Mine
Blaenau Ffestiniog,
Gwynedd LL41 3NB
Tel: (01766) 830704
Walk into the enormous underground chambers blasted out of the mountains by miners working the slate cliffs by candlelight. Visit the working slate mill, railway centre, exhibition hall, winding house, miners' cottages and museums.

15 Llechwedd Slate Caverns
Blaenau Ffestiniog,
Gwynedd LL41 3NB
Tel: (01766) 830306
The Miners' Tramway and Deep Mine take you through floodlit tunnels and caverns where Victorian working conditions are re-created. Attractions include demonstrations

of slate engraving, a smithy, slate mill, Victorian shops, bank and police station.

16 Criccieth Castle
Criccieth, Gwynedd LL52 0DP
Tel: (01766) 522227
Established about 1230 by Llywelyn the Great, the castle is perched on a rocky peninsula.

17 Ffestiniog Railway
Porthmadog, Gwynedd LL49 9NF
Tel: (01766) 512340
Steam engines, including the unique Double Fairlei type, haul both historic and modern corridor carriages, with 1st and 3rd class, licensed buffet and observation cars.

18 Portmeirion Italianate Village
Penrhyndeudraeth,
Gwynedd LL48 6ER
Tel: (01766) 770228
A fantasy village built by Sir Clough Williams Ellis between 1925 and 1972, consisting of colourwashed buildings, fountains, statues, columns and fake facades, more reminiscent of Italy than Wales.

19 Harlech Castle
Harlech, Gwynedd LL46 2YH
Tel: (01766) 780552
One of the 'iron ring' fortresses built 1283-89. Its imposing, twin-towered

gatehouse now contains an exhibition entitled 'A Castle and its People'.

20 Bala Lake Railway
The Station, Llanuwchllyn,
Bala, Gwynedd LL23 7DD
Tel: (01678) 540666
A delightfull nine-mile return journey by narrow-gauge steam train along the shores of Llyn Tegid (Bala Lake) and through part of the beautiful Snowdonia National Park.

21 Coed Y Brenin Visitor Centre
Nr Ganllwyd, Gwynedd LL40 2HY
Tel: (01341) 440666
Over 50 miles of walks, picnic sites, an arboretum, nature reserve and visitor centre. The centre includes displays featuring wildlife, geology and gold mining, and an audio-visual show.

22 The Talyllyn Railway and Narrow Gauge Railway Museum
Wharf Station, Tywyn,
Gwynedd LL36 9EY
Tel: (01654) 710472
Steam trains, about half main line size, run on a narrow-gauge single line. The Narrow Gauge Railway Museum houses a display of locomotives, wagons, signals and other rescued items.

23 Corris Craft Centre
Corris, Nr Machynlleth,
Powys SY20 9SP
Tel: (01654) 761249
You can see a variety of fascinating crafts being practised by skilled workers and buy their quality gifts and crafts, including pyrography by the country's leading exponent.

24 Powis Castle
Nr Welshpool SY21 8RF
Tel: (01938) 554336
The ancestral home of the Herbert family since 1587. Attractions include the Clive of India collection of Indian treasure and unique 18th century garden.

25 Centre For Alternative Technology
Machynlleth,
Powys SY20 9AZ
Tel: (01654) 702400
The Centre's work is based on the principles of conservation and care for the Earth's resources. Water-powered cliff railway, wind, water and solar-powered exhibits, organic gardens, wave power and Britain's best insulated house.

26 Vale of Rheidol Railway
Park Avenue,
Aberystwyth,
Powys SY23 1PG
Tel: (01970) 625819
First opened in 1902, the line clings to the hillside, offering spectacular views as it climbs to Devil's Bridge, where you'll find superb walks, deep gorges and waterfalls.

27 Elan Valley Visitor Centre
Elan Village,
Rhayader,
Powys LD6 5HP
Tel: (01597) 810898
The spectacular Elan Valley lakes are the most scenic reservoirs in Mid Wales. The centre houses interesting exhibitions on wildlife, water, farming and history.

28 Cambrian Woollen Mill
Llanwrtyd Wells,
Powys LD5 4SD
Tel: (01591) 610211
Manufacturers of Welsh flannels. All processes from wool dyeing to the woven cloth can be seen. 'Welsh Wool Experience' educational tours for all the family. Large shop.

29 Museum of the Welsh Woollen Industry
Dre-fach Felindre,
Llandysul SA44 5UP
Tel: (01559) 370929
Dre-fach Felindre was once one of the busiest wool producing areas in Wales. The museum houses working exhibitions tracing woollen cloth from fleece to fabric. Also craft workshops, an extensive collection of tools and equipment, and shop.

30 Llangloffan Farmhouse Cheese Centre
Castle Morris,
Nr Fishguard,
Pembrokeshire SA62 5ET
Tel: (01348) 891241
Cheeses are made by hand from the milk of the farm's own herd of cows. The three stages of cheese making are demonstrated each morning. Visitors are also welcome to stroll around the farm.

31 Oakwood Park
Canaston Bridge, Narberth,
Pembrokeshire SA67 8DF
Tel: (01834) 891373
*Wales' top theme park set in 80
acres of beautiful Pembrokeshire
countryside. Action-packed day out
with exciting rides and attractions
for all ages. Superb value
all-inclusive entrance price.*

32 Pembroke Castle
Pembroke SA71 4LA
Tel: (01646) 681510
*The walls enclose a large inner
ward and the Great Keep, nearly
80 foot high. One of the smaller
towers is said to be the birthplace
of Harri Tudur, who became Henry
VII, first of the Tudors.*

**33 Manor House Wildlife and
Leisure Park**
St Florence, Nr Tenby,
Pembrokeshire SA70 8RJ
Tel: (01646) 651201
*A 12-acre wooded park with birds,
animals, aquarium, reptiles, model
railway exhibition, falconry
demonstrations, beautifull gardens
with floral displays, childrens' play
area with go-karts and giant slide.*

34 Folly Farm
Begelly, Kilgetty,
Pembrokeshire SA68 0XA
Tel: (01834) 812731
*Experience a 200-acre dairy farm
at work. See the milking parlour in
action. Hand-milk a cow or
bottle-feed a young animal and see
the museum of dairying bygones.*

35 Pembrey Country Park
Pembrey SA16 0EJ
Tel: (01554) 833913
*A 520-acre park Blue Flag and
Premier Seaside Award winner
1992. Forest walks, dry ski slope,
birdwatching, play areas, picnic
sites, pony trekking and a
narrow-gauge railway.*

36 Dan-Yr-Ogog Showcaves
Abercraf, Glyntawe,
Swansea SA9 1GJ
Tel: (01639) 730284
*Situated within the splendour of the
Brecon Beacons National Park,
Dan-yr-Ogof is probably the most
spectacular series of showcaves in
the country with the largest and
longest chambers in Britain.*

**37 Swansea Maritime and
Industrial Museum**
Maritime Quarter,
Swansea SA1 1SN
Tel: (01792) 650351
*Boat and transport displays; also a
fully operational woollen mill.
Lightship, steam tug, etc moored on
the quayside. Tram shed annexe
dedicated to first passenger-carrying
railway, the Mumbles Railway.*

38 Penscynor Wildlife Park
Cilfrew,
Nr Neath SA10 8LF
Tel: (01639) 642189
*An exciting day out for all the
family. Among the trees, ponds and
streams are tropical birds, monkeys
and free-flying parrots. Also
sea-lions, penguins and
chimpanzees.*

**39 Brecon Beacons Mountain
Centre**
Libanus, Nr Brecon,
Powys LD3 8ER
Tel: (01874) 623366
*The best starting point for
any exploration of the Brecon
Beacons National Park.*

40 Margam Park
Port Talbot SA13 2TJ
Tel: (01639) 881635
*800 acres of parkland and forest
with adventure playground, boating,
pony rides, Fairytale Land, maze,
farm trail, road train, castle and
abbey ruins and audio-visual
display.*

**41 Afan Argoed Countryside
Centre**
Afan Forest Park,
Cynonville,
Port Talbot SA12 9LL
Tel: (01639) 850564
*The park occupies a mountainside,
which visitors can explore via ten
way-marked and guided walks. The
Welsh Miners' Museum features
the life and times of the South
Wales miner.*

42 Brecon Mountain Railway
Pant Station, Dowlais,
Nr Merthyr Tydfil CF48 2UP
Tel: (01685) 722988
*One of Wales' 'Great Little Trains',
this narrow-gauge line runs for two
miles from its terminus at Pant to a
scenic lakeside halt in the foothills
of the Beacons.*

43 Big Pit
Blaenafon NP4 9XP
Tel: (01495) 790311
*Big Pit closed as a working colliery
in 1980, exactly 100 years after it
first produced coal. The pit is now a
museum where visitors can discover
how miners worked and lived.*

44 Tintern Abbey
Tintern NP8 1RF
Tel: (01291) 689251
*The impressive ruins of Tintern
Abbey are set against the green
wooded slopes of the Wye Valley.*

45 Caerleon Roman Fortress
High Street, Caerleon,
Nr Newport NP6 1AE
Tel: (01633) 422518
*See the remains of the fortress
baths, the amphitheatre and the
barracks with explanatory displays.
Also Roman Legionary Museum.*

46 Tredegar House
Newport NP1 9YW
Tel: (01633) 815880
Magnificent 17thC mansion.

Dazzling state rooms. Craft workshops, gardens and 17thC stable block with orangery.

47 Caerphilly Castle
Caerphilly CF8 1JL
Tel: (01222) 883143
One of the greatest surviving medieval castles of the western world. Its famous leaning tower outleans that of Pisa.

48 The Rhondda Heritage Park
Lewis Merthyr,
Coed-Cae Road,
Trehafod CF37 7NP
Tel: (01443) 682036
On the former Lewis Merthyr and Ty-Mawr colliery site, the multi-media Black Gold exhibition offers insight into the lives of miners and their families.

49 Castell Coch
Tongwynlais,
Nr Cardiff
Tel: (01222) 810101
A mix of Gothic fantasy and timeless fairytale.

50 Cardiff Castle
Cardiff CF1 2RB
Tel: (01222) 822083
A blend of genuine ruins - Roman wall, Norman stone keep - and Victorian fantasy. 1st The Queen's Dragoon Guards and Welch Regiment Museums.

51 Museum of Welsh Life
St Fagans,
Cardiff CF5 6XB
Tel: (01222) 569441
The heritage of Wales' rural life is displayed in a vast collection of authentically erected buildings where Welsh people have lived and worked. Crafts people demonstrate traditional skills.

52 National Museum and Gallery
Cathays Park,
Cardiff CF1 3NP
Tel: (01222) 397951
The story of Wales from the earliest times. Re-created prehistoric scenes, dinosaur and mammoth skeletons and lively displays of animal and plant life capture children's imaginations. Superb art collection including Impressionist and post-Impressionist, silver and ceramics, coins, medals and shells.

53 Techniquest
Stuart Street,
Cardiff CF1 6BW
Tel: (01222) 475475
World-renowned 'hands-on' science and technology centre. Lots of fascinating models and exhiblts for visitors to touch, feel and experience.

54 Welsh Industrial and Maritime Museum
Bute Street,
Cardiff CF1 6AN
Tel: (01222) 481919
An imaginative complex, part of the National Museum of Wales, telling the story of industry and transport in Wales: steam engines, a huge colliery ventilating fan, early cars, bikes, shipping gallery and railway exhibits.

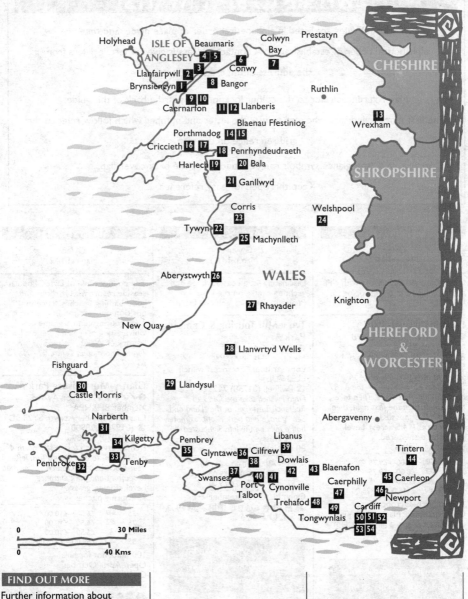

Holyhead

ISLE OF ANGLESEY

Beaumaris

Colwyn Bay

Prestatyn

Llanfairpwll 2 3

Brynsiengyn 1 4 5

6 Conwy

7

CHESHIRE

8 Bangor

Ruthlin

9 10

Caernarfon

11 12 Llanberis

Blaenau Ffestiniog

13

Wrexham

Porthmadog 14 15

Criccieth 16 17

18 Penrhyndeudraeth

Harlech 19

20 Bala

SHROPSHIRE

21 Ganllwyd

Corris

23

Welshpool

24

Tywyn 22

25 Machynlleth

Aberystwyth 26

WALES

27 Rhayader

Knighton

New Quay

28 Llanwrtyd Wells

HEREFORD & WORCESTER

Fishguard

29 Llandysul

30

Castle Morris

Narberth

Abergavenny

31

Kilgetty

Pembrey

Libanus

33 34

35

Glyntawe 36 Cilfrew 39

Tintern

Tenby

38 Dowlais

44

Pembroke 32

37

40 41

Cynonville

42

43 Blaenafon

45 Caerleon

Swansea

Port Talbot

Caerphilly

46

Trehafod 48

47

Newport

49

Cardiff

Tongwynlais

50 51 52

53 54

0   30 Miles

0   40 Kms

FIND OUT MORE

Further information about holidays and attractions in Wales is available from:

Wales Tourist Board,
Brunel House, 2 Fitzalan Road,
Cardiff CF2 1UY.
Tel: (01222) 499909
Fax: (01222) 485031

WHERE TO STAY (WALES)

Parks in Wales are listed in alphabetical order of place name, and then in alphabetical order of establishment. A contact address is given where it differs from the address of the establishment.

Map references refer to the colour location maps at the back of this guide.

The first number indicates the map to use; the letter and number which follow refer to the grid reference on the map.

At-a-glance symbols can be found inside the back cover flap.

Keep this open for easy reference.

ABERPORTH

Dyfed
Map ref 1A2

Quiet Cardigan Bay resort with cliff, sands, bathing and boat-slipping facilities.

Pilbach Caravan Park
⊖✓✓✓✓✓ Dragon Award
Member BH&HPA
Betws Ifan, Rhydlewis, Llandysul
SA44 5RT
☎ Rhydlewis (01239) 851434
South from Aberystwyth on the A487 turn left onto the B4333. Then take the first left, then the first right, then the first left. Signposted.
5.8 hectares (14.5 acres). Level, grassy, hard, sheltered.
65 touring pitches

50	🚐	£8.00—£9.75
5	🚚	£8.00—£9.75
10	⛺	£8.00—£9.75
7	🏠	£115.00—£325.00

Open March–October
Cards accepted: Mastercard, Visa

The map references refer to the colour maps towards the end of the guide. The first figure is the map number; the letter and figure which follow indicate the grid reference on the map.

ABERSOCH

Gwynedd
Map ref 1A1

Fascinating little coastal village and yachting centre on the Lleyn Peninsula. Beaches, golf and fishing.

Tyn y Mur Touring & Camping Park ⚠
⊖✓✓✓✓
Member BH&HPA/NCC
Lon Garmon, Abersoch, Pwllheli
LL53 7UL
☎ Pwllheli (01758) 712328
From Pwllheli take the A499 to Abersoch, turn right at the "Land and Sea" garage and park is approximately half a mile on the left. Signposted.
Level, grassy.
80 touring pitches

40	🚐	£10.00—£11.00
40	🚚	£8.00—£9.00
52	⛺	£8.00—£9.00

Open March–September

A key to symbols can be found inside the back cover flap.

All accommodation in this guide has been graded, or is awaiting a grading, by a trained Tourist Board inspector.

ABERYSTWYTH

Dyfed
Map ref 1A2

The county town of Dyfed. Popular seaside resort with harbour and good bathing beaches. Its central position on Cardigan Bay makes it a good touring centre. Home of University College and National Library of Wales.
Tourist Information Centre ☎ (01970) 612125

Glan-y-Mor Leisure Park ⚠
⊖✓✓✓✓✓ Dragon Award
Member BH&HPA
Clarach Bay, Aberystwyth SY23 3DT
☎ (01970) 828900
Fax (01970) 828890
From Aberystwyth take A487 north 4 miles (6km) to Bow Street. Turn left near Black Lion for Clarach. Follow road to seafront and park entrance.
Level, sloping, grassy.
75 touring pitches

25	🚐	£6.50—£10.00
25	🚚	£6.50—£10.00
25	⛺	£6.50—£10.00
55	🏠	£99.00—£375.00

100 units not for hire
Open April–October
Cards accepted: Access, Visa, Switch/Delta

[Ad] See display advertisement on page 209

Please mention this guide when making your booking.

Midfield Caravan Park

⊖✓✓✓
Member BH&HPA
Southgate, Aberystwyth SY23 4DX
☎ (01970) 612542
Situated 1.5miles (3km) south east of Aberystwyth on A4120, 200 yards from the junction with A487 main north to south road. Signposted.
3.2 hectares (8 acres). Level, sloping, grassy, sheltered.
75 touring pitches

75	🚐	£7.90—£8.20
75	🚏	£7.90—£8.20
75	⛺	£7.90—£8.20

57 units not for hire
Open March–October
🛶🚲📷🏕🔌🏧🛒🚿⚡🚻♿🚮🛁☻⛰♨

Ocean View Caravan Park

⊖✓✓✓✓
Member BH&HPA
Clarach Bay, Aberystwyth SY23 3DT
☎ (01970) 623361
A487 Aberystwyth to Machynlleth Road, turn off to B4572 for Clarach Bay.
Level, grassy, hard.
25 touring pitches

20	🚐	£6.00—£8.00
5	🚏	£6.00—£8.00
2	⛺	£95.00—£185.00

🚗🛶P🚲🏕🔌🛒🚿⚡🚻♿🚮🏧 ☻⛰Ü🅿☻

Little Kings Park Caravan Park

⊖✓✓✓✓
Member BH&HPA
Amroth, Narberth SA67 8PG
☎ Llanteg (01834) 831330
Take A477 from St. Clears through Llanteg, turn left at sign to Ludchurch. Amroth. Signposted 0.5 miles (1km) on right to Ludchurch. Signposted.
Level, grassy.
95 touring pitches

35	🚐	£7.00—£15.00
20	🚏	£7.00—£15.00
40	⛺	£7.00—£9.00
17	⛺	£110.00—£360.00

Open March–September
🚲🏕🔌⚡🛒🚿♿🍴📷🚮🏧🛶☻⛰♨🛁
☻

Small market town on Bala Lake, the largest natural sheet of water in Wales. Mountain scenery, fishing, walking and boating.
Tourist Information Centre ☎ (01678) 521021

Pen-y-Garth Camping & Caravan Park 🏔

⊖✓✓✓✓ Dragon Award
Member BH&HPA
Rhosygwaliau, Bala LL23 7ES
☎ (01678) 520485
Off B3491 at Lake Vyrnwy signpost. Park in 600 yards. Signposted.
8 hectares (20 acres). Level, grassy, hard, sheltered.
63 touring pitches

35	🚐	£6.00—£8.00
35	🚏	£6.00—£8.00
28	⛺	£5.00—£8.00
6	⛺	£120.00—£250.00

45 units not for hire
Open March–October
Cards accepted: Access
🛶P🚲🏕🔌🏧🛒🚿⚡🚻♿✕🍴📷🚮
🛁☻⛰Ü🅿♨🛎📞☻

The 🏔 symbol after an establishment name indicates that it is a Regional Tourist Board member.

Popular seaside resort at the mouth of the beautiful Mawddach estuary, on the edge of the Snowdonia National Park.

Hendre Mynach Touring Caravan and Camping Park

⊖✓✓✓✓
Barmouth LL42 1YR
☎ (01341) 280262
Site is situated 0.5 miles (1km) north of Barmouth on the A496 Barmouth Harlech Road. Signposted.
4 hectares (10 acres). Level, sloping, grassy, stony, hard, sheltered.
220 touring pitches

45	🚐	£7.00—£11.00
45	🚏	£7.00—£10.00
180	⛺	£7.00—£9.00

Open March–October
🛶🚗🚲🏕🔌🛒🚿⚡🚻♿✕🍴📷🚮🏧
☻⛰Ü♨☻

Parc Caerelwan

⊖✓✓✓✓✓ Dragon Award
Member BH&HPA/NCC
Talybont, Barmouth LL43 2AX
☎ Dyffryn (01341) 247236
Fax (01341) 247711
Turn left off the A496 at Talybont village, go down the beach road and it is the first park after the railway bridge on the right hand side. Signposted.
2.8 hectares (7 acres). Level, grassy, hard, sheltered.

60	⛺	£84.00—£315.00

Open March–October
Cards accepted: Access, Visa, Switch/Delta
🛶P🚲🏕🔌⚡🚻♿🛒🍴📷🚮🛁☻⛰
Ü🅿♨

BARMOUTH

Continued

Trawsdir ⚠

❸✓✓✓✓
Llanaber, Barmouth LL42 1RR
☎ (01341) 280611 & 280999
Fax (01341) 280250
A496 Barmouth to Harlech Road.
Signposted.
Level, sloping, grassy.
25 touring pitches

25	🚐	£7.50—£15.00

Open March–October
🅿🄿⊙🄝🅀❄🛁🍳☕🎖🔲🚿🚲⊙∪
🏧♿

BETWS-Y-COED

Gwynedd
Map ref 1B1

Village surrounded by woods, hills, glens and rivers.
Tourist Information Centre ☎ (01690) 710426

Cwmlanerch Caravan Park

❸✓✓
Betws-y-Coed LL24 0BG
☎ (01690) 710363
On B5106 Betws-y-Coed to Conwy road. 1 mile (2km) from Betws-y-Coed. Signposted.
1 hectares (2.5 acres). Level, grassy, hard, sheltered.
17 touring pitches

16	🚐	£6.00—£7.50
16	🚲	£6.00—£7.50
1	🚐	£90.00—£190.00

Open March–October
🄿⊙🄝🅀❄🛁☕⊙♿♿

Please check prices and other details at the time of booking.

The ⚠ symbol after an establishment name indicates that it is a Regional Tourist Board member.

BORTH

Dyfed
Map ref 1A2

Small seaside holiday resort strung out along the landward side of the road, facing the sea wall. Blue Flag beach.

Cambrian Coast Holiday Park ⚠

❸✓✓✓✓ Dragon Award
Member BH&HPA
Borth SY24 5JU
☎ Aberystwyth (01970) 871233
Fax (01970) 871856
Take A487 from Cardigan through Aberstwyth. Take next left signposted to Borth. B4353 Cambrian Coast Holiday Park signposted from Borth. Signposted.
Level, grassy.
50 touring pitches

25	🚐	£6.50—£10.00
5	🚲	£6.50—£10.00
20	🅰	£6.50—£10.00
30	🚐	£69.00—£339.00

100 units not for hire
Open April–October
Cards accepted: Access, Visa, Switch/Delta
🄿⊙🄝🅀❄🛁☕⊙🎖✗🍳🔲❄🚿
⊙♿🍴🍷∪🏧♪♿🅃🄐
[Ad] See display advertisement on page 209

BRECON

Powys
Map ref 1B3

Market town situated at the junction of the rivers Usk and Honddu. Excellent base for exploring the Brecon Beacons National Park.
Tourist Information Centre ☎ (01874) 622485

Anchorage Caravan Park

❸✓✓✓✓
Member BH&HPA
Bronllys, Brecon LD3 0LD
☎ Talgarth (01874) 711246
On A438, 8 miles (12km) northeast of Brecon and on west side of Bronllys village. Signposted.
5.2 hectares (13 acres). Level, sloping, grassy, hard, sheltered.
110 touring pitches

60	🚐	£6.00
10	🚲	£6.00
40	🅰	£6.00

75 units not for hire
🄿⊙🄝🅀❄🛁☕⊙📺🔲🍳❄🚿🚐⊙
🏧♿

Brynich Caravan Park

❸✓✓✓✓✓
Member BH&HPA
Brecon LD3 7SH
☎ (01874) 623325
Fax (01874) 623325
1 mile east of Brecon on A470 (Builth Wells) near roundabout with A40 (Abergavenny). Signposted.
5.6 hectares (14 acres). Level, grassy, hard, sheltered.
130 touring pitches

50	🚐	£7.50—£8.50
30	🚲	£7.50—£8.50
50	🅰	£7.50—£8.50

Open Easter–October
🄿⊙🄝🅀❄🛁☕⊙🚲🔲🍳❄🚿🚐⊙🏧
♿♿
[Ad] See display advertisement on this page

CAERNARFON

Gwynedd
Map ref 1A1

Ancient county town famous for its magnificent and well preserved medieval castle, the birthplace of Edward I and scene of the investiture of the Prince of Wales in 1969.
Tourist Information Centre ☎ (01286) 672232

Bryn-Gloch Caravan and Camping Park

❸✓✓✓✓✓
Betws Garmon, Caernarfon LL54 7YY
☎ Waunfawr (01286) 650216
Entrance directly off A4085 Caernarfon to Beddgelert road. Signposted.
4.8 hectares (12 acres). Level, grassy, hard.
100 touring pitches

80	🚐	£6.00—£8.00
20	🚲	£6.00—£8.00
80	🅰	£6.00—£8.00
13	🚐	£99.00—£260.00

---

4 units not for hire
Cards accepted: Access

🔌🚐🖵🔆🔥🏃🕯️🛁🕯️🅿️🛒✕♨️📺🍴
🖵🕯️☀️🚰⛰️🔱🛶↔️🏕️
Ad See display advertisement on this page

Cadnant Valley Camping and Caravan Park
ⵔ✓✓✓✓✓
Member BH&HPA
Llanberis Road, Caernarfon
LL55 2DF
☎ (01286) 673196
On A4086 only 0.5 miles from Caernarfon centre. Follow signs for Llanberis from Caernarfon. Entrance on left just before Fire Station. Signposted.
2 hectares (5 acres). Level, grassy, hard, sheltered.
60 touring pitches

33	🚐	£6.50—£8.10
7	🚚	£6.50—£8.10
20	▲	£4.00—£8.10

Open March–October

🚗🚐🖵🔆🔥🏃🕯️🛁🕯️☀️🍴🖵🕯️🚰☀️✕🕯️

Plas Gwyn Caravan Park
ⵔ✓✓✓✓✓
Llanberis Road, Llanrug, Caernarfon
LL55 2AQ
☎ (01286) 672619
Fax (01286) 672619
From Caernarfon take A4086 for 3 miles (5km). Park on right. From Llanberis take A4086 for 2.5 miles (4.5km). Park on left. Signposted.
1.4 hectares (3.5 acres). Level, sloping, grassy, sheltered.
30 touring pitches

30	🚐	£6.50—£7.50
5	🚚	£6.00—£8.00
15	▲	£5.00—£6.50
6	🏕️	£95.00—£220.00

12 units not for hire
Open April–October

🚗🅿️🏃🕯️🛁🕯️☀️🔋🍴🖵☀️🚰🏨☀️

Tourist Information Centre ☎ (01239) 613230

Cenarth Falls Holiday Park
ⵔ✓✓✓✓✓
Member BH&HPA
Cenarth, Newcastle Emlyn SA38 9JS
☎ Newcastle Emlyn (01239) 710345
Signposted from A484, on the outskirts of Cenarth. Signposted.
4.8 hectares (12 acres). Level, grassy, sheltered.
30 touring pitches

20	🚐	£7.75—£12.75
20	🚚	£7.75—£12.75
10	▲	£7.75—£12.75
7	🏕️	£106.00—£423.00

79 units not for hire
Open March–December
Cards accepted: Access, Visa, Switch/Delta

🚗🅿️🖵🔆🔥🏃🕯️🛁🕯️☀️🔋✕♨️📺🖵🖵🕯️🚰⛰️↩️🎵☀️

Popular seaside resort with sands, bathing and a pier. Ideal centre for touring Snowdonia.
Tourist Information Centre ☎ (01492) 530478

Bron-Y-Wendon Touring Caravan Park ⛰️
ⵔ✓✓✓✓✓
Bron-Y-Wendon, Wern Road, Llanddulas, Colwyn Bay LL22 8HG
☎ (01492) 512903
Follow the A55 into North Wales and take the Llanddulas junction (A547). Turn right opposite the Shell garage and head for the sea. Bron-Y-Wendon is approximately 0.25 miles. Signposted.

3.2 hectares (8 acres). Level, sloping, grassy, hard.
130 touring pitches

110	🚐	£8.00—£9.00
20	🚚	£8.00—£9.00

Open March–October
Cards accepted: Visa

🅿️🖵🔆🔥🏃🕯️🛁🕯️☀️📺🖵🖵🕯️🔋🚰☀️⛰️☀️

Fascinating medieval fortress town at the mouth of the River Conwy, enclosed by massive walls and dominated by striking 13th C castle. Sheltered harbour and small fishing fleet.
Tourist Information Centre ☎ (01492) 592248

Conwy Touring Park
ⵔ✓✓✓✓
Trefriw Road, Conwy LL32 8UX
☎ (01492) 592856
Fax (01492) 580024
Take the A55 into Conwy, turn left at Conwy Castle onto the B5106 and travel 1.5 miles. Sign on the left of the road. Signposted.
28 hectares (70 acres). Level, grassy, hard, sheltered.
319 touring pitches

319	🚐	£4.85—£9.95
100	🚚	£4.85—£9.95
75	▲	£4.00—£9.95

Open April–October
Cards accepted: Access, Visa

🖵🔆🏃🕯️🛁🕯️☀️🔋♨️🖵🖵🕯️🔋🚰☀️⛰️🎵☀️
Ad See display advertisement on page 212

COWBRIDGE

South Glamorgan
Map ref 1B3

Small, old-world borough with an Edwardian gatehouse. Parts of 13th-14th C walls are still standing. Good shops.

Llandow Touring Caravan Park ⚲

⊖✓✓✓✓
Member BH&HPA
Llandow, Cowbridge CF7 7PB
☎ Llantwit Major (01446) 794527 & 792462
A48 to Cowbridge. Bypass Cowbridge, first left onto B4268. Stay on road until you see brown signs, do not go to Llandow village.
2 hectares (5 acres). Level, grassy, hard.
100 touring pitches

60	🚐	£6.00—£8.00
20	🚏	£6.00—£8.00
20	⛺	

Open February–November

CRICKHOWELL

Powys
Map ref 1B3

Charming country town on the River Usk. Good centre for exploring Brecon Beacons and Black Mountains.

Riverside Caravan Camping Park

⊖✓✓✓✓
Member BH&HPA
New Road, Crickhowell NP8 1AY
☎ (01873) 810397
Fax (01873) 811989
Off New Road in Crickhowell between A40 and A4077. Entrance 400 yards on the right from the A40. Signposted.
1.4 hectares (3.5 acres). Level, grassy, sheltered.
55 touring pitches

35	🚐	£5.50
20	🚏	£4.50
20	⛺	£5.00

20 units not for hire
Open March–October

CWMCARN

Gwent
Map ref 1B3

Tourist Information Centre ☎ (01495) 272001

Cwmcarn Forest Drive Campsite

⊖✓✓✓✓
Nantcarn Valley, Cwmcarn, Cross Keys, Newport NP1 7FA
☎ Cross Keys (01495) 272001
From the M4 junction 28 (Risca) go north onto A467 following signs for Risca then Brynmawr. After 7 miles (11km) park is on right hand side. Signposted.
0.8 hectares (2 acres). Grassy, hard.
35 touring pitches

35	🚐	£4.70—£5.80
35	🚏	£4.70—£5.80
35	⛺	£3.60—£5.80

DOLGELLAU

Gwynedd
Map ref 1B2

This grey-walled, slate-roofed market town is near the head of the Mawddach estuary. Splendid touring centre and excellent base for walking in the southern section of the Snowdonia National Park and the Caed-y-Brenin Forest.
Tourist Information Centre ☎ (01341) 422888

Tanyfron Caravan and Camping Park

⊖✓✓✓✓✓
Member BH&HPA
Arran Road, Dolgellau LL40 2AA
☎ (01341) 422638
Fax (01341) 422638
Off A470 from Welshpool take left turn after Little Chef. Signposted Dolgellau. 0.5 mile on left. Signposted.
1.4 hectares (3.5 acres). Level, sloping, grassy, hard, sheltered.
43 touring pitches

7	🚐	£7.50—£8.50
6	🚏	£7.00—£8.00
30	⛺	£7.00—£10.00
1	🏠	£100.00—£150.00

DULAS

Gwynedd
Map ref 1A1

Tyddyn Isaf Camping and Caravan Park ⚲

⊖✓✓✓✓✓ Dragon Award
Member BH&HPA
Lligwy Bay, Dulas LL70 9PQ
☎ Moelfre (01248) 410203
Fax (01248) 410667
A5025 turn right to Lligwy Beach at Brynrefail then turn off 0.5 miles towards the beach on the right hand side. Signposted.
Sloping, grassy.
80 touring pitches

80	🚐	£10.00—£15.00
80	🚏	£8.50—£12.00
80	⛺	£8.50—£9.00
10	🏠	£100.00—£275.00

40 units not for hire
Open March–October

FISHGUARD

Dyfed
Map ref 1A2

Picturesque little town perched high above its harbour. Fine cliff scenery.
Tourist Information Centre ☎ (01348) 873484 or 872037

Fishguard Bay Caravan Park

⊖✓✓✓✓
Member BH&HPA
Dinas Cross, Newport SA42 0YD
☎ Dinas Cross (01348) 811415
Fax (01348) 811425
Take A487 from Fishguard towards Cardigan. Turning on your left. Signposted.
2.4 hectares (6 acres). Sloping, grassy.
20 touring pitches

20	🚐	£7.50—£10.00
10	🚏	
20	⛺	
13	🏠	£130.00—£310.00

37 units not for hire
Open March–December
Cards accepted: Access, Visa

Tregroes Touring Park
⊖✓✓
Fishguard SA65 9QF
☎ (01348) 872316
A40 from Fishguard south for 1 mile (2km). Take turning to Manorowen. Signposted.
4 hectares (10 acres). Level, grassy.
45 touring pitches

25	🚐	£6.00—£7.00
10	🚙	£6.00—£7.00
10	⛺	£6.00—£7.00

Open April–October
Cards accepted: Access
🎱📻🕭🛆🐾🚾📺🗄☺🔍⚠↙🏋
🛆🛝

HARLECH
Gwynedd
Map ref 1A1

Harlech Castle, a 13th C stronghold built by Edward I, dominates this little town on the shores of Tremadog Bay.

Pant Mawr Caravan Park
⊖✓✓✓
Member BH&HPA
Ffordd Uchaf, Harlech LL46 2SS
☎ (01766) 780226
From Harlech high street going south, turn left after main car park. Pant Mawr is 300 yds on left just after right hand bend.
Sloping, grassy, sheltered.

10	🚐	£70.00—£260.00

Open April–October
Cards accepted: Access
P🕭🛆🚿♦☺🛝

HAVERFORDWEST
Dyfed
Map ref 1A3

Pleasant market town with steep streets, fine church and Norman castle.
Tourist Information Centre ☎ (01437) 763110

Scamford Caravan Park 🏔
⊖✓✓✓✓
Member BH&HPA
Keeston, Haverfordwest SA62 6HN
☎ Camrose (01437) 710304
Fax (01437) 710304

Take A487 from Haverfordwest. After 4 miles (6km) turn right at sign for Keeston. Signposted.
1.4 hectares (3.5 acres). Level, grassy.
5 touring pitches

5	🚐	£5.00—£7.00
5	🚙	£5.00—£7.00
25	🚐	£90.00—£315.00

Open March–October
🚐🎱🕭🛆🐾☺🗄📺♦🛆☺⚠Ս
🛆Ⓣ☺
[Ad] See display advertisement on this page

LITTLE HAVEN
Dyfed
Map ref 1A3

Picturesque village with extensive sands, on St Bride's Bay.

Hasguard Cross Caravan Park
⊖✓✓✓✓
Member BH&HPA
Little Haven, Haverfordwest, Pembrokeshire SA62 3SL
☎ Broad Haven (01437) 781443
From Haverfordwest follow Dale signs B4327. After 7 miles turn right for Little Haven. Entrance 200 yards on the right . Signposted.
1.3 hectares (3.25 acres). Level.
25 touring pitches

25	🚐	£5.00—£7.00
25	🚙	£5.00—£7.00
6	🚐	£85.00—£255.00

29 units not for hire
🚐P🕭🛝🛆♦☺✕⛾🗄☺♦🚐☺
🔍⚠Ս🛆Ⓣ

Redlands Touring Caravan Park 🏔
⊖✓✓✓✓
Member BH&HPA
Little Haven, Haverfordwest, Pembrokeshire SA62 3SJ
☎ Broadhaven (01437) 781300 & 781457
Fax (01437) 781093
From Haverfordwest take B4327 Dale road for 6.5 miles (11km). Site is signposted on right. Do not approach via Broad Haven
2 hectares (5 acres). Level, grassy.
63 touring pitches

63	🚐	£6.50—£7.50
63	🚙	£6.50—£7.50
63	⛺	

Open April–September
🚐🎱🕭🛝🛆♦⛾♦🚐☺🛆

LLANDOVERY
Dyfed
Map ref 1B3

Small market town by the rivers Tywi, Bran and Gwydderig. Good fishing.

Erwlon Caravan and Camping Park
⊖✓✓✓✓
Member BH&HPA
Llandovery SA20 0RD
☎ (01550) 720332
Adjoining the A40 from Brecon to Llandovery. Signposted within 1km of Llandovery.
3.2 hectares (8 acres). Level, grassy, hard, sheltered.
40 touring pitches

40	🚐	£5.00—£7.00
40	🚙	£5.00—£7.00
40	⛺	£5.00—£7.00

🚐P🎱🕭🛝🛆♦☺🗄☺♦☺🛆

LLANDRINDOD WELLS
Powys
Map ref 1B2

The leading spa resort in Wales, situated 100 feet above sea level. Variety of mineral springs, Victorian architecture. Good touring centre.
Tourist Information Centre ☎ (01597) 822600

Disserth Caravan & Camping Park
⊖✓✓✓✓
Member BH&HPA
Disserth, Howey, Llandrindod Wells LD1 6NL
☎ (01597) 860277 & 0374 225399
Fax (01597) 860277
From Llandrindod Wells take A483 south for 3 miles (5km). Turn right at sign for Disserth 1 mile and Newbridge-on-Wye 2.5 miles (4km). Park 1 mile (2km) on left by church. Signposted.

Continued ▶

LLANDRINDOD WELLS
Continued

1.4 hectares (3.5 acres). Level, grassy, sheltered.
45 touring pitches

20	🚐	£6.25—£7.50
5	🚏	£6.25—£7.50
20	⛺	£6.25—£7.50
2	🏠	£95.00—£275.00

19 units not for hire
Open March—October

🅰️🅿️🄰🄰🄲🄰🄰🄲🄰✕🍴🖥️🖥️⚡
🚗⊙🄰🄰⊛

LLANDUDNO
Gwynedd
Map ref 1B1

Well-known seaside resort with two magnificent sandy bays, one enclosed by the headlands of Great Orme and Little Orme, the other stretching from the west to the Conwy Estuary. The rock-strewn heights of Great Orme's Head dominate the town and may be reached by cable car or tramway.
Tourist Information Centre ☎ (01492) 876413

Penrhyn Hall Farm Caravan Park
⊖✓✓✓✓✓
Member BH&HPA
Penrhyn Bay, Llandudno LL30 3EE
☎ Colwyn Bay (01492) 549207
From Colwyn Bay take the B5115 signs for Llandudno site 2.5 miles (5km) from Colwyn Bay. Entrance to site is at bottom of Penrhyn Hill off a roundabout. Signposted.
2.8 hectares (7 acres). Level, sloping, grassy, hard, sheltered.
10 touring pitches

8	🚐	£9.50—£11.00
2	🚏	£9.50—£11.00

151 units not for hire
Open April—October

🅰️🅿️🄰🄰🄲🄰🄰🄲🖥️⚡🚗⊙🄰
🄰🄰

LLANGORSE
Powys
Map ref 1B3

Lakeside Caravan and Camping Park
⊖✓✓✓✓
Member BH&HPA
Llangorse Lake, Llangorse, Brecon LD3 7TR
☎ (01874) 658226
Fax (01874) 658430

From the A40 at Bwlch take the B4560 to Llangorse. Follow signs for lake.
1.6 hectares (4 acres). Level, grassy, sheltered.
40 touring pitches

40	🚐	£6.50—£8.50
40	🚏	£6.50—£8.50
40	⛺	£6.50—£8.50
10	🏠	£135.00—£185.00

72 units not for hire
Open April—November
Cards accepted: Access, Visa

🅰️🄰🄰🄲🄰🄰🄲⚡✕🍴🖥️🖥️⚡🚗⊙
🄰🄰🄰🄰🄰🄰🄰

MERTHYR TYDFIL
Mid Glamorgan
Map ref 1B3

Market and industrial town, former iron and steel capital of the world. Cyfarthfa Castle (1825) houses a museum.
Tourist Information Centre ☎ (01685) 379884

Grawen Farm Caravan and Camping Park
⊖✓✓✓
Cwm Taff, Cefn Coed, Merthyr Tydfil CF48 2HS
☎ (01685) 723740
4 miles (6km) from Merthyr Tydfil on A470 Brecon Brecons Road. Third farm on left. Signposted.
1.6 hectares (4 acres). Level, grassy, hard.
55 touring pitches

15	🚐	£5.50—£7.00
10	🚏	£5.00—£6.00
30	⛺	£5.00—£6.00

Open April—October
Cards accepted: Access, Visa

🅰️🄰🄰🄲🄰🄰🄲🄰🖥️⚡⊙🄰🄰🄰

MONMOUTH
Gwent
Map ref 1B3

Historic market town, birthplace of Henry V, with unique 13th C gateway built across the Monnow.

Bridge Caravan Park Camping Site
⊖✓✓✓✓✓
Dingestow, Monmouth NP5 4DY
☎ Dingestow (01600) 740241
From A449 trunk road take junction for Raglan and Abergavenny and follow signs. Signposted.
2 hectares (5 acres). Level, grassy, hard, sheltered.
74 touring pitches

40	🚐	£7.00—£8.50
9	🚏	£7.00—£8.50
25	⛺	£7.00—£7.00
3	🏠	£90.00—£150.00

Open April—October

🅰️🄰🄰🄲🄰🄰🄲🄰🄰🖥️🖥️⚡🚗⊙
🄰🄰

Monmouth Caravan Park
⊖✓✓✓
Rockfield Road, Monmouth NP5 3BA
☎ (01600) 714745
Level, grassy, hard.
40 touring pitches

30	🚐	£7.00—£7.00
10	🚏	£6.00—£6.00
12	⛺	£5.50—£6.00

Open March—October

🅿️🄰🄰🄲🄰🄰🄲🄰🄰🖥️⊙🄰🄰🄰

NARBERTH
Dyfed
Map ref 1A3

Market town north of Tenby. The ruins of a Norman castle crown the summit of a hill.
Tourist Information Centre ☎ (01834) 860061

Noble Court Holiday Park 𝕸
⊖✓✓✓✓✓
Member BH&HPA
Noble Court, Redstone Road, Narberth SA67 7ES
☎ (01834) 861191 & 861484
Off the A40, trunk road onto B4313 to Narberth. Park is 0.5 miles on the left side. Signposted.
12 hectares (30 acres). Level, sloping, grassy, hard, sheltered.
92 touring pitches

92	🚐	£8.00—£13.50
50	🚏	£8.00—£13.50
30	⛺	£8.00—£13.50

60 units not for hire
Open March—October
Cards accepted: Access, Visa

🅰️🅿️🄰🄰🄲🄰🄰🄲✕🍴🖥️⚡
🚗⊙🄰🄰🄰🄰🄰

NEW QUAY
Dyfed
Map ref 1A2

Quay West Holiday Resort
⊖✓✓✓✓
Member BH&HPA/NCC
New Quay SA45 9SE
☎ Reservations/free brochure
(01442) 248668
Fax (01442) 232459
Follow the signs to Aberystwyth taking the A487 coastal trunk road. On reaching Llanarth, turn onto the

B4342. New Quay is situated between Cardigan and Aberystwyth. Signposted. 40.5 hectares (100 acres). Level, sloping, grassy.

280	🏕	£80.00—£450.00

245 units not for hire
Open March–November
Cards accepted: Access, Visa, Switch/Delta
♠ P ⟲ ♨ ♿ × ⚲ (📷 ⊘ ✦ 🚐 ☺ ♦ 🏔 ♒ ♨ ∪ ♖ ♪ ♫ ⚹ T
Ad See display advertisement inside front cover

NEWPORT

Gwent
Map ref 1B3

The third largest town in Wales with seaport and steelworks. Interesting castle and cathedral.
Tourist Information Centre ☎ *(01633) 842962*

Tredegar House & Park
⊖✓✓✓✓
Newport NP1 9YW
☎ (01633) 815880
Fax (01633) 815895
Follow signposts from A48/M4 (junction 28). Signposted.
1.6 hectares (4 acres). Level, grassy, hard, sheltered.
60 touring pitches

30	⚲	£7.00—£9.00
30	▲	£5.00—£7.00

Open April–September
Cards accepted: Access, Visa, Switch/Delta
♠ P ⚲ ⟲ ♨ ♿ × (📷 ⊘ ⚲ ☺ 🏔 ♒ ⚹

PENDINE

Dyfed
Map ref 1A3

Pendine Holiday Village
⊖✓✓✓
Member BH&HPA/NCC
Marsh Road, Pendine, Carmarthen SA33 4NZ
☎ Reservations/free brochure (01442) 248668
Fax (01442) 232459
Take A40 trunk road from Carmarthen to St Clears. Pendine/Pentywyn is signposted to the left along the A4066 some 8 miles from the junction of the A40.
24 hectares (60 acres). Level, sloping, grassy, hard, sheltered.

30	⚲	£7.00—£16.50
10	▲	£7.00—£13.00
130	🏕	£120.00—£489.00

Open March–October
Cards accepted: Access, Visa, Switch/Delta
♠ ⚲ ♿ ♨ (📷 ⊘ ✦ 🚐 ☺ 🏔 ♒ ♖ × ✕
Ad See display advertisement inside front cover

PENMAENMAWR

Gwynedd
Map ref 1B1

Holiday resort at the foot of Penmaenmawr Mountain, with excellent sands and bathing, sailing and golf.

Pendyffran Hall Caravan Park
⊖✓✓✓
Glan Y Afon Road, Penmaenmawr LL34 6UF
☎ (01492) 623219
Situated off A55 Expressway between Conwy - Penmaenmawr which is signposted. Signposted.
38.4 hectares (96 acres). Level, grassy, stony, sheltered.
100 touring pitches

25	⚲	£6.00—£9.00
75	⚲	£6.00—£9.00
75	▲	£6.00—£9.00

153 units not for hire
Open March–October
♠ P ⚲ ⟲ ♨ ♿ ♨ ♖ TV (📷 ⊘ 🚐 ☺

Woodlands Camping Park
⊖✓✓✓
Member BH&HPA
Pendyffrann Hall, Penmaenmawr LL34 6UF
☎ Aberconwy (01492) 623219
Off the A55 between Conwy and Penmaenmawr. Pass through illuminated tunnel then take 1st turning left towards Dwylgyfychi. Then 2nd turn on left is park entrance. Signposted.
38.4 hectares (96 acres). Level, grassy, stony, sheltered.
75 touring pitches

25	⚲	£6.00—£8.50
75	⚲	£6.00—£8.50
75	▲	£6.00—£8.50

150 units not for hire
Open March–October
♠ P ⚲ ♨ ♿ ♨ ♖ TV (📷 ⊘ 🚐 ☺ ♦ ✕

All accommodation in this guide has been graded, or is awaiting a grading, by a trained Tourist Board inspector.

PORTHMADOG

Gwynedd
Map ref 1A1

Delightful seaside resort with a good harbour and some fine sandy bays. Wonderful views across the estuary to the mountains beyond. Trips into the hills on the narrow gauge Festiniog Railway.
Tourist Information Centre ☎ *(01766) 512981*

Black Rock Touring & Camping Park ♦
⊖✓✓✓✓✓
Member BH&HPA/NCC
Black Rock Sands, Morfa Bychan, Porthmadog LL49 9LU
☎ (01766) 513919
A492 from Porthmadog to Morfa Bychan. Continue for 3 miles (5km) then pass beach entrance bear right to park. Signposted.
Level, grassy, sheltered.
150 touring pitches

30	⚲	£10.00—£11.00
30	⚲	£8.00—£9.00
120	▲	£8.00—£9.00

Open March–September
♠ ⚲ ⟲ ♨ ♿ ♨ ⟲ (📷 ⊘ 🚐 ☺ 🏔 ⚹ ✕ ∪ ♦ ®

Greenacres Holiday Park
⊖✓✓✓✓
Member BH&HPA/NCC
Morfa Bychan, Porthmadog LL49 9YB
☎ Reservations/free brochure (01442) 248668
Fax (01442) 232459
After arriving at Porthmadog High St, turn between Woolworths and main Post Office towards Black Rock Sands. Park is along this road on other side of village of Morfa Bychan.
Level, grassy.
80 touring pitches

80	⚲	£7.20—£18.00
200	🏕	£109.00—£538.00

740 units not for hire
Open March–October
Cards accepted: Access, Visa, Switch/Delta
♠ ⟲ ♨ ♿ ♨ ♖ × ♨ (📷 ⊘ 🚐 ☺ ♦ 🏔 ♒ ∪ ♖ ♪ ♫ ⚹ T
Ad See display advertisement inside front cover

A key to symbols can be found inside the back cover flap.

PORTSKEWETT

Gwent
Map ref 1B3

St Pierre Caravan Park
☻✓✓✓✓✓
Portskewett, Chepstow NP6 4TT
☎ Chepstow (01291) 425114
From A48 roundabout take the turning for Caldicot. Then the small turning for Portskewett. Follow road round. Park is on the left. Signposted.
Level, grassy.
50 touring pitches

50	🚐	£10.00
50	🚲	£10.00
50	⚕	£8.00

Open March–October and Christmas
P🏁🛁🔥♨☗🎡🛢⚡🚙☉∪🗙♠

PRESTATYN

Clwyd
Map ref 1B1

Lido Beach Holiday Park
☻✓✓✓✓
Member BH&HPA/NCC
Central Beach, off Bastion Road, Prestatyn LL19 7EU
☎ Reservations/free brochure (01442) 248668
Fax (01442) 232459
Take turn off for Prestatyn off the A55 and follow the signs for the Nova Centre, go down Bastion Road and we are the fourth turning on the left.
Level, grassy.
50 touring pitches

50	🚐	£10.00—£17.00
44	🚲	£10.00—£17.00
60	⚕	£110.00—£450.00

560 units not for hire
Open April–October
Cards accepted: Access, Visa, Switch/Delta
🏁🖤🔥☗🎡🛢⚡🚙🔍♠🆃◎
Ad See display advertisement inside front cover

Nant Mill Farm Camp Site ⋀
☻✓✓✓✓
Prestatyn LL19 9LY
☎ (01745) 852360
On A548 half a mile east of Prestatyn town centre. Signposted.
2 hectares (5 acres). Level, sloping, grassy, sheltered.
150 touring pitches

150	🚐	£8.00—£10.00
150	🚲	£8.00—£10.00
150	⚕	£8.00—£10.00

Open April–October
🏁🖤🔥♨☗🎡🛢⚡🚙☉⚏♠

Tan-y-Don Caravan Park
☻✓✓✓✓✓
Member BH&HPA/NCC
263 Victoria Road, Prestatyn LL19 7UT
☎ (01745) 853749
Fax (01745) 854147
On A548 coast road approximately 200 yards from Ffrith Beach. Entrance in Sandhurst Road. Signposted.
Level, grassy, hard, sheltered.
8 touring pitches

8	🚐	£8.00—£12.00
8	🚲	£8.00—£12.00
3	⚕	£65.00—£315.00

64 units not for hire
Open March–October
Cards accepted: Access, Visa
🏁🖤P🖤🔥♨☗🎡🛢⚡🚙⚡🚙☉⚏🗙

ST DAVIDS

Dyfed
Map ref 1A3

A place of pilgrimage for over eight centuries, situated on the rugged western peninsula within easy reach of some of Britain's finest cliffs and bays. Interesting cathedral.
Tourist Information Centre ☎ (01437) 720392

Caerfai Bay Caravan and Tent Park
☻✓✓✓✓
Member BH&HPA
St Davids, Haverfordwest SA62 6QT
☎ St David's (01437) 720274
Fax (01437) 721422
Off A487 (Haverfordwest-St David's) in St David's, at signpost to Caerfai. Park is at road end, 0.75 mile, on the right. Signposted.
4 hectares (10 acres). Level, sloping, grassy.
83 touring pitches

28	🚐	£6.00—£9.00
10	🚲	£4.50—£5.00
45	⚕	£4.50—£5.00
4	⚕	£100.00—£295.00

27 units not for hire
Open April–October
🏁🖤🔥♨☗🎡🛢⚡🚙☉♠

The symbols in each entry give information about services and facilities. A 'key' to these symbols appears at the back of this guide.

SAUNDERSFOOT

Dyfed
Map ref 1A3

Small resort near Tenby with fine sands and a harbour.

Moreton Farm Leisure ⋀
☻✓✓✓✓
Member BH&HPA
Moreton, Saundersfoot SA69 9EA
☎ (01834) 812016
Fax (01834) 811890
On A478 Tenby Road, 2m (3k) from roundabout at Kilgetty. Signposted 400 yards from Wooden. Entrance on left opposite chapel. Signposted.
4.8 hectares (12 acres). Level, sloping, grassy, sheltered.
60 touring pitches

20	🚐	£8.00—£10.50
40	⚕	£5.00—£7.00

Open March–November
🏁🖤P🖤🔥♨☗🎡🛢⚡🚙⚡🚙☉⚏∪🌙🗙♠◎

TALSARNAU

Gwynedd
Map ref 1A1

Small village overlooking the beautiful Traeth Bay estuary. Good centre for exploring Snowdonia and the Vale of Ffestiniog.

Barcdy Touring Caravan and Camping Park ⋀
☻✓✓✓✓✓
Member BH&HPA
Talsarnau LL47 6YG
☎ Penrhyndeudraeth (01766) 770736
Travelling south via Trawfynydd take left turning at Maentwrog onto A496. Site is 4 miles along on the left. Signposted.
4.8 hectares (12 acres). Level, sloping, grassy, sheltered.
78 touring pitches

38	🚐	£6.50—£8.50
10	🚲	£6.50—£8.50
40	⚕	£6.50—£8.50
2	⚕	£160.00—£240.00

27 units not for hire
Open April–October
🏁🖤🖤🔥♨☗🎡🛢⚡🚙⚡🚙☉🗙♠🆃◎

The ⋀ symbol after an establishment name indicates that it is a Regional Tourist Board member.

TENBY

Dyfed
Map ref 1A3

Town with colourful harbour, superb sands, cliff-top hotels and ancient walls and gateways. It stands on a rocky promontory on Carmarthen Bay and is an ideal centre for exploring the coast.
Tourist Information Centre ☎ *(01834) 842402*

Kiln Park Holiday Centre ▲▲
☉✓✓✓✓
Member BH&HPA/NCC
Marsh Road, Tenby SA70 7RB
☎ Reservations/free brochure
(01442) 248668
Fax (01442) 232459
Follow A478 to Tenby, then follow signs for Penally. Park is half-mile on LH side.
48 hectares (120 acres). Level, grassy.
280 touring pitches

100	⚎	£7.70—£21.00
180	⛺	£6.60—£10.62
	⛺	£131.0—£598.00

Open March–October
Cards accepted: Access, Visa, Switch/Delta

🔥⚑♨☊⛁⚡✗🍴〖📶◨⚊🚐☺🔍⚑
🎏🔄🚻⚲🏹✂♫♨Ⓣ◉
Ad See display advertisement inside front cover

Lydstep Beach Holiday Resort ▲▲
☉✓✓✓
Member BH&HPA/NCC
Lydstep Haven, Tenby SA70 7SB
☎ Reservations/free brochure
(01442) 248668
Fax (01442) 232459
From Tenby take A4139 towards Penally then follow main road for about 3 miles. Site is on your left.
36 hectares (90 acres). Sloping.

120	⛺	£109.00—£576.00

5 units not for hire
Open March–October
Cards accepted: Access, Visa, Switch/Delta

⚑P☊⚡✗🍴〖📶◨⚊⚊↔🚐☺♫
🎏♨Ⓣ◉
Ad See display advertisement inside front cover

WELSHPOOL

Powys
Map ref 1B2

Tourist Information Centre ☎ *(01938) 552043*

Henllan Caravan Park
☉✓✓✓✓✓
Member BH&HPA/NCC
Llangyniew, Welshpool SY21 9EJ
☎ Llanfair Caereinon (01938) 810343
Fax (01938) 810554
0.5 miles (1km) off A458 Welshpool to Dolgellau Road. 6 miles (10km) west of Welshpool. 2 miles (3km) east of Llanfair Caereinion. Site beside river in hilly country. Signposted.
2.4 hectares (6 acres). Level.
10 touring pitches

10	⚎	£7.00—£10.00
1	⛺	

60 units not for hire
Open March–October

🔥⚑P☊♨☊⚡✗🍴TV〖◨⚊
🚐☺⚑♨🚻⚲🏹♫♨Ⓣ

WREXHAM

Clwyd
Map ref 1B1

Busy market town with medieval church.
Tourist Information Centre ☎ *(01978) 292015*

Plassey Touring Caravan and Leisure Park ▲▲
☉✓✓✓✓✓
Eyton, Wrexham LL13 0SP
☎ Bangor-on-Dee (01978) 780277
Fax (01978) 780 019
From Chester take the A483 South for Wrexham and Oswestry. Take the exit for Bangor-on-Dee (B5426). The entrance is 2 1/2 miles on the left. Follow Brown signs for Plassey. Signposted.
96 hectares (240 acres). Level, grassy, sheltered.
100 touring pitches

100	⚎	£8.50—£10.50
10	⛺	£8.50—£10.50
10	⛺	£8.50—£10.50

Open March–October
Cards accepted: Access, Visa, Switch/Delta

⚑P◨⚑☊♨☊⚡⚡✗🍴TV〖
◨⚊🚐🔍⚑♨🚻⚲♫🏹♨⚑◉

COUNTRY CODE

Always follow the Country Code 🐾 Enjoy the countryside and respect its life and work 🐾 Guard against all risk of fire 🐾 Fasten all gates 🐾 Keep your dogs under close control 🐾 Keep to public paths across farmland 🐾 Use gates and stiles to cross fences, hedges and walls 🐾 Leave livestock, crops and machinery alone 🐾 Take your litter home 🐾 Help to keep all water clean 🐾 Protect wildlife, plants and trees 🐾 Take special care on country roads 🐾 Make no unnecessary noise

USE YOUR *i*'s

There are more than 550 Tourist Information Centres throughout England offering friendly help with accommodation and holiday ideas as well as suggestions of places to visit and things to do. There may well be a centre in your home town which can help you before you set out. You'll find the address of your nearest Tourist Information Centre in your local Phone Book.

AT-A-GLANCE SYMBOLS

Symbols at the end of each accommodation entry give useful information about services and facilities. A key to symbols can be found inside the back cover flap.

Keep this open for easy reference.

CHECK THE MAPS

The colour maps at the back of this guide show all the cities, towns and villages for which you will find accommodation entries.

Refer to the town index to find the page on which it is listed.

INFORMATION PAGES

USEFUL ADDRESSES
ADRESSES UTILES/NÜTZLICHE ANSCHRIFTEN/
NUTTIGE ADRESSEN/INDIRIZZI UTILI

Automobile Association

Written enquiries: The Campsites Editor, AA Publishing, Fanum House, Basingstoke, Hampshire RG21 4EA.

Routes can be prepared, avoiding steep gradients if specified. Please write to: Routes Request, Fanum House, 26-32 Park Row, Bristol BS1 5LY.

The Automobile Association inspects and classifies camping and caravanning parks in the UK and Ireland and awards pennant ratings to parks with touring facilities on a rising scale of one to five, based on amenities and quality. It publishes annually a guide priced at £7.99, to more than a thousand parks with pennant ratings in the UK and Ireland, and the guide is available from bookshops and AA shops. There are however, no free leaflets available, and no information about caravans to rent for self-catering holidays.

British Holiday & Home Parks Association Ltd

Chichester House, 6 Pullman Court, Great Western Road, Gloucester GL1 3ND.

Brochure requests (01452) 413041; other enquiries (01452) 526911; Fax (01452) 307226.

The BH&HPA is recognised as the official representative body of the Parks Industry in the UK.

Member parks are located all over Britain. The parks are situated within some of the most spectacular locations that Britain can offer, from the breathtaking scenery of the Scottish Highlands, the beautiful coastal landscape of Cornwall, to the splendid mountains and lakes of North Wales and Northern Ireland. Parks can also be found nearby historic cities such as Oxford and Cambridge, and Shakespeare's city of Stratford-upon-Avon. Castles and historic sites are within reach of many BH&HPA parks.

Member parks offer pitches for touring caravans, tent and motor homes, caravan holiday homes and chalets to let, and holiday home ownership. The type of park ranges from the large multi-facility park to the smaller park run by a farm. So there is something to suit all needs.

Many parks can offer facilities such as swimming pools, restaurants and bars, and others are ideally situated near sailing and horse riding facilities, for instance, if you wish to have an activity-oriented holiday. For those seeking the peace and tranquillity of the countryside, there are small rural parks to choose from.

BH&HPA jointly produces a set of full colour guides to holiday parks covering Scotland, Wales, Western England, Southern England, Northern England and Eastern England. These are available free-of-charge by calling (01452) 413041.

The Camping and Caravanning Club

Greenfields House, Westwood Way, Coventry, West Midlands CV4 8JH. Tel: (01203) 694995.
Operates a national network of 84 camping and caravanning parks throughout Britain, most of which are open to non-members.

The club publishes a detailed guide to the above 84 sites, a Big Sites book listing 4500 parks in Britain and Ireland and an accompanying map with all these sites plotted on, useful for route planning. These are all available free to members.

Foreign visitors can obtain the above guides and map for £9.50 plus postage and by quoting their Camping Card International (CCI) number. Foreign visitors without a CCI may obtain the guide to the 84 Club parks open to them through temporary membership at £10.00 plus postage for three months membership.

The Caravan Club

East Grinstead House, East Grinstead, West Sussex RH19 1UA.
Tel: (01342) 326944;
Fax (01342) 410258.

Europe's premier club for trailer caravanners, motor caravanners and trailer tent users. A network of some 200 sites and 3000 small '5 van' sites (members only) are listed in the Sites Directory & Handbook. Members' benefits are available to any foreign visitor who in his own country is a member of a club affiliated to the Caravan Club through the AIT, FICC or the FIA, providing a Camping Card International (CCI) provided by the home touring organisation can be produced. The Sites Directory & Handbook is available free to UK members from the Club's headquarters. These can be posted overseas but a charge will be made. Contact the club's Information Officers for further details on any caravanning matter.

Forestry Commission

231 Corstorphine Road, Edinburgh EH12 7AT. Tel: (0131) 334 0303; Fax (0131) 334 0849.

Forest Holidays, run by Forest Enterprise, an executive agency of the Forestry Commission, have almost 30 camping and caravan sites in the scenic forest locations throughout the UK. Choose from the Scottish Highlands, the New Forest, Snowdonia National Park, the Forest of Dean, or the banks of Loch Lomond. Some sites are open all year.

Advance bookings accepted for many sites. Dogs welcome on most sites. For a unique forest experience, call the Forestry Commission for a brochure on (0131) 334 0303.

The Motor Caravanners' Club

22 Evelyn Close, Twickenham TW2 7BN. Tel: (0181) 893 3883. Club authorised to issue the Camping Card International (CCI). Club produces a monthly magazine 'Motor Caravan' for all its members.

Royal Automobile Club

RAC House, PO Box 100, Bartlett Street, South Croydon CR2 6XW. Members of motoring organisations affiliated to the FIA (Federation International de l'Automobile) and AIT (Alliance Internationale de Tourisme) can benefit from reciprocal services offered by the RAC who will undertake for members the planning of individual routes for caravan or camping journeys, having regard to road conditions, gradients and the towing vehicle when a caravan is involved. The RAC publishes an annual guide to Camping and Caravanning sites in Great Britain and Ireland listing nearly 3000 sites.

STANDARDS FOR CARAVAN AND CAMPING PARKS

NORMES REQUISES POUR LES TERRAINS DE CAMPING ET POUR CARAVANES/REGELN FÜR CAMPING- UND CARAVANPLÄTZE/AAN CARAVAN EN CAMPINGPARKEN GESTELDE EISEN/NORME IMPOSTE AI CAMPEGGI PER TENDE E ROULOTTES

These standards should be read in conjunction, where applicable, with the Caravan Sites and Control of Development Act 1960, and, where applicable, the Public Health Act 1936.

A The Park

1 The park must have planning permission and site licence readily available, if applicable.

2 Facilities must be clean and in wholesome condition.

3 The park must be well managed and maintained and kept in a clean and presentable manner and attention paid to the road-side sign and entrance.

4 The park must have reception arrangements at appropriate times where advice and assistance can be obtained if necessary.

5 The park operator must be capable of arranging or carrying out repairs to caravans and equipment.

6 Supplies of gas and replacement bottles together with essential (where applicable) spares must be available at all reasonable times.

7 Where provided, all toilet blocks and washing facilities must be lit internally and externally during the hours of darkness, whilst the park is open.

8 All shower blocks must have internal lighting.

9 Where washing and/or shower facilities are provided, an adequate supply of hot and cold water must be available at all reasonable times.

10 A proprietary first-aid kit must be readily available. Emergency notices must be prominently displayed giving details and location of park, contact, telephone, doctor, fire service, local hospital and other essential services.

11 It is the park operators responsibility to ensure that all caravans offered for hire on the park have insurance cover for public liability as letting caravans and comply with the Consumer Protection Act.

12 The park owner must have fire fighting equipment and notices which conform with the conditions of the site licence.

13 All electricity installations on the park both internally and externally must have the appropriate safety certification.

14 Parks providing pitches for touring units must provide facilities for chemical disposal unless specifically prohibited by local authorities.

15 Lighting should be appropriate to the size and type of park.

16 Adequate provision to be made for refuse disposal.

17 The intended use of facilities must be indicated by signage.

NB: Parks providing NO toilet facilities make this clear in all promotional literature and advertising.

B Visitor Information

The booking form must be accompanied by details of the park, stating clearly:

1   A description of the park and its amenities, e.g:

a) Whether cars park by caravans or in a car park.

b) Whether or not pets are allowed.

c) Details of shower and bath facilities.

d) Whether a grocery shop is on site or the distance to nearest shop.

e) Licensed bar.

f) Laundry facilities.

g) Dancing, entertainments.

h) Television room.

i) Sports facilities.

j) Public transport to and from park.

k) Distance from sea and accessibility to beach (coastal parks only).

2   The prices for the pitch for the period booked and details of any further charges, e.g. electricity, gas, showers, awnings as well as any optional charges, e.g. holiday insurance.

Note: If Value Added Tax (VAT) is not included in the total charge, this must be clearly stated.

3   Any special conditions for payment of deposits or balance.

4   Wherever possible, a map showing the location of the park and its proximity to main centres and attractions.

5   If bookings in advance are necessary during the summer months.

C Caravan Holiday Homes and Chalets

1   All caravans must be of proprietary make.

2   All caravans/chalets must be in good state of internal and external repair and decoration with no internal dampness.

3   The caravans/chalets must not be occupied by more than the number of persons for which they are designed by the manufacturer ie four persons in a 4-berth.

4   Equipment must be provided as listed below. An inventory of this equipment must be available for each caravan/chalet.

5   All caravans/chalets must have adequate storage space for luggage and food for the maximum number of occupants.

6   All doors, windows, skylights and all ventilation in the caravan/chalet must function correctly. All windows must be properly fitted with opaque curtains or blinds.

7   All caravans/chalets must have adequate internal lighting.

8   All caravans/chalets must be thoroughly cleaned and checked before every letting and equipment maintained and replaced as necessary.

9   Where linen is provided it must be changed on each change of occupier and as appropriate during lets of 2 weeks or more. All mattresses must be in sound condition.

10 The sink and its waste pipe must be in sound condition with a draining board. A fixed impervious work top for food preparation must be provided.

11 All caravans/chalets must have a fridge and a cooker with at least two boiling rings. The cooker must be in a sound and clean condition and functioning properly.

12 All caravans/chalets must have adequate heating.

13 All caravans must have safe steps or equivalent, to each external door.

14 All caravans must have a supply of hot and cold water.

D Inventory of Equipment for Caravan Holiday-Homes and Chalets

The accommodation should contain the following:

1 per caravan/chalet
Kettle
Teapot
Tea caddy
Saucepan & lid (large, medium & small)
Frying pan
Colander
Oven roasting tray
Casserole dish
Carving knife and fork
Bread knife
Bread/cake container
Bread/chopping board
Fish slice
Small vegetable knife
Tin opener
Corkscrew/bottle opener
Potato peeler
Large fruit dish
Butter dish
Sugar dish
Tray
Milk jug
Condiment set (2 piece)
Washing-up bowl
Dustpan and brush
Broom
Floor cloth
Pot scourer/dish mop
Bucket
Mirror
Doormat
Covered kitchen refuse container
Fire extinguisher/blanket
Smoke detector

2 per caravan/chalet
Table spoons
Mixing bowls or basins
Bread/cake plates
Dusters
Ash trays

Per bed
3 blankets or 1 continental quilt and cover (for winter lettings, or letting very early or late in the season the scale of bedding to be increased and adequate heating provided)
1 pillow per person

1 per person
Knife (table & dessert)
Fork (table & dessert)
Spoon (dessert & tea)
Plate (large & small)
Tea cup and saucer
Cereal/soup plate
Tumbler
Egg cup

4 per person
Coat-hangers

E Information for Hirers

The booking form should be accompanied by details of the park and caravan(s)/chalet(s) stating clearly:

1 The accommodation size (length and width) of the caravan and the number of berths. This shall not exceed the maximum number of berths as defined by the manufacturer.

2 Whether caravans are connected to:
Mains water
Mains drainage
Mains sewerage
Electricity (stating voltage)
Piped gas (stating LPG or Natural)

3 Type of lighting:
Electricity or Gas

4 Type of cooking:
Electricity or Gas

5 A full description of park and its amenities.

6 Wherever possible a map showing the location of the park and its proximity to main centres and attractions.

7 The charges for the accommodation/pitch for the period booked and details of any further additional charges, for example, electricity, gas, showers etc, as well as any optional charges, eg holiday insurance.

Note: If VAT is payable it must be included in the quoted price.

F Standards for Disabled Guests

The park may or may not be able to accommodate severely disabled guests (e.g. those in wheelchairs). Those that welcome them and wish to be so designated in publications, must conform to the following standards.

1 The entrance to the caravan must be equipped with a ramp whose gradient does not exceed 1 in 12 and a turning platform of at least 122cm (48ins) by 122cm (48ins).

2 All doors must have a clear opening width of at least 75cm (29.5ins).

3 In bedrooms, WCs and/or WCs in toilet blocks, used by the disabled, the clearance around beds, washbasins and WCs etc. must be at least 75cm (29.5ins) and there must be turning space of 122cm (48ins) by 122cm (48ins).

G Code of Conduct

In addition to fulfilling its statutory obligations, the park management undertakes to observe the following Code of Conduct:

1 To ensure high standards of courtesy, cleanliness, catering and service appropriate to the type of site.

2 To describe fairly to all visitors and prospective visitors, the amenities, facilities and service provided by the park, whether by advertisement, brochure, word of mouth, or any other means, and to allow visitors to see pitches, if requested, before booking.

3 To make clear to visitors exactly what is included in all prices quoted for pitches, meals and refreshments, including service charges, taxes and other surcharges. Details of cancellation procedures and charges for additional services or facilities available should also be made clear.

4 To adhere to, and not to exceed, prices current at the time of occupation for accommodation or other services.

5 To advise visitors at the time of booking and subsequent to any change, if the pitch offered is on another park and the location of the park and any difference in the comfort and amenities from the pitch previously booked.

6 To give each visitor, on request, details of payment due and receipt, if required.

7 To deal promptly and courteously with all enquiries, requests, reservations, correspondence and complaints from visitors.

8 To allow a National Tourist Board representative reasonable access to the establishment, on request, to confirm that the Code of Conduct is being observed.

9 The operator must also comply with the provisions of the caravan industry Codes of Practice.

USE YOUR i's

There are more than 800 Tourist Information Centres throughout Britain offering friendly help with accommodation and holiday ideas as well as suggestions of places to visit and things to do. You'll find the address of your nearest Tourist Information Centre in your local Phone Book.

ENGLAND - EVENTS 1997
MANIFESTATIONS EN ANGLETERRE EN 1997
VERANSTALTUNGEN IN ENGLAND 1997
EVENEMENTEN IN ENGELAND IN 1997
CALENDARIO DEGLI AVVENIMENTI IN INGHILTERRA NEL 1997

Below is a selection of events taking place in England throughout the coming year. *N.B. As changes often occur after press date it is advisable to confirm the information given with the local Tourist Information Centre when you get to England.*

Vous trouverez ci-dessous un choix de manifestations devant de dérouler en Angleterre dans le courant de l'année. *N.B. Etant donné que des modifications sont susceptibles de survenir après la date de mise sous presse, nous vous conseillons de vous faire confirmer, une fois arrivé en Angleterre, les reseignements donnés dans ce guide auprès du Centre d'Information Touristique de la région où vous séjournez.*

Nachstehend finden Sie eine Auswahl der 1996 in England stattfindenden Veranstaltungen. *N.B. Da nach Redaktionsschluß oft Änderungen vorkommen, ist es ratsam, sich die Angaben bei Ihrer Ankunft in England vom jeweiligen Tourist Information Centre bestätigen zu lassen.*

Hieronder vindt u een keuze uit de evenementen die er het komende jaar in Engeland zullen plaatsvinden. *N.B. Eventuele veranderingen vinden vaak pas na de persdatum*

plaats. Het is daarom raadzaam de gegeven informatie na aankomst in Engeland bij het plaatselijke Toeristen Informatie Bureau te controleren.

Riportiamo una selezione degli avvenimenti che si svolgeranno in Inghilterra nel corso dell'anno prossimo. *N.B. Dal momento che dopo la data di stampa si verificano spesso dei cambiamenti, si consiglia di verificare l'esattezza delle informazioni riportate in questa guida rivolgendosi, dopo l'arrivo in Inghilterra, al Tourist Information Centre del luogo.*

January 1997

2-13 January*
43rd London International Boat Show
Earls Court Exhibition Centre,
Warwick Road, London SW5
Contact: (01784) 473377

6 January
Old Custom: Haxey Hood Game
The Village, Haxey,
North Lincolnshire
Contact: (01427) 752845

9-12 January
Autosports International
National Exhibition Centre,
Birmingham, West Midlands
Contact: (0171) 402 2555

February 1997

7-16 February
Great St Valentine's Fair
City Centre,
Leeds, West Yorkshire
Contact: (0113) 247 4293

9 February*
Chinese New Year Celebrations: Year of the Ox
Centered on Gerrard Street
and Leicester Square,
London, WC2
Contact: (0171) 734 5161

9-14 February*
The Wordsworth Winter School
Dove Cottage & Wordsworth Museum, Town End,
Grasmere, Cumbria
Contact: (015394) 35544

20-23 February
Harrogate Antique and Fine Art Fair
Royal Baths Assembly Rooms,
Crescent Road, Harrogate,
North Yorkshire
Contact: (01823) 323363

March 1997

6-9 March
Crufts Dog Show
National Exhibition Centre,
Birmingham, West Midlands
Contact: (0171) 4936651

11-13 March
Cheltenham Gold Cup National Hunt Racing Festival
Cheltenham Racecourse,
Cheltenham, Gloucestershire
Contact: (01242) 513014

13 March-6 April
Daily Mail Ideal Home Exhibition
Earls Court Exhibition Centre,
Warwick Road,
London SW5
Contact: (01895) 677677

22 March-6 April
Easter Activities
Salford Museum & Art Gallery,
Peel Park, The Crescent,
Salford, Greater Manchester
Contact: (0161) 736 2649

28 March
Old Custom: Pace Egg Plays
Various venues in and around
Hebden Bridge,
West Yorkshire
Contact: (01422) 843831

29 March*
Oxford and Cambridge Boat Race
River Thames, London

April 1997

3-5 April
Grand National Meeting
Aintree Racecourse,
Ormskirk Road,
Aintree, Merseyside
Contact: (0151) 523 2600

8 April
Old Custom: World Coal Carrying Championship
Royal Oak Public House,
Owl Lane, Ossett,
West Yorkshire

11-13 April
2nd North East Knitting and Needlecraft Exhibition
Leeds University Exhibition
& Conference Centre,
Willow Terrace Road,
Leeds, West Yorkshire
Contact: (0117) 970 1370

11-13 April
County Spring Flower Show - 100th Anniversary
The Lost Gardens of Heligan,
Heligan, Pentewan, Cornwall
Contact: (01872) 74057

13 April*
London Marathon
Greenwich Park, London SE10
Contact: (0171) 620 4117

19-20 April
Bike Expo 97
Sheffield Arena, Broughton Lane,
Sheffield, South Yorkshire
Contact: (01484) 605555

26-27 April
Centennial Orchid Society
The Floral Halls,
Marine Parade, Southport,
Merseyside

26-27 April
Rainbow Craft Fair
Meols Hall, Churchtown,
Southport, Merseyside
Contact: (01704) 28326

27 April
Three Peaks Race
Playing Field,
Horton-in-Ribblesdale,
North Yorkshire
Contact: (0113) 258 5586

May 1997

2-3 May
Nottinghamshire County Show
Newark and Notts Show Ground,
Winthorpe, Nottinghamshire
Contact: (01636) 610642

2-4 May
Cleethorpes Beer Festival
Winter Gardens, Kingsway,
Cleethorpes,
North East Lincolnshire
Contact: (01472) 692925

3 May
Gawthorpe Maypole Procession
High Street, Gawthorpe,
Ossett, West Yorkshire

3-5 May*
Rochester Sweeps Festival
Various venues, Rochester, Kent
Contact: (01634) 843666

3-5 May*
Spalding Flower Parade and Springfields Country Fair
Springfields Show Gardens,
Spalding, Lincolnshire
Contact: (01775) 724843

3-25 May
Brighton International Festival
Various venues,
Brighton, East Sussex
Contact: (01273) 676926

4-5 May
Kids International
Telford Town Park,
Telford, Shropshire
Contact: (01952) 203009

8-11 May
Living Crafts Exhibition
Hatfield House, Hatfield,
Hertfordshire
Contact: (01582) 761235

10-25 May
Bournemouth International Festival
Various venues,
Bournemouth, Dorset
Contact: (01202) 297327

16-18 May
Keswick Jazz Festival
Keswick, Cumbria
Contact: (01900) 602122

17 May
Football: FA Challenge Cup Final
Wembley Stadium, London
Contact: (0171) 402 7151

20-23 May
Chelsea Flower Show
Royal Hospital Chelsea,
Royal Hospital Road London SW3

24 May-9 June
Salisbury Festival
Various venues, Salisbury, Wiltshire
Contact: (01722) 323883

25-26 May
Southend Air Show
Western Esplanade,
Southend-on-Sea, Essex

25-26 May*
North Shields Fishquay Festival
North Shields, Tyne and Wear
Contact: (0191) 257 5544

28-29 May
Corpus Christi Carpet of Flowers and Floral Festival
Cathedral of Our Lady and
St Philip Howard,

Cathedral House,
Arundel, West Sussex
Contact: (01903) 882297

28-31 May
The Royal Bath and West Show
The Royal Bath & West
Showground,
Shepton Mallet, Somerset
Contact: (01749) 822200

29-31 May*
Dickens Festival
Various venues, Rochester, Kent
Contact: (01634) 843666

30 May-1 June
Great Garden and Countryside Festival
Holker Hall and Gardens,
Cark in Cartmel, Cumbria
Contact: (015395) 58838

June 1997

1 June*
229th Royal Academy Summer Exhibition
Royal Academy of Arts,
Burlington House, Piccadilly,
London W1
Contact: (0171) 494 5615

5-7 June
South of England Agricultural Show
South of England Showground,
Ardingly, West Sussex
Contact: (01444) 892048

13-29 June
50th Aldeburgh Foundation of Music and the Arts
Snape Maltings Concert Hall,
Snape, Suffolk
Contact: (01728) 452935

14 June*
Durham Regatta
River Wear, Durham
Contact: (0191) 383 1594

14 June*
Trooping the Colour - The Queen's Birthday Parade
Horse Guards Parade,
London SW1
Contact: (0171) 414 2479

25-26 June
Royal Norfolk Show 97
The Showground, Dereham Road,
Norwich, Norfolk
Contact: (01603) 748931

28-29 June
Middlesex Show
Uxbridge Showground,
Park Road, Uxbridge, London
Contact: (01895) 252131

28-29 June
Royal Air Force Waddington Air Show
RAF Waddington, Lincolnshire
Contact: (01522) 726100

28-29 June
Vintage Vehicle Rally
Meols Hall, Churchtown,
Southport, Merseyside
Contact: (01704) 28326

30 June-3 July
The Royal Show
National Agricultural Centre,
Stoneleigh Park, Warwickshire
Contact: (01203) 696969

July 1997

1-31 July*
Hull International Festival
Various venues, Hull,
Kingston-upon-Hull
Contact: (01482) 615623

2-6 July
Henley Royal Regatta
Henley-on-Thames, Oxfordshire
Contact: (01491) 572153/4

3-20 July
The Exeter Festival
Various venues, Exeter, Devon
Contact: (01392) 265118

5-6 July
International Kite Festival
Northern Playing Fields,
Washington, Tyne and Wear
Contact: (0191) 514235

6-22 July
Chichester Festivities
Various venues,
Chichester, West Sussex
Contact: (01243) 785718

8-10 July
Great Yorkshire Show
Great Yorkshire Showground,
Harrogate, North Yorkshire
Contact: (01423) 561536

9-12 July
Claremont Fete Champetre
Claremont Landscape Garden,
Portsmouth Road, Esher, Surrey
Contact: (01372) 453401

11-13 July*
British Grand Prix 97
Silverstone, Northamptonshire
Contact: (01327) 857271

11, 12, 13 July
Swanage Jazz Festival
Various venues,
Swanage, Dorset
Contact: (01929) 422885

11-20 July .
"Ways with Words"
Literature Festival
Dartington Hall,
Dartington, Devon
Contact: (01803) 867311

12-13 July
Durham County Show
Clondyke Garden Centre,
Lambton Park,
Chester-Le-Street, Durham
Contact: (0191) 3885459

15-26 July
The Royal Tournament
Earls Court Exhibition Centre,
Warwick Road,
London SW5
Contact: (0171) 370 8202

19 July
Cumberland County Show
Rickerby Park,
Carlisle, Cumbria
Contact: (01228) 560364

19-20 July
Holkham Country Fair
Holkham Hall,
Wells-next-the-Sea, Norfolk
Contact: (01328) 830367

19-27 July
Whitstable Oyster Festival
Whitstable Harbour, Kent
Contact: (01227) 273570

19 July-2 August
King's Lynn Festival 97
King's Lynn Arts Centre,
King Street,
King's Lynn, Norfolk
Contact: (01553) 774725

25 July
Horse Racing: Glorious
Goodwood
Goodwood Racecourse,
Goodwood,
West Sussex
Contact: (01243) 774107

26-27 July
Cumbria Steam Gathering
Cark Airfield, Flookburgh,
Cumbria
Contact: (015242) 71584

26-31 July*
Teesside International
Eisteddfod
Middlesbrough Festival Town
Centre,
Middlesbrough,
Tees Valley
Contact: (01642) 327088

August 1997

1-8 August
43rd Sidmouth International
Festival of Folk Arts
The Arena and other Venues,
Sidmouth, Devon

2-9 August
Cowes Week
Cowes, Isle of Wight
Contact: (01983) 293303

2-17 August
International Gilbert and
Sullivan Festival
Buxton Opera House,
Water Street,
Buxton, Derbyshire
Contact: (01422) 359161

6-7 August
167th Bakewell Show
The Showground, Coombs Road,
Bakewell, Derbyshire
Contact: (01629) 812736

8-10 August
Bristol International Balloon Fiesta
Ashton Court Estate,
Long Ashton, Bristol
Contact: (0117) 953 5884

8-10 August
Lowther Horse Driving Trials and Country Fair
Lowther Castle,
Lowther, Cumbria
Contact: (01931) 712378

9-16 August*
Billingham International Folklore Festival
Queensway, Billingham,
Tees Valley
Contact: (01642) 558212

15-16 August
Shrewsbury Flower Show
Quarry Park, Shrewsbury,
Shropshire
Contact: (01743) 364051

15-17 August
International Birdwatching Fair
Egleton Reserve,
Rutland Water, Oakham,
Leicestershire
Contact: (01572) 770651

15-17 August
Northampton Hot Air Balloon Festival
Northampton Racecourse,
St. George's Avenue,
Northampton, Northamptonshire
Contact: (01604) 233500

16-22 August
Whitby Folk Week
Various venues,
Whitby, North Yorkshire
Contact: (01757) 708424

20 August
Weymouth Carnival
The Seafront,

Weymouth, Dorset
Contact: (01305) 772444

21-26 August
International Beatles Festival
Various venues,
Liverpool, Merseyside
Contact: (0151) 236 9091

22-25 August
Clacton Jazz Festival
Various venues,
Clacton-on-Sea, Essex
Contact: (01255) 425501

23-30 August
Bude Jazz Festival
Various venues,
Bude, Cornwall
Contact: (01684) 566956

24 August
Leicester International Air Display
Leicester Airport,
Gartree Road,
Leicester, Leicestershire
Contact: (0116) 259 2360

25 August
Mathew Street Festival
Cavern Quarter,
Liverpool City Centre,
Mathew Street,
Liverpool
Contact: (0151) 236 9091

27-31 August
Great Dorset Steam Fair
South Down,
Tarrant Hinton,
Dorset
Contact: (01258) 860361

28 August
Buckinghamshire County Show
Weedon Park, Weedon,
Aylesbury, Buckinghamshire
Contact: (01296) 83734

28 August
Muncaster Country Fair and Sheepdog Trials
Muncaster, Ravenglass,
Cumbria
Contact: (01229) 717608

29-31 August
Shepway Festival
The Leas, Folkestone, Kent
Contact: (01303) 852321

30 August
Hesket Newmarket Agricultural Show
Hog House Field, Hudscales,
Hesket Newmarket, Cumbria
Contact: (016974) 78663

September 1997

4 September
The Blenheim International Horse Trials
Blenheim Palace,
Woodstock, Oxfordshire
Contact: (01993) 813335

5-7 September
Swanage Folk Festival
Various venues,
Swanage, Dorset
Contact: (01929) 427490

6-7 September
Chatsworth Country Fair
Chatsworth House and Garden,
Bakewell, Derbyshire
Contact: (01328) 830367

6-7 September
Kirby Lonsdale Victorian Fair
Kirkby Lonsdale, Cumbria
Contact: (015242) 71237

13 September
Romsey Show
Broadlands Park,
Romsey, Hampshire
Contact: (01794) 517521

13-14 September
Essex Steam Rally and Craft Fair
Barleylands Farm Museum,
Billericay, Essex
Contact: (01268) 532253

13-21 September
Southampton International Boat Show
Western Esplanade,
Southampton, Hampshire
Contact: (01784) 473377

20-21 September
Newbury and Royal County of Berkshire Show
Newbury Showground,
Chieveley, Berkshire
Contact: (01635) 247111

28 September
Urswick Rushbearing
Urswick Church, Urswick,
Ulverston, Cumbria

October 1997

1-5 October
Horse of the Year Show
Wembley Arena, Empire Way,
Wembley, London
Contact: (01203) 693088

9-19 October
Norfolk and Norwich Festival 97
Various venues,
Norwich, Norfolk
Contact: (01603) 614921

10-18 October*
Hull Fair
Walton Street Fairground, Hull,
Kingston-upon-Hull
Contact: (01482) 615623

10-19 October
Cheltenham Festival of Literature
Town Hall, Imperial Square,
Cheltenham, Gloucestershire
Contact: (01242) 521621

11-25 October
Canterbury Festival
Various venues.
Canterbury, Kent
Contact: (01227) 455600

12 October
World Conker Championships
The Village Green,
Ashton, Northamptonshire

16-26 October
The London Motor Show
Earls Court Exhibition Centre,
Warwick Road, London SW5

19 October
Trafalgar Day Parade - The Sea Cadet Corps
Trafalgar Square, London WC2
Contact: (0171) 928 8978

November 1997

1 November
Grand Firework Spectacular
Leeds Castle,
Leeds, Kent
Contact: (01622) 765400

1 November
Firework Displays
Christchurch Park,
Ipswich, Suffolk

1 November
Bonfire and Firework Display
Meols Hall,
Churchtown, Southport,
Merseyside
Contact: (01704) 28326

6 November
Bridgwater Guy Fawkes Carnival
Town Centre,
Bridgwater, Somerset
Contact: (01278) 425344

8 November
Lord Mayor's Show
City of London
Contact: (01992) 505306

20 November
Biggest Liar in the World Competition
Bridge Inn, Wasdale,
Santon Bridge,
Cumbria
Contact: (01946) 67575

December 1997

18-22 December
Olympia International Showjumping Championships
Olympia,
Hammersmith Road,
London W14
Contact: (0171) 370 8202

30 December*
Carlisle Races Christmas Meet
Carlisle Racecourse,
Durdar, Cumbria
Contact: (016973) 42634

31 December
Allendale Baal Festival
Market Square,
Allendale,
Northumberland
Contact: (01434) 683763

SCOTLAND - EVENTS 1997

11 October '96 -8 February
Pride & Passion
The National Burns
Exhibition
Dick Institute,
Kilmarnock
Contact: (01563) 526401

28 January
Up Helly Aa
Traditional Viking Fire Festival
Lerwick, Shetland
Contact: (01595) 693768

16 January-2 February*
Celtic Connections
Glasgow Royal Concert Hall,
Glasgow
Contact: (0141) 332 6633

22-28 February
75th Inverness Music Festival
Inverness
Contact: (01463) 233902

25 February-1 March
Festival of One Act Plays
Aberdeen Arts Centre,
Aberdeen
Contact: (01224) 641122

3-8 March*
Glenshee Snow Fun Week
Glenshee,
Perthshire
Contact: (01250) 875509

21-23 March
Cairngorm Snow Festival
Aviemore
Contact: (01479) 861261

22 March-6 April
Edinburgh International
Science Festival
Various venues, Edinburgh
Contact: (0131) 220 3977

28 March-15 December
William Wallace 700th
Anniversary Exhibition
Smith Art Gallery & Museum,
Stirling
Contact: (01786) 471917

3-6 April*
Shetland Folk Festival
Various venues, Shetland
Contact: (01595) 694757

20 April
Fiddlers Rally
Oban
Contact: (01631) 710488

1-24 May*
Mayfest
Glasgow
Contact: (0141) 552 6612

2 May-11 October
Pitlochry Festival Theatre
Pitlochry, Perthshire
Contact: (01796) 472680

21 May-1 June*
Perth Festival of the Arts
Perth
Contact: (01738) 621031

22-25 May
Orkney Traditional Folk
Festival
Various venues, Orkney
Contact: (01856) 850773

23 May-1 June
Dumfries & Galloway Arts
Festival
Various venues in Dumfries and
Galloway
Contact: (01387) 260447

23 May-7 June
The Second Annual
Highland Festival
Various venues throughout the
Highlands and Islands.
Contact: (01463) 719000

24-25 May
Loch Fyne Food Fair
Loch Fyne, Argyll
Contact: (01499) 600217

26 May-1 June
International Children's
Festival
Edinburgh
Contact: (0131) 554 6297

5-7 June*
The Perth Scottish Rally
Perth
Contact: (0141) 204 4999

20-25 June
St Magnus Festival
Kirkwall,
Stromness, Orkney
Contact: (01859) 872669

27 June-6 July
11th International Jazz
Festival
Various venues,
Glasgow
Contact: (0141) 552 3572

28 June-16 August
Aberdeen Arts Carnival
Aberdeen Arts Centre,
Aberdeen
Contact: (01224) 635208

6-18 July
**Feis Bharraigh (Barra
Festival)**
Isle of Barra,
Western Isles
Contact: (01871) 810667

12-15 July
Cutty Sark Tall Ships Race
Aberdeen
Contact: (01224) 252150

17-20 July
**1997 Open Golf
Championship**
Royal & Ancient Golf Club
of St Andrews
Royal Troon, Ayrshire
Contact: (01334) 472112

25 July
Langholm Common Riding
Langholm,
Dumfriesshire
Contact: (01387) 380428

1-8 August
**West Highland Yachting
Week**
Crinin, Oban,
Tobermory
Contact: (01631) 563309

1-23 August
Edinburgh Military Tattoo
Edinburgh Castle,
Edinburgh
Contact: (0131) 225 1188

10-30 August
International Festival
Edinburgh
Contact: (0131) 226 4001

16 August
**World Pipe Band
Championships**
Glasgow
Contact: (0141) 221 5414

16-17 August*
**Scottish Championship
Horse Trials**
Thirlestane Castle,
Lauder,
Berwickshire
Contact: (01896) 860242

6 September
**Braemar Royal Highland
Gathering**
Braemar,
Aberdeenshire
Contact: (01339) 755377

12-13 September
**Battle of Stirling Bridge -
Theatre Event**
Stirling
Contact: (01786) 443122

13 September
**RAF Leuchars Battle of
Britain Airshow**
Leuchars,
Fife
Contact: (01334) 839000

9-18 October*
**Aberdeen Alternative
Festival**
Aberdeen
Contact: (01224) 635822

10-17 October
**Royal National Mod -
Inverness**
An Comunn Gaidhealach
Contact: (01463) 231226

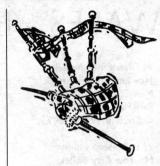

17 October*
**The Massed Bands of the
Royal Air Force Concert
Tour**
Royal Concert Hall,
Glasgow
Contact: (01285) 713300

8 November
**Dunvegan Castle Fireworks
Spectacular**
Dunvegan Castle,
Isle of Skye Contact: (01470)
521206

31 December
Edinburgh's Hogmanay
Various venues,
Edinburgh
Contact: (0131) 557 1700

* Provisional Dates

WALES - EVENTS 1997

14 December-25 January
Jack and the Beanstalk
New Theatre,
Park Place, Cardiff
Contact: (01222) 878889

22 December-5 January
Moscow City Ballet:
Swan Lake/Cinderella
St David's Hall,
The Hayes, Cardiff
Contact: (01222) 878444

1 January
Saundersfoot New Year's
Day Charity Swim
Saundersfoot Beach,
Saundersfoot, Pembrokeshire
Contact: (01834) 813039

1 February
Five Nations Championship
Rugby International - Wales
v Ireland
Cardiff Arms Park,
Westgate Street, Cardiff
Contact: (01222) 390111

22 February-30 September
Bi-Centenary of the Last
Invasion of Britain
Areas in Pencaster, Goodwick
and Fishguard,
Pembrokeshire
Contact: (01348) 873208

23 February
West Wales Antique and
Collectors Fair
Leisure Complex,
Kiln Park Holiday Centre,
Marsh Road,
Tenby
Contact: (01834) 812634

1 March
Cwmbach Choir - Annual
St David's Day Concert
The Coliseum,
Mount Pleasant Street,
Trecynon,
Aberdare
Contact: (01685) 881188

4 March-19 April
Shared Language
Exhibition
Newport Museum & Art Gallery,
John Frost Square,
Newport
Contact: (01633) 840064

6-8 March
Festival of Male Voice Praise
Brangwyn Hall,
The Guildhall,
Swansea
Contact: (01792) 851307

7-9 March
Llanwrtyd Wells Folk
Weekend
Various venues in Llanwrtyd
Wells
Contact: (01591) 610666

15 March
Five Nations Championship
Rugby International - Wales
v England
Cardiff Arms Park,
Westgate Street,
Cardiff
Contact: (01222) 390111

29-31 March
Welsh Camping and
Caravanning Show
Royal Welsh Showground,
Llanelwedd,
Builth Wells
Contact: (01597) 825984

26 April
Festival Concert
Deeside College,
Kelsterton Road,
Connah's Quay, Deeside
Contact: (01352) 732940

3-9 May
Bodedern and District
Festival
Heol yr Eglwys, Bodedern,
Contact: (01407) 740858

5-10 May
Llandrindod Wells Drama
Festival
Albert Hall Theatre,
Ithon Road,
Llandrindod Wells
Contact: (01597) 822283

23 May-1 June
The Hay Festival
Various venues in Hay-on-Wye
Contact: (01497) 821217

24 May -28 November
The Schubert Brahms
Experience
Y Tabernacl, Heol Pencallt,
Machynlleth
Contact: (01650) 521352

24-31 May
Hay Children's Festival of
the Arts
The Community Centre,
Hay-on-Wye,
Herefordshire
Contact: (01544) 328424

9-21 June '97
A Passion Play 'Behold the Man'
Margain Park,
Margain, Port Talbot
Contact: (01639) 813578

14-20 June
The Barmouth to Fort William Three Peaks Yacht Race
The Quay, Barmouth
Contact: (01341) 280298

15 June-21 July
Cardiff Singer of the World
St David's Hall,
The Hayes, Cardiff
Contact: (01222) 878444

20-22 June
Gwyl Ifan (Folk Dance Festival)
Various locations in Cardiff and surrounding areas
Contact: (01222) 563989

4-6 July
The Ninth North Wales Bluegrass Music Festival
Civic Hall, Bodlondeb Park and various venues in Conwy
Contact: (01492) 580454

8-13 July
Llangollen International Musical Eisteddfod
Royal International Pavilion,
Llangollen
Contact: (01978) 860236

14-26 July
Gower Music Festival
Various locations in Gower,
Swansea
Contact: (01792) 207924

17-26 July
The Welsh Proms
St David's Hall, The Hayes,
Cardiff
Contact: (01222) 878444

21-24 July
The Royal Welsh Show
Royal Welsh Showground,
Llanelwedd, Builth Wells
Contact: (01982) 553683

23-30 July
Ian Rush International Soccer Tournament
U.C.W. Playing Fields,
Llanbadarn Fawr,
Aberystwyth
Contact: (01938) 553631

2 August
Brecon County Show
The Showground,
The Walton, Brecon
Contact: (01568) 708760

2-9 August
National Eisteddfod of Wales
Bala, Meirionydd,
Contact: (01222) 763777

8-10 August
Brecon Jazz Festival
Various venues in Brecon
Contact: (01874) 625557

9 August
Eglwysbach Show
Cae Hemblas, Eglwysbach,
Colwyn Bay
Contact: (01492) 650529

9 August
Chepstow Agricultural Show
Howick Farm, Howick,
Nr Chepstow
Contact: (01291) 627655

15-17 August
Welsh Kennel Club Championship Dog Show
Royal Welsh Showground,
Llanelwedd,
Builth Wells
Contact: (01792) 843490

19-21 August
Pembrokeshire County Show
County Showground,
Withybush,
Haverfordwest,
Pembrokeshire
Contact: (01437) 764331

20 August
Vale of Glamorgan Agricultural Show
Penllyn Castle Park,
Cowbridge
Contact: (01446) 772027

28 August
Monmouthshire Show
Vauxhall Fields,
Monmouth,
Contact: (01291) 691160

13 September
Usk Show
Usk Showground,
Gwernesney,
Usk
Contact: (01291) 672379

2 December
Royal Welsh Agricultural Winter Fair
Royal Welsh Showground,
Llanelwedd,
Builth Wells
Contact: (01982) 553683

NORTHERN IRELAND - EVENTS 1997

4 January
International Cross-Country Athletics
Barnett's Demesne, Belfast
Contact: (01232) 602707

8-15 March
Opera Northern Ireland Spring Season
Madame Butterfly, Puccini
Grand Opera House, Belfast
Contact: (01232) 381241

17 March
St Patrick's Day Celebrations
Armagh, Downpatrick and Newry
Armagh - Contact:
(01861) 524640
Downpatrick - Contact:
(01396) 610831
Newry - Contact:
(01693) 67226

18 March
Horse Ploughing Match & Heavy Horse Show
Ballycastle
Contact: (012657) 62530

29 March
International Football
Northern Ireland v Portugal
World Cup qualifying match
Windsor Park, Belfast
Contact: (01232) 669458

12-16 May
Fermanagh Classic Fishing Festival
Fermanagh Lakeland
Contact: (01365) 323110

17 May
North West 200 Motorcycling

Portstewart circuit
Contact: (01265) 51199 or
(0850) 384663

6-8 June*
Jazz & Blues Festival
Holywood
Contact: (01232) 710793

14 June
Kilbroney 2000
Rostrevor
Rally of vintage and veteran cars, motorcycles and lorries
Contact: (01693) 67226

28 June
European Pipe Band Championship
Bangor
Contact: (01232) 833811

29 June
Northern Ireland International Air Show
Londonderry
Contact: (0113) 2675127

2-6 July
Coalisland International Music Festival
Coalisland
Contact: (01846) 623000 (day)
or (01868) 748809 (eves)

12 July
Battle of the Boyne Commemorations
Belfast and 18 other centres
Contact: (01232) 322801

24-27 July*
Senior British Open Tournament
Royal Portrush Golf Club
Contact: (01265) 822311

28 July-3 August*
Fiddler's Green Folk Festival
Rostrevor
Contact: (016937) 38577
or (016937) 39819

25-26 August
Oul' Lammas Fair
Ballycastle
Ireland's oldest traditional fair
Contact : (012657) 62024

25-28 September*
Balcas International Horse Trials
Ulster Lakeland Equestrian Park,
Necarne, Irvinestown
Contact: (01396) 821166/828734

5-6 September*
Appalachian & Blue Grass Music Festival
Ulster-American Folk Park,
Omagh
Contact: (01662) 243292

15-16 October
Northern Ireland Ploughing Championships
Bishopscourt, Downpatrick
Contact: (01232) 370222/777466

10 November
Belfast Festival at Queen's
Queen's University campus and
other venues,
Belfast
Contact: (01232) 667687

15-22 November
Foyle Film Festival
Londonderry
Contact: (01504) 260562

* Provisional Dates

TOURIST INFORMATION IN BRITAIN

INFORMATION POUR LES TOURISTES EN GRANDE-BRETAGNE
TOURISTEN-INFORMATION IN GROSSBRITANNIEN
TOERISTISCHE INFORMATIE IN GROOT-BRITTANNIE
INFORMAZIONI PER TURISTI IN GRAN BRETAGNA

One of the pleasures of visiting a country is discovering the unusual, as well as seeing the better known places of interest.

To help you explore Britain, to see both the major sites and the fascinating attractions off the beaten track, there is a country-wide service of Tourist Information Centres (TICs), each ready and able to give advice and directions on how best to enjoy your holiday in Britain. A comprehensive list can be obtained from BTA offices overseas.

Call in at these centres while travelling - you'll find them in most towns and many villages - and make use of the help that awaits you. Much development of Tourist Information Centre services has taken place in recent years and you should have no difficulty in locating them as most are well signposted and the use of the following international symbol is becoming more common:

You can rest assured that the Tourist Information Centres in the places you visit will be ready to give you all the help you need when you get to Britain, particularly on matters of detailed local information.

Accommodation Reservation Services

Wherever you go in Britain, you will find TICs which can help and advise you about all types of accommodation. Details of Park Finding Services are outlined on page 18.

The British Travel Centre

The British Travel Centre combines BTA, British Rail, Roomcentre and other big names to offer the most comprehensive information and booking service in London - and it's all under one roof, just 2 minutes' walk from Piccadilly Circus.

The British Travel Centre will book rail, air and car travel, reserves sightseeing tours, theatre tickets and accommodation, change currency and, of course, provide information in many languages on the whole of Britain. There is also a bookshop and giftshop within the Centre.

Open 7 days a week, 9.00 to 18.30 Monday to Friday, 10.00 to 16.00 Saturday and Sunday (extended Saturday opening during mid-May to September) at 12 Regent Street, Piccadilly Circus, London SW1Y 4PQ.

Please note that the British Travel Centre will be moving in 1997 to a new location close to Piccadilly Circus.

Tourist Organisations

Here is an address list of official tourist organisations in all parts of Britain. All these offices welcome personal callers, except those marked.

London

London Tourist Board and Convention Bureau
Tourist Information Centre
Victoria Station Forecourt
London SW1
Opening daily 09.00 to 20.30
(Reduced hours in winter)
Tel: 0171-730 3488 (Mons to Sats)
Information on London and England only.

Northern Ireland

Northern Ireland Tourist Board
11 Berkeley Street,
London W1X 5AD
Tel: 0171-493 0601

Scotland

Scottish Tourist Board
19 Cockspur Street,
London SW1Y 5BL
Tel: 0171-930 8661

Wales

Wales Tourist Board
12 Regent Street,
London SW1Y 4PQ
Tel: 0171 409 0969

British Tourist Authority
Thames Tower,
Black's Road,
Hammersmith,
London W6 9EL
(written enquiries only)

England

There are 10 regional tourist boards in England and a network of some 500 information centres. Look out for the sign shown above.

English Tourist Board
Thames Tower, Black's Road,
Hammersmith, London W6 9EL
(written enquiries only)

Northern Ireland

Northern Ireland Tourist Board
St Anne's Court, North Street,
Belfast BT1 1NB
Tel: (01232) 231221

Scotland

The Scottish Tourist Board has a substantial network of local tourist boards, backed up by more than 150 information centres.

Scottish Travel Centre
14 South St Andrews Street
Edinburgh EH2 2AZ
Tel: (0131) 332 2433

Wales

Wales has three Regional Marketing Councils and a network of more than 60 information centres to help you.

Wales Tourist Board
Brunel House,
2 Fitzalan Road,
Cardiff CF2 1UY
Tel: (01222) 499909
(telephone and written enquiries only)

CHECK THE MAPS

The colour maps at the back of this guide show all the cities, towns and villages for which you will find accommodation entries.

Refer to the town index to find the page on which it is listed.

AT-A-GLANCE SYMBOLS

Symbols at the end of each accommodation entry give useful information about services and facilities. A key to symbols can be found inside the back cover flap.

Keep this open for easy reference.

BTA OVERSEAS OFFICES

Argentina
BTA
Avenida Cordoba 645
2nd Floor
1054 Buenos Aires
Tel: (1) 314 6735
Fax: (1) 314 8955
(open to public 1000-1300 only)

Australia
BTA
8th Floor, University Centre
210 Clarence Street
Sydney, NSW 2000
Tel: (2) 267 4555
Fax: (2) 267 4442

Belgium
BTA
306 Avenue Louise
1050 Brussels
Tel: (2) 646 35 10
Fax: (2) 646 39 86

Canada
BTA
111 Avenue Road, Suite 450
Toronto
Ontario M5R 3J8
Tel: (416) 925 6326
Fax: (416) 961 2175

Czech & Slovak Republics
BTA
Kaprova 13
110 01 Prague 1
PO Box 264
Tel: (2) 232 7213
Fax: (2) 232 7469

Denmark
BTA
Møntergade 3
1116 Copenhagen K
Tel: 33 33 91 88
Fax: 33 14 01 36

France
BTA
Maison de la
Grande-Bretagne
19 rue des Mathurins
75009 Paris
Tel: 44 51 56 20
Fax: 44 51 56 21
Minitel: 3615 BRITISH

Germany
BTA
Taunusstrasse 52-60
60329 Frankfurt
Tel: (69) 238 0711
Fax: (69) 238 0717

Hong Kong
BTA
Room 1504, Eton Tower
8 Hysan Avenue
Causeway Bay
Hong Kong
Tel: 2882 9967
Fax: 2577 1443

Ireland
BTA
18-19 College Green
Dublin 2
Tel: (1) 670 8000
Fax: (1) 670 8244

Italy (Milan)
BTA
Corso Magenta 32
20123 Milano
Tel: (2) 7201 0078
Fax: (2) 7201 0086

Italy (Rome)
BTA
Corso Vittorio Emanuele 337
00186 Rome
Tel: (6) 68806821
Fax: (6) 6879095 (incoming only)

Japan - Osaka
BTA
OCAT Building, 4th Floor
1-chome, 4-1 Minatomachi
Naniwa-ku
Osaka 556
Tel: (6) 635 3093
Fax: (6) 635 3095

Japan Tokyo
BTA
Akasaka Twin Tower 1F
2-17-22 Akasaka
Minato-ku
Tokyo
Tel: (3) 5562 2550
Fax: (3) 5562 2551

Korea
BTA
Anglican Church Building
3-7 Chung-dong
Choong-ku
Seoul 100-120
Tel: (2) 723 8266-8
Fax: (2) 720 6066

Netherlands
BTA
Aurora Gebouw (5e)
Stadhouderskade 2
1054 ES Amsterdam
Tel: (20) 685 50 51
Fax: (20) 618 68 68

New Zealand
BTA
3rd Floor, Dilworth Building
Corner Queen & Customs
Streets
Auckland 1
Tel: (9) 303 1446
Fax: (9) 377 6965

Norway
BTA
Nedre Slotts Gt 21, 4 etasje
N-0157 Oslo
Postbox 1554 Vika
N-0117 Oslo
Tel: 22 42 47 45
Fax: 22 42 48 74

Portugal
BTA
Rua Luciano Cordeiro
123 2°Dt°
1050 Lisbon
Tel: (1) 312 9020
Fax: (1) 312 9030

Singapore
BTA
24 Raffles Place
#19-06 Clifford Centre
Singapore 048621
Tel: 535 2966
Fax: 534 4703

South Africa
BTA
Lancaster Gate
Hyde Park Lane
Hyde Lane, Hyde Park
Sandton 2196 (Visitors);
PO Box 41896
Craighall 2024 (Postal address)
Tel: (11) 325 0343
Fax: (11) 325 0344

Spain
BTA
Torre de Madrid 6/5
Pza. de España 18
28008, Madrid
Tel: (91) 541 13 96
Fax: (91) 542 81 49

Sweden
BTA
Box 3102, 103 62 Stockholm
(Postal address);
Klara Norra Kyrkogata 29,
S 111 22 Stockholm (Visitors)
Tel: (8) 4401 700
Fax: (8) 21 31 29

Switzerland
(Information office only)
BTA
Limmatquai 78,
CH-8001 Zurich
Tel: (1) 261 42 77
Fax: (1) 251 44 56

Taiwan
BTA
7th Floor
Fu Key Building
99 Jen Ai Road
Section 2
Taipei 10625
Tel: 2 351 0991
Fax: 2 392 6653

USA - Chicago
BTA
625 N Michigan Avenue
Suite 1510
Chicago IL 60611
(personal callers only)

USA - New York
BTA
7th Floor
551 Fifth Avenue
New York
NY 10176-0799
Tel: 1 800 GO 2 BRITAIN
or (212) 986 2200
Fax: (212) 986 1188

MILEAGE CHART

The distances between towns on the mileage chart are given to the nearest mile, and are measured along routes based on the quickest travelling time, making maximum use of motorways or dual-carriageway roads. The chart is based upon information supplied by the Automobile Association.

	Aberdeen	Aberystwyth	Barnstaple	Birmingham	Brighton	Bristol	Cambridge	Cardiff	Carlisle	Carmarthen	Colchester	Dorchester	Dover	Edinburgh	Exeter	Fort William	Glasgow	Gloucester	Guildford	Holyhead	Hull	Inverness	Kendal	Leeds	Lincoln	Liverpool	Maidstone	Manchester	Middlesbrough	Newcastle	Norwich	Nottingham	Oxford	Penzance	Perth	Plymouth	Sheffield	Southampton	Stranraer	Taunton	York
Aberystwyth	468																																								
Barnstaple	603	211																																							
Birmingham	431	123	178																																						
Brighton	606	285	206	171																																					
Bristol	514	128	100	88	169																																				
Cambridge	462	214	267	97	120	171																																			
Cardiff	534	117	129	108	203	46	205																																		
Carlisle	232	236	372	196	375	282	257	302																																	
Carmarthen	517	50	190	169	264	107	266	67	285																																
Colchester	515	289	291	171	112	195	48	229	310	290																															
Dorchester	596	203	94	170	121	62	180	121	364	182	208																														
Dover	586	325	272	207	81	206	124	239	401	300	116	201																													
Edinburgh	125	335	471	296	474	382	334	401	99	384	387	463	458																												
Exeter	587	195	55	161	176	84	251	113	356	174	276	54	244	455																											
Fort William	156	446	582	406	584	492	467	511	209	495	520	574	611	133	566																										
Glasgow	147	332	468	293	471	379	354	398	96	381	407	461	498	47	452	102																									
Gloucester	479	111	126	53	155	36	150	66	247	127	170	118	192	346	110	457	343																								
Guildford	564	222	174	128	44	106	91	139	332	200	103	98	97	431	147	541	428	100																							
Holyhead	460	105	341	165	344	251	260	206	228	155	334	333	370	327	325	438	324	216	301																						
Hull	361	227	321	134	260	231	139	251	170	312	192	313	264	232	305	380	266	196	239	218																					
Inverness	106	494	630	455	633	540	516	560	258	543	569	622	659	157	614	65	173	505	591	485	428																				
Kendal	279	190	326	150	329	236	245	256	47	239	319	318	355	146	310	257	143	201	286	181	164	305																			
Leeds	328	173	309	115	262	220	146	239	123	222	199	302	271	199	293	332	219	185	220	165	59	318	72																		
Lincoln	387	201	276	99	208	187	88	206	182	267	141	245	212	258	260	392	278	152	166	204	47	440	176	72																	
Liverpool	358	111	274	99	277	184	193	204	126	167	267	266	303	225	258	335	222	149	234	103	128	384	79	74	140																
Maidstone	547	283	233	168	50	167	85	200	362	261	77	162	41	419	206	572	458	153	58	330	225	620	316	233	173	264															
Manchester	352	131	262	86	264	172	160	191	120	180	213	254	291	220	246	330	216	137	222	122	98	378	74	44	85	35	249														
Middlesbrough	276	244	359	172	319	269	199	288	95	293	252	351	323	148	343	281	191	234	277	235	89	308	84	64	123	144	281	114													
Newcastle	234	274	389	202	350	300	229	319	59	323	282	381	354	105	373	238	153	265	307	265	142	266	101	95	154	175	311	145	39												
Norwich	487	276	329	159	169	233	63	267	282	328	59	242	173	359	313	492	378	212	161	321	150	540	276	172	103	240	131	185	223	254											
Nottingham	393	160	235	53	195	145	86	164	188	226	139	227	218	264	219	398	284	110	153	174	92	446	148	74	38	108	176	71	129	160	118										
Oxford	503	159	170	68	109	74	81	107	271	168	124	115	146	370	154	481	367	48	67	239	189	529	225	171	130	173	106	161	227	257	161	103									
Penzance	697	305	110	271	288	194	361	223	466	284	386	166	356	565	110	675	561	129	259	433	414	724	419	403	369	367	317	355	451	482	423	328	264								
Perth	86	382	518	343	521	428	379	448	146	431	432	510	504	42	502	102	61	393	479	373	277	114	193	245	304	272	462	266	193	151	404	311	418	612							
Plymouth	628	236	61	202	219	125	292	154	397	214	317	97	287	496	45	606	492	150	190	364	345	655	350	334	300	298	248	286	382	413	354	259	195	78	543						
Sheffield	366	167	272	86	233	183	122	202	162	263	175	265	247	238	257	371	246	148	191	158	65	420	125	36	47	79	204	38	103	133	147	44	141	366	283	297					
Southampton	570	221	140	134	66	76	131	139	338	200	158	54	152	437	109	547	434	99	48	306	256	596	291	237	196	240	112	227	293	324	193	170	66	221	484	152	207				
Stranraer	239	342	478	303	481	388	363	408	106	391	417	470	507	133	462	186	84	353	438	333	276	265	153	229	288	232	465	226	201	163	389	295	378	572	153	503	268	444			
Taunton	555	162	50	129	158	51	218	80	323	141	243	45	224	422	34	533	419	77	126	291	227	581	277	260	227	225	184	212	309	340	280	186	121	144	469	75	223	91	429		
York	321	201	316	129	276	226	156	245	117	250	209	308	280	193	300	326	213	191	234	192	38	375	91	25	81	102	238	72	50	88	181	87	184	410	238	341	60	251	223	267	
London	545	238	216	120	59	120	60	153	314	214	62	129	78	413	200	523	409	102	30	281	187	572	267	199	136	215	38	203	254	285	115	131	56	310	460	241	168	80	419	167	211

ACCOMMODATION COUPONS

▶ **Complete this coupon and mail it direct to the park in which you are interested. Do not send it to the British Tourist Authority. Remember to enclose a stamped addressed envelope (or international reply coupon).**

▶ **Tick as appropriate and complete the reverse side if you are interested in making a booking.**

❑ *Please send me a brochure or further information, and details of prices charged.*
❑ *Please advise me, as soon as possible, if accommodation is available as detailed overleaf.*

Name: *(BLOCK CAPITALS)*

Address:

Postcode:

Telephone number: *Date:*

Where to Stay 1997
Camping & Caravan Parks

BTA
British Tourist Authority

▶ **Complete this coupon and mail it direct to the park in which you are interested. Do not send it to the British Tourist Authority. Remember to enclose a stamped addressed envelope (or international reply coupon).**

▶ **Tick as appropriate and complete the reverse side if you are interested in making a booking.**

❑ *Please send me a brochure or further information, and details of prices charged.*
❑ *Please advise me, as soon as possible, if accommodation is available as detailed overleaf.*

Name: *(BLOCK CAPITALS)*

Address:

Postcode:

Telephone number: *Date:*

Where to Stay 1997
Camping & Caravan Parks

BTA
British Tourist Authority

ACCOMMODATION COUPONS

▶ **Complete this side if you are interested in making a booking.**

▶ **Please read the information on pages 17-19 before confirming any booking.**

Please advise me if a pitch or accommodation is available as detailed below.

From (date of arrival): _____ To (date of departure): _____

or alternatively from: _____ To: _____

Adults _____ Children _____ (ages _____)
Please give the number of people and ages of children

Type of pitch/accommodation required: _____

_____

Other/special requirements: _____

_____

▶ **Please enclose a stamped addressed envelope (or international reply coupon).**

▶ **Complete this side if you are interested in making a booking.**

▶ **Please read the information on pages 17-19 before confirming any booking.**

Please advise me if a pitch or accommodation is available as detailed below.

From (date of arrival): _____ To (date of departure): _____

or alternatively from: _____ To: _____

Adults _____ Children _____ (ages _____)
Please give the number of people and ages of children

Type of pitch/accommodation required: _____

_____

Other/special requirements: _____

_____

▶ **Please enclose a stamped addressed envelope (or international reply coupon).**

ACCOMMODATION COUPONS

▶ *Complete this coupon and mail it direct to the park in which you are interested.*
Do not send it to the British Tourist Authority. Remember to enclose a stamped
addressed envelope (or international reply coupon).

▶ *Tick as appropriate and complete the reverse side if you are interested in*
making a booking.

❑ *Please send me a brochure or further information, and details of prices charged.*
❑ *Please advise me, as soon as possible, if accommodation is available as detailed overleaf.*

Name: _____ (BLOCK CAPITALS)

Address: _____

_____

Postcode: _____

Telephone number: _____ Date: _____

Where to Stay 1997
Camping & Caravan Parks

BTA
British Tourist Authority

▶ *Complete this coupon and mail it direct to the park in which you are interested.*
Do not send it to the British Tourist Authority. Remember to enclose a stamped
addressed envelope (or international reply coupon).

▶ *Tick as appropriate and complete the reverse side if you are interested in*
making a booking.

❑ *Please send me a brochure or further information, and details of prices charged.*
❑ *Please advise me, as soon as possible, if accommodation is available as detailed overleaf.*

Name: _____ (BLOCK CAPITALS)

Address: _____

_____

Postcode: _____

Telephone number: _____ Date: _____

Where to Stay 1997
Camping & Caravan Parks

BTA
British Tourist Authority

ACCOMMODATION COUPONS

▶ **Complete this side if you are interested in making a booking.**

▶ **Please read the information on pages 17-19 before confirming any booking.**

Please advise me if a pitch or accommodation is available as detailed below.

From (date of arrival): _____   To (date of departure): _____

or alternatively from: _____   To: _____

Adults _____   Children _____   (ages _____)
Please give the number of people and ages of children

Type of pitch/accommodation required: _____

_____

Other/special requirements: _____

_____

▶ **Please enclose a stamped addressed envelope (or international reply coupon).**

▶ **Complete this side if you are interested in making a booking.**

▶ **Please read the information on pages 17-19 before confirming any booking.**

Please advise me if a pitch or accommodation is available as detailed below.

From (date of arrival): _____   To (date of departure): _____

or alternatively from: _____   To: _____

Adults _____   Children _____   (ages _____)
Please give the number of people and ages of children

Type of pitch/accommodation required: _____

_____

Other/special requirements: _____

_____

▶ **Please enclose a stamped addressed envelope (or international reply coupon).**

ACCOMMODATION COUPONS

▶ **Complete this coupon and mail it direct to the park in which you are interested. Do not send it to the British Tourist Authority. Remember to enclose a stamped addressed envelope (or international reply coupon).**

▶ **Tick as appropriate and complete the reverse side if you are interested in making a booking.**

❏ Please send me a brochure or further information, and details of prices charged.

❏ Please advise me, as soon as possible, if accommodation is available as detailed overleaf.

Name: _____ (BLOCK CAPITALS)

Address: _____

_____

_____ Postcode: _____

Telephone number: _____ Date: _____

Where to Stay 1997
Camping & Caravan Parks

BTA
British Tourist Authority

▶ **Complete this coupon and mail it direct to the park in which you are interested. Do not send it to the British Tourist Authority. Remember to enclose a stamped addressed envelope (or international reply coupon).**

▶ **Tick as appropriate and complete the reverse side if you are interested in making a booking.**

❏ Please send me a brochure or further information, and details of prices charged.

❏ Please advise me, as soon as possible, if accommodation is available as detailed overleaf.

Name: _____ (BLOCK CAPITALS)

Address: _____

_____

_____ Postcode: _____

Telephone number: _____ Date: _____

Where to Stay 1997
Camping & Caravan Parks

BTA
British Tourist Authority

ACCOMMODATION COUPONS

▶ **Complete this side if you are interested in making a booking.**

▶ **Please read the information on pages 17-19 before confirming any booking.**

Please advise me if a pitch or accommodation is available as detailed below.

From (date of arrival): _____   To (date of departure): _____

or alternatively from: _____   To: _____

Adults _____   Children _____   (ages _____)

Please give the number of people and ages of children

Type of pitch/accommodation required: _____

_____

Other/special requirements: _____

_____

▶ **Please enclose a stamped addressed envelope (or international reply coupon).**

▶ **Complete this side if you are interested in making a booking.**

▶ **Please read the information on pages 17-19 before confirming any booking.**

Please advise me if a pitch or accommodation is available as detailed below.

From (date of arrival): _____   To (date of departure): _____

or alternatively from: _____   To: _____

Adults _____   Children _____   (ages _____)

Please give the number of people and ages of children

Type of pitch/accommodation required: _____

_____

Other/special requirements: _____

_____

▶ **Please enclose a stamped addressed envelope (or international reply coupon).**

ADVERTISEMENT COUPONS

▶ **Complete this coupon and mail it direct to the advertiser from whom you would like to receive further information. Do not send it to the British Tourist Authority.**

To (advertiser's name): _____

Please send me a brochure or further information on the following, as advertised by you in the British Tourist Authority's **Where to Stay 1997** *Camping & Caravan Parks:*

_____

_____

▶ **Complete this coupon and mail it direct to the advertiser from whom you would like to receive further information. Do not send it to the British Tourist Authority.**

To (advertiser's name): _____

Please send me a brochure or further information on the following, as advertised by you in the British Tourist Authority's **Where to Stay 1997** *Camping & Caravan Parks:*

_____

_____

▶ **Complete this coupon and mail it direct to the advertiser from whom you would like to receive further information. Do not send it to the British Tourist Authority.**

To (advertiser's name): _____

Please send me a brochure or further information on the following, as advertised by you in the British Tourist Authority's **Where to Stay 1997** *Camping & Caravan Parks:*

_____

_____

ADVERTISEMENT COUPONS

Name: _____ (BLOCK CAPITALS)

Address: _____

_____

_____ Postcode: _____

Telephone Number: _____ Date: _____

Where to Stay 1997
Camping & Caravan Parks

BTA 🏴
British Tourist Authority

Name: _____ (BLOCK CAPITALS)

Address: _____

_____

_____ Postcode: _____

Telephone Number: _____ Date: _____

Where to Stay 1997
Camping & Caravan Parks

BTA 🏴
British Tourist Authority

Name: _____ (BLOCK CAPITALS)

Address: _____

_____

_____ Postcode: _____

Telephone Number: _____ Date: _____

Where to Stay 1997
Camping & Caravan Parks

BTA 🏴
British Tourist Authority

ADVERTISEMENT COUPONS

▶ **Complete this coupon and mail it direct to the advertiser from whom you would like to receive further information. Do not send it to the British Tourist Authority.**

To (advertiser's name): _____

Please send me a brochure or further information on the following, as advertised by you in the British Tourist Authority's **Where to Stay 1997** *Camping & Caravan Parks:*

_____

▶ **Complete this coupon and mail it direct to the advertiser from whom you would like to receive further information. Do not send it to the British Tourist Authority.**

To (advertiser's name): _____

Please send me a brochure or further information on the following, as advertised by you in the British Tourist Authority's **Where to Stay 1997** *Camping & Caravan Parks:*

_____

▶ **Complete this coupon and mail it direct to the advertiser from whom you would like to receive further information. Do not send it to the British Tourist Authority.**

To (advertiser's name): _____

Please send me a brochure or further information on the following, as advertised by you in the British Tourist Authority's **Where to Stay 1997** *Camping & Caravan Parks:*

_____

ADVERTISEMENT COUPONS

Name: _____ (BLOCK CAPITALS)

Address: _____

_____

Postcode: _____

Telephone Number: _____ Date: _____

Where to Stay 1997
Camping & Caravan Parks

BTA 🏴
British Tourist Authority

Name: _____ (BLOCK CAPITALS)

Address: _____

_____

Postcode: _____

Telephone Number: _____ Date: _____

Where to Stay 1997
Camping & Caravan Parks

BTA 🏴
British Tourist Authority

Name: _____ (BLOCK CAPITALS)

Address: _____

_____

Postcode: _____

Telephone Number: _____ Date: _____

Where to Stay 1997
Camping & Caravan Parks

BTA 🏴
British Tourist Authority

INDEX TO PARKS
REPERTOIRE DES TERRAINS/PLATZVERZEICHNIS/
REGISTER VAN CAMPINGS/INDICE DEI CAMPEGGI

THE QUALITY Q IS YOUR

SURE SIGN

OF WHERE TO STAY

CARAVAN, CHALET AND CAMPING PARKS

Throughout Britain, the tourist boards now inspect over 1,200 holiday parks, every year, to help you find the ones that suit you best.

THE GRADES: 1-5 ✓s within the Q for quality symbol tell you the quality standard of what is provided. The more ✓s, the higher the standard.

More detailed information on the **Quality Q** is given in free *SURE SIGN* leaflets, available from any Tourist Information Centre.

We've checked them out before you check in!

INDEX TO TOWNS
ANNUAIRE PAR VILLES/STÄDTEVERZEICHNIS/
INDEX VAN STEDEN/INDICE DELLE CITTÀ

254

MAP I

A

B

Dublin
Dun Laoghaire

MERSEYSIDE
M58
A565
A570
M62
LIVERPOOL
A57
Liverpool
M53
A550
M56

Dulas

ISLE OF
ANGLESEY

Holyhead

Prestatyn

Llandudno
Conwy
Penmaenmawr
Colwyn
Bay
Flint
FLINTSHIRE
Chester
A55
A494
CHESHIRE
A54

Bangor
A5
A55

CONWY
A470

Caernarfon

A487

Betws-y-Coed
A470
DENBIGHSHIRE
A483
Wrexham
WREXHAM
A41
A495

SNOWDONIA
A470
Porthmadog
NATIONAL PARK
Talsarnau
Harlech
GWYNEDD
Bala
A5
A5
A495
A5

Abersoch
A494

ENGLAND

Barmouth
A470
A487
Dolgellau
A458
A483
Welshpool
A458
Shrewsbury
A49
SHROPSHIRE

Borth
A487
A44
A470
A489
A49

See map 2 for Key to Maps

Aberystwyth

A487
A465
A44
A483
POWYS
A470

CEREDIGION

A44
Llandrindod
Wells
A49

SEE MAPS 3 & 5

New Quay
A487
Aberporth
A487
Cardigan
A484
A485
A482
A483
A470
A438
HEREFORD
AND
WORCESTER
A44
A4112
A438
A49

Fishguard
A40
A487
Llandovery
A40
Brecon
Llangorse
A470
A465
A49

St. David's
PEMBROKESHIRE COAST
NATIONAL PARK
CARMARTHENSHIRE
Carmarthen
A40
A483
BRECON BEACONS
NATIONAL PARK
Crickhowell
A465
Monmouth
A40

PEMBROKESHIRE
A40
A4067
A470
BLAENAU
GWENT
MONMOUTHSHIRE
A449
A4042
A449

Little Haven
Haverfordwest
Narberth
A477
Pendine
Amroth
Saundersfoot
Milford
Haven
M4
Llanelli
SWANSEA
A48
NEATH
PORT TALBOT
A465
Merthyr
Tydfil
Aberdare
RHONDDA
CYNON TAFF
Cwmbran
Cwmcarn
CAERPHILLY
Caerphilly
Cwmbran
Newport
NEWPORT
M48
M4

Pembroke
Rosslare
Tenby
SWANSEA
BRIDGEND
VALE OF
CARDIFF
M4
M4
M5

Porthcawl
A48
Cowbridge
GLAMORGAN
CARDIFF
Penarth
NORTH
Bristol

Cork
Cardiff-
Wales
Barry
SOMERSET

N

0   25 Miles
0   40 Kilometres

Produced by COLIN EARL Cartography

257

MAP 2

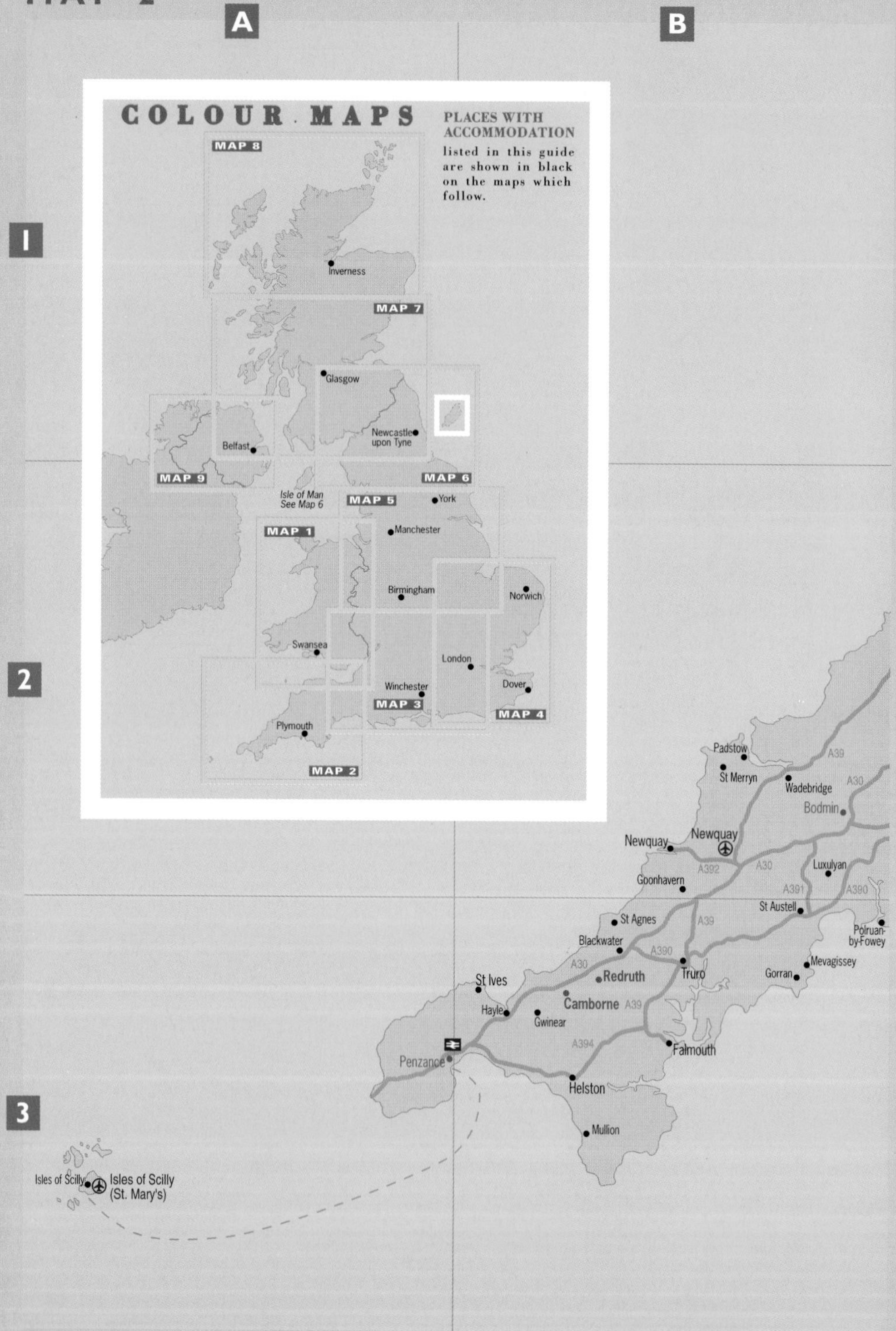

A B

1

COLOUR MAPS

PLACES WITH ACCOMMODATION listed in this guide are shown in black on the maps which follow.

MAP 8

Inverness

MAP 7

Glasgow

Newcastle upon Tyne

Belfast

MAP 9

Isle of Man See Map 6

MAP 6

MAP 5

York

MAP 1

Manchester

Birmingham

Norwich

Swansea

London

Dover

Winchester

MAP 3

MAP 4

Plymouth

MAP 2

2

Padstow

St Merryn

A39

Wadebridge

A30

Bodmin

Newquay

Newquay

A392

A30

Luxulyan

Goonhavern

A391

A390

St Agnes

A39

St Austell

Polruan-by-Fowey

Blackwater

A390

Truro

Gorran

Mevagissey

St Ives

Redruth

Hayle

Camborne

A39

Gwinear

A394

Falmouth

Penzance

Helston

3

Mullion

Isles of Scilly

Isles of Scilly (St. Mary's)

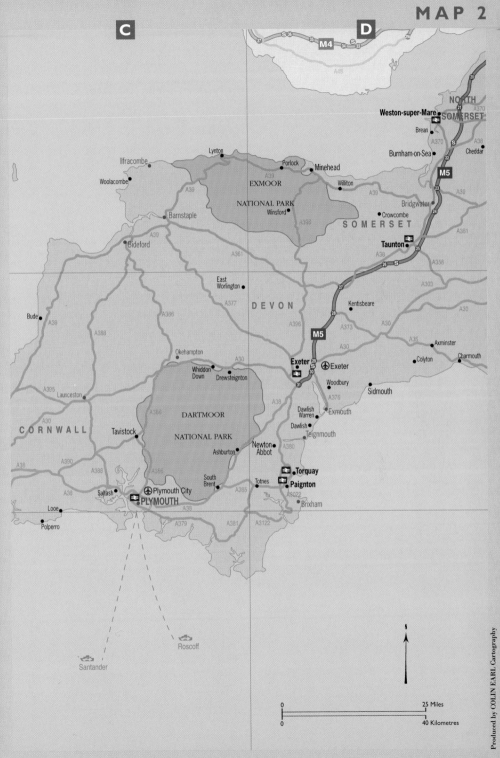

MAP 2

C

D

M4

NORTH SOMERSET

Weston-super-Mare

Brean

Burnham-on-Sea

Cheddar

Lynton

Porlock

Minehead

Ilfracombe

Woolacombe

EXMOOR NATIONAL PARK

Williton

M5

Winsford

Crowcombe

Bridgwater

Barnstaple

SOMERSET

Bideford

Taunton

East Worlington

DEVON

Kentisbeare

Bude

Okehampton

Axminster

Colyton

Charmouth

Whiddon Down

Drewsteignton

Launceston

Exeter

Exeter

Woodbury

Sidmouth

CORNWALL

DARTMOOR NATIONAL PARK

Dawlish Warren

Exmouth

Tavistock

Dawlish

Teignmouth

Ashburton

Newton Abbot

Totnes

Torquay

South Brent

Paignton

Saltash

Plymouth City

PLYMOUTH

Brixham

Looe

Polperro

Santander

Roscoff

N

0   25 Miles

0   40 Kilometres

259

MAP 3

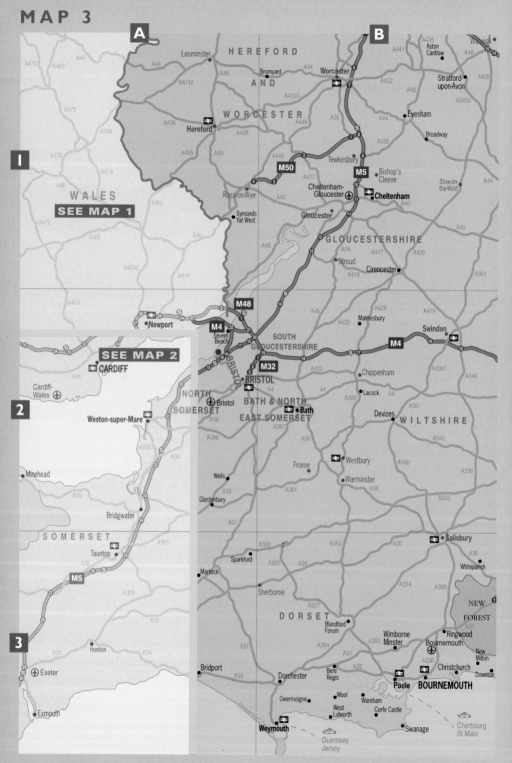

A **B**

I

HEREFORD
Leominster
Bromyard
Worcester
AND
Hereford
WORCESTER
A4112
A4103
A422
A441
Aston Cantlow
Warwick
Stratford-upon-Avon
A46
A429
A3400
Evesham
Broadway
Stow-on-the-Wold
A44

M50
Ross-on-Wye
Symonds Yat West
Tewkesbury
Bishop's Cleeve
M5
Cheltenham-Gloucester
Cheltenham
Gloucester
GLOUCESTERSHIRE
Stroud
Cirencester
A417
A419
A361

WALES
SEE MAP 1

M48
Newport
M4
Severn Beach
SOUTH
GLOUCESTERSHIRE
M32
BRISTOL
Malmesbury
A433
Swindon
M4
A346
A4361
A419

2
SEE MAP 2
CARDIFF
Cardiff-Wales
Weston-super-Mare
NORTH
SOMERSET
Bristol
BATH & NORTH
EAST SOMERSET
BRISTOL
Bath
Chippenham
Lacock
Devizes
WILTSHIRE
A342
A338

Minehead
Frome
Westbury
Warminster
A360
A36
A303

Bridgwater
Wells
Glastonbury
A368
A367
A361

SOMERSET
Taunton
M5
Sparkford
Martock
Sherborne
Salisbury
Whiteparish
A36
A338
Blandford Forum

3
Honiton
Exeter
Exmouth
Bridport
Dorchester
Bere Regis
Owermoigne
Wool
West Lulworth
Wareham
Corfe Castle
Swanage
Weymouth
DORSET
NEW FOREST
Ringwood
Wimborne Minster
BOURNEMOUTH
Poole
Christchurch
Downton
New Milton
Guernsey
Jersey
Cherbourg
St Malo

260

MAP 3

Produced by COLIN EARL Cartography

MAP 4

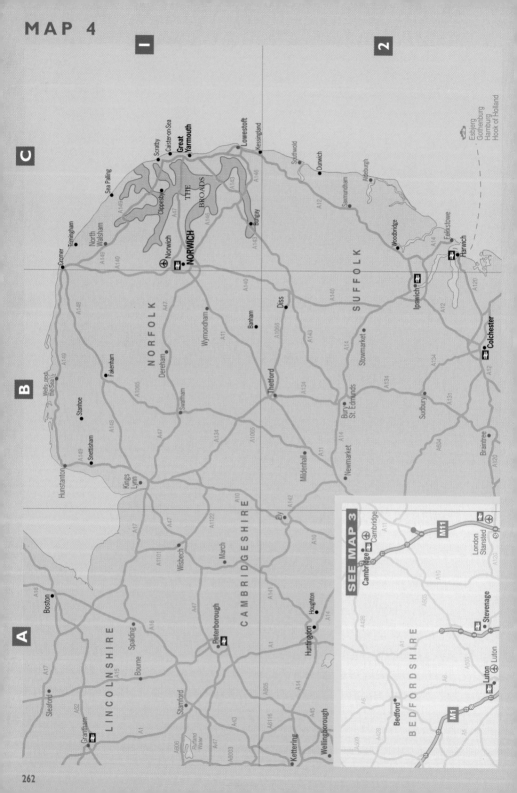

Esbjerg
Gothenburg
Hamburg
Hook of Holland

Caister-on-Sea
Scratby
Great
Yarmouth
Lowestoft
Kessingland

Sea Palling
THE
BROADS
A143
A146
Southwold
Dunwich

A149
Happisburgh
Clippesby
A47
Bungay
A146
Aldeburgh
Saxmundham

Trimingham
North
Walsham
Norwich
NORWICH
A140
A143
A12
Woodbridge
Felixstowe

Cromer
A148
A140
A140
S U F F O L K
Harwich

Wells-next-
the-Sea
A148
Dereham
Swaffham
A11
Wymondham
Banham
Diss
A1066
A143
A14
Stowmarket
A140
Ipswich
A12
A120

Stanhoe
N O R F O L K
A1065
A47
Thetford
A134
Bury
St. Edmunds
A134
A131
Sudbury
A604
Colchester
A12

Snettisham
A149
A148
A134
A1065
A11
Mildenhall
Newmarket
A14
Braintree
A120

Hunstanton
Kings
Lynn
A17
A47
A1122
A142
Ely
A10
A604

Boston
A16
Spalding
A47
A1101
Wisbech
March
A1147
C A M B R I D G E S H I R E
A10

Sleaford
A17
A52
Bourne
A16
A47
A605
Houghton
Huntingdon
A14
A1

Grantham
A607
Stamford
A43
A6116
Rutland
Water
A47
Peterborough
A605
A14
A45
Kettering
Wellingborough

L I N C O L N S H I R E
A15
A1

SEE MAP 3
Cambridge
Cambridge
A11
M11
London
Stansted
A10
Stevenage
A505
A1
B E D F O R D S H I R E
Bedford
A6
Luton
Luton
M1
A5

262

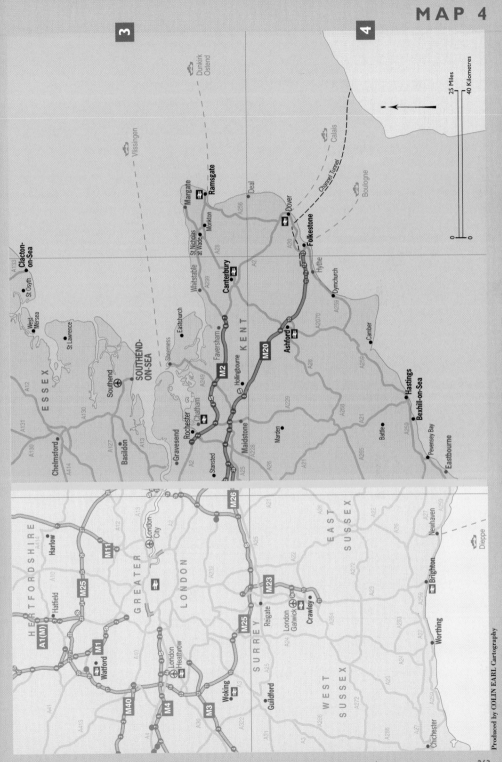

MAP 4

3

4

Produced by COLIN EARL Cartography

MAP 5

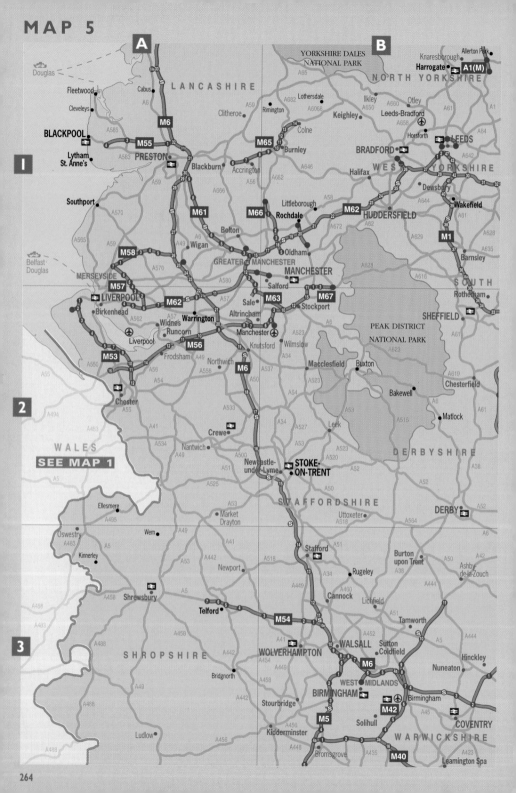

A

B

YORKSHIRE DALES
NATIONAL PARK

Knaresborough
Allerton Park
Harrogate   A1(M)

NORTH YORKSHIRE

Douglas

LANCASHIRE

Fleetwood   Cabus
Cleveleys
                          Clitheroe   Rimington   Lothersdale
                                                                    Ilkley   Otley
BLACKPOOL   Colne   Keighley   Leeds-Bradford
                 M6   Horsforth   LEEDS
                M55   PRESTON   M65   Burnley   BRADFORD
Lytham   Blackburn   Accrington   WEST YORKSHIRE
St. Anne's   Dewsbury
                                                                    Halifax   Wakefield
Southport   M1

                    M61   Bolton   Littleborough   Barnsley
            M58   Wigan   Oldham   M66   Rochdale   M62   HUDDERSFIELD
MERSEYSIDE   SOUTH
            M57   LIVERPOOL   M62   Sale   Salford   MANCHESTER   Rotherham
                 Birkenhead   M63   Altrincham   M67   Stockport
                          M56   Widnes Runcorn Manchester   Wilmslow   SHEFFIELD
            M53   Frodsham   Northwich   Knutsford   Macclesfield   Buxton
                                        M6   Chesterfield
Liverpool   Bakewell
                 Chester   Matlock
                              Crewe   Leek   PEAK DISTRICT
WALES   Nantwich   NATIONAL PARK
SEE MAP 1   DERBYSHIRE
                          Newcastle-
                          under-Lyme   STOKE-
                          ON-TRENT   DERBY
            Ellesmere   STAFFORDSHIRE
Oswestry   Wem   Uttoxeter
Kinnerley   Market   Stafford   Burton
                          Drayton   Newport   Rugeley   upon Trent   Ashby
            Shrewsbury   Cannock   Lichfield   de-la-Zouch
                                        Telford   M54   Tamworth
                                              SHROPSHIRE   Walsall   Hinckley
            SHROPSHIRE   WOLVERHAMPTON   Sutton   Nuneaton
                          Bridgnorth   M6   Coldfield
                                        WEST MIDLANDS
                                        BIRMINGHAM   Birmingham
                          Stourbridge   M42
                              M5   Solihull   COVENTRY
                          Kidderminster   WARWICKSHIRE
Ludlow   Bromsgrove   M40   Leamington Spa

264

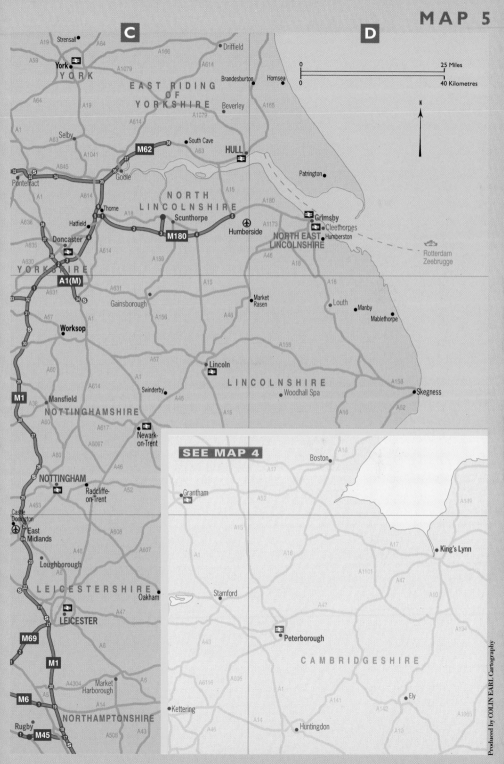

MAP 5

C **D**

| 0 | 25 Miles |
| 0 | 40 Kilometres |

N

Strensall
A19
Driffield
A64
A166
Brandesburton
Hornsea
A59
A1079
A614
York
YORK
EAST RIDING OF YORKSHIRE
Beverley
A64
A19
A1079
A165
Selby
A63
South Cave
HULL
A19
Patrington
Ponterfract
A1041
M62
A63
A645
Goole
A614
NORTH LINCOLNSHIRE
A15
Thorne
A18
Scunthorpe
A180
Grimsby
Cleethorpes
Hatfield
M180
Humberside
NORTH EAST LINCOLNSHIRE
Humberston
Doncaster
A1173
Rotterdam Zeebrugge
A614
A150
A46
A18
A630
YORKSHIRE
A15
A16
A631
A1(M)
Gainsborough
Market Rasen
Louth
Manby
A635
A156
A46
Mablethorpe
Worksop
A57
A1
A155
Skegness
M1
A60
A1
A158
A614
Mansfield
Swinderby
Lincoln
LINCOLNSHIRE
A52
NOTTINGHAMSHIRE
A46
Woodhall Spa
A617
A16
Newark-on-Trent
A9097
A46
NOTTINGHAM
Radcliffe-on-Trent
A52
A453
Castle Donington
East Midlands
A606
A46
A607
Loughborough
A6
LEICESTERSHIRE
Oakham
LEICESTER
A47
M69
A6
M1
A8
Market Harborough
A6
M6
A4304
A5
A14
Rugby
M45
NORTHAMPTONSHIRE
A508
A43

SEE MAP 4

Grantham
A52
Boston
A16
A17
A149
A15
King's Lynn
A17
A1
A16
A47
A10
Stamford
A47
A1101
Peterborough
A134
A43
CAMBRIDGESHIRE
A6116
A605
A1
A141
Ely
A1065
Kettering
A14
Huntingdon
A142
A10
A46

Produced by COLIN EARL Cartography

265

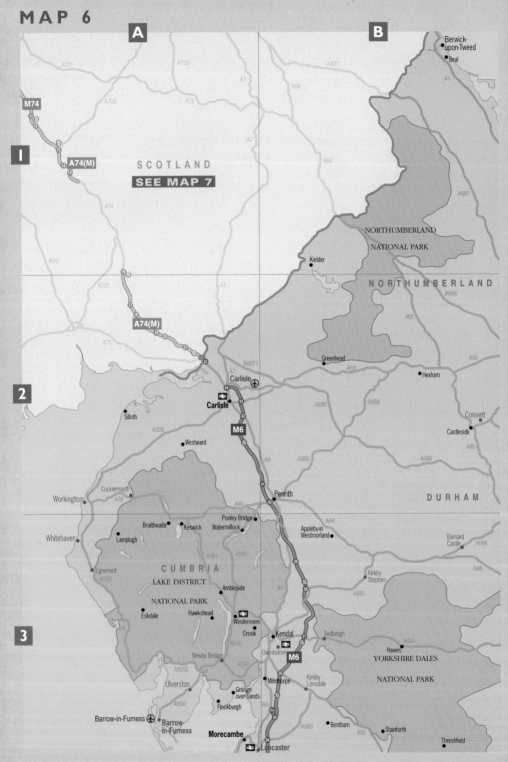

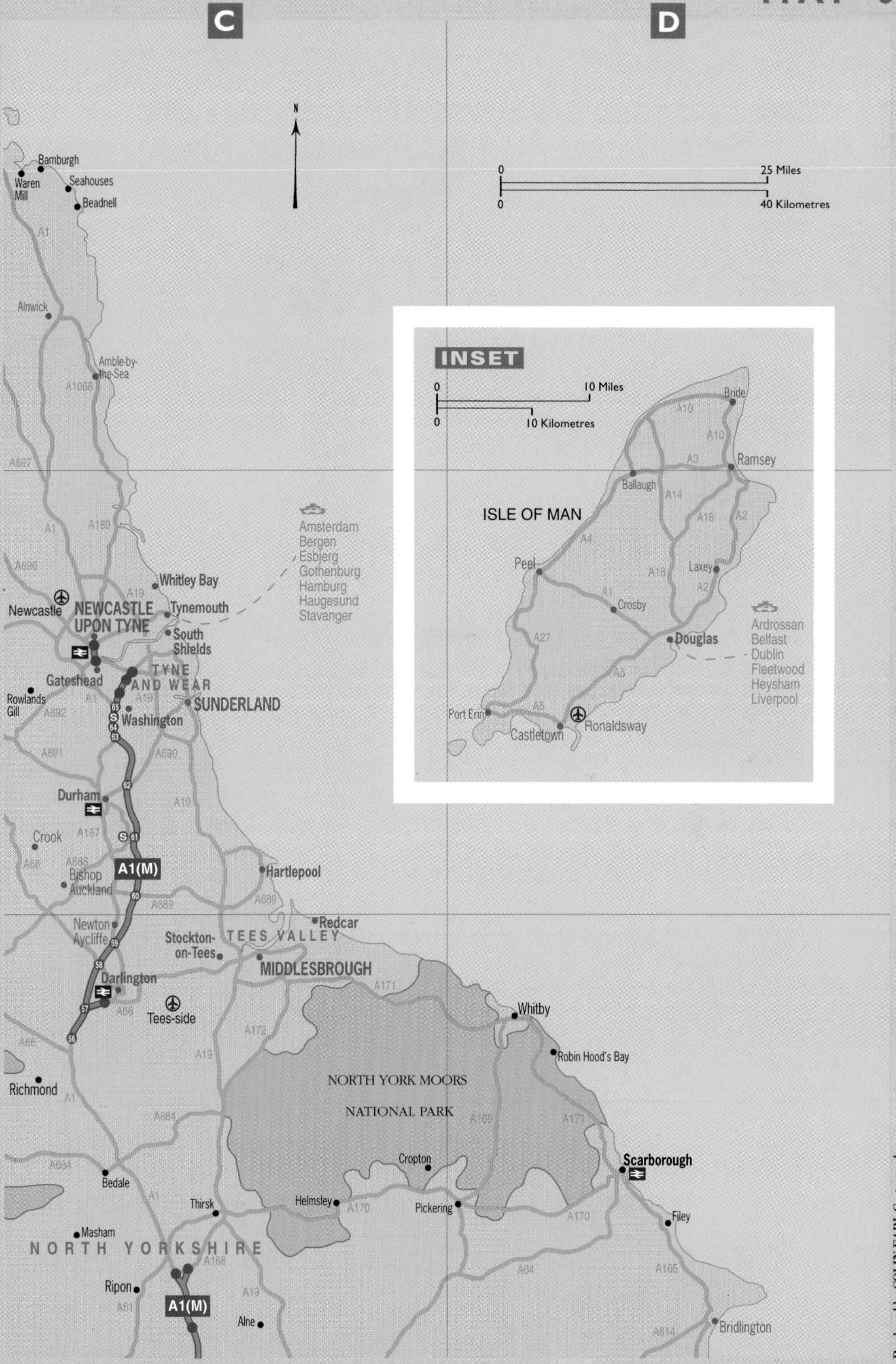

MAP 6

C   D

N

Bamburgh
Waren Mill
Seahouses
Beadnell
A1

Alnwick

Amble-by-the-Sea
A1068

A697

A1 A189

A696

Whitley Bay
A19
Newcastle   NEWCASTLE UPON TYNE   Tynemouth
South Shields
Gateshead   TYNE AND WEAR
Rowlands Gill   A692   SUNDERLAND
Washington
A691   A690
Durham
Crook   A167
A68   A688   Bishop Auckland
A1(M)
A669
Newton Aycliffe
Stockton-on-Tees   TEES VALLEY
Darlington
A66   Tees-side   MIDDLESBROUGH   A171

Richmond
A1
A684
Bedale
Thirsk
Masham
NORTH YORKSHIRE
Ripon
A61   A1(M)   A19
Alne

0   25 Miles
0   40 Kilometres

Amsterdam
Bergen
Esbjerg
Gothenburg
Hamburg
Haugesund
Stavanger

INSET
0   10 Miles
0   10 Kilometres

Bride
A10
A10
Ramsey
Ballaugh   A3
A14   A18   A2
ISLE OF MAN
A4
Peel   Laxey
A18   A2
Crosby   A1
A27
Douglas
A5
Port Erin   A5
Castletown   Ronaldsway

Ardrossan
Belfast
Dublin
Fleetwood
Heysham
Liverpool

Hartlepool
A689
Redcar

Whitby
Robin Hood's Bay
A172
A19
NORTH YORK MOORS
NATIONAL PARK   A169   A171
Cropton
Helmsley   Scarborough
A170   Pickering   Filey
A170   A64
A165
Bridlington
A814

267

MAP 7

A **B**

HIGHLAND

COLL

TIREE

Fort William
Glen Nevis

A830
A82
A86

Glencoe

A828

A82

ISLAND
OF
MULL

Oban

A85

Ardlui

A82

A84

Inveruglas
Inveraray

Arrochar

Aberfoyle

Inverbeg

STIRL

COLONSAY

A83

ARGYLL AND BUTE

A816

A83

Balloch

A811

Lochgilphead

Greenock
INVERCLYDE

Glasgow

JURA

Wemyss Bay
Skelmorlie

M8

1

2

3

17

22

GLASGOW
RENFREWSHIRE

A76

Lochwinnoch

4

ISLAY

A737

A77

NORTH AYRSHIRE

A63

Ardrossan

Irvine

Kilmarnock

A71

EAST

ISLE
OF
ARRAN

Prestwick
Ayr

A77

A76

Campbeltown

A70

SOUTH
AYRSHIRE

A713

GALLOWAY
FOREST PARK

DUMFRIES

Coleraine

A77

Cairnryan

Leswalt

Stranraer

A75

Larne

Portpatrick

Auchenmalg

NORTHERN

Sandhead

IRELAND

SEE MAP 9

BELFAST

Douglas

268

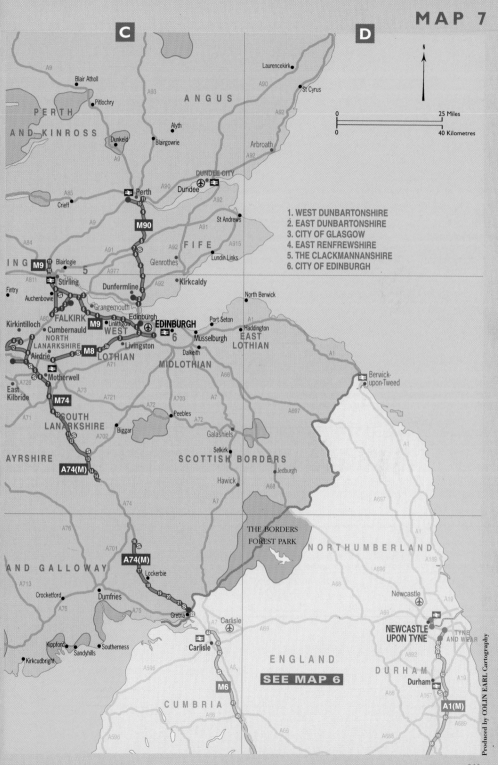

MAP 7

C **D**

N

0 — 25 Miles
0 — 40 Kilometres

1. WEST DUNBARTONSHIRE
2. EAST DUNBARTONSHIRE
3. CITY OF GLASGOW
4. EAST RENFREWSHIRE
5. THE CLACKMANNANSHIRE
6. CITY OF EDINBURGH

Blair Atholl
Pitlochry
PERTH
Dunkeld
AND KINROSS
Crieff
Blairgowrie
Alyth
ANGUS
Laurencekirk
St Cyrus
Arbroath
A93
A9
A90
A92

DUNDEE CITY
Dundee
Perth
M90
A90
A91
A977
Glenrothes
FIFE
St Andrews
A915
Lundin Links
Kirkcaldy
A92

Blairlogie
M9
Stirling
Auchenbowie
Dunfermline
Fintry
Kirkintilloch
FALKIRK
Grangemouth
Edinburgh
EDINBURGH
North Berwick
Port Seton
Haddington
EAST
LOTHIAN
Musselburgh
M9
Cumbernauld
NORTH
LANARKSHIRE
Linlithgow
WEST
LOTHIAN
Livingston
Dalkeith
MIDLOTHIAN
M8
Airdrie
Motherwell
East
Kilbride
M74
SOUTH
LANARKSHIRE
Biggar
Peebles
Galashiels
Selkirk
SCOTTISH BORDERS
Hawick
Jedburgh
AYRSHIRE
A74(M)
Berwick-upon-Tweed

THE BORDERS
FOREST PARK
NORTHUMBERLAND
AND GALLOWAY
A74(M)
Lockerbie
Crocketford
Dumfries
Gretna
Carlisle
Kippford
Sandyhills
Southerness
Kirkcudbright
Newcastle
NEWCASTLE
UPON TYNE
TYNE
AND WEAR
ENGLAND
SEE MAP 6
DURHAM
Durham
CUMBRIA
M6
A1(M)

MAP 8

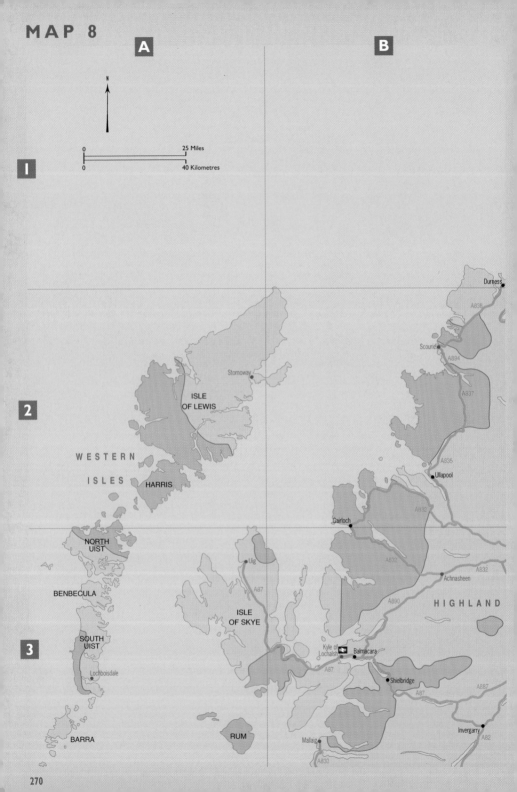

A

B

N

0 ——————————— 25 Miles
0 ——————————— 40 Kilometres

1

2

Durness

A838

Scourie

A894

Stornoway

A837

ISLE
OF LEWIS

A835

Ullapool

WESTERN

ISLES

HARRIS

A832

Gairloch

NORTH
UIST

Uig

A832

A850

BENBECULA

A87

Achnasheen

A890

HIGHLAND

ISLE
OF SKYE

SOUTH
UIST

Kyle of
Lochalsh

Balmacara

3

Lochboisdale

A87

Shielbridge

A887

A87

Invergarry

A82

Mallaig

BARRA

RUM

A830

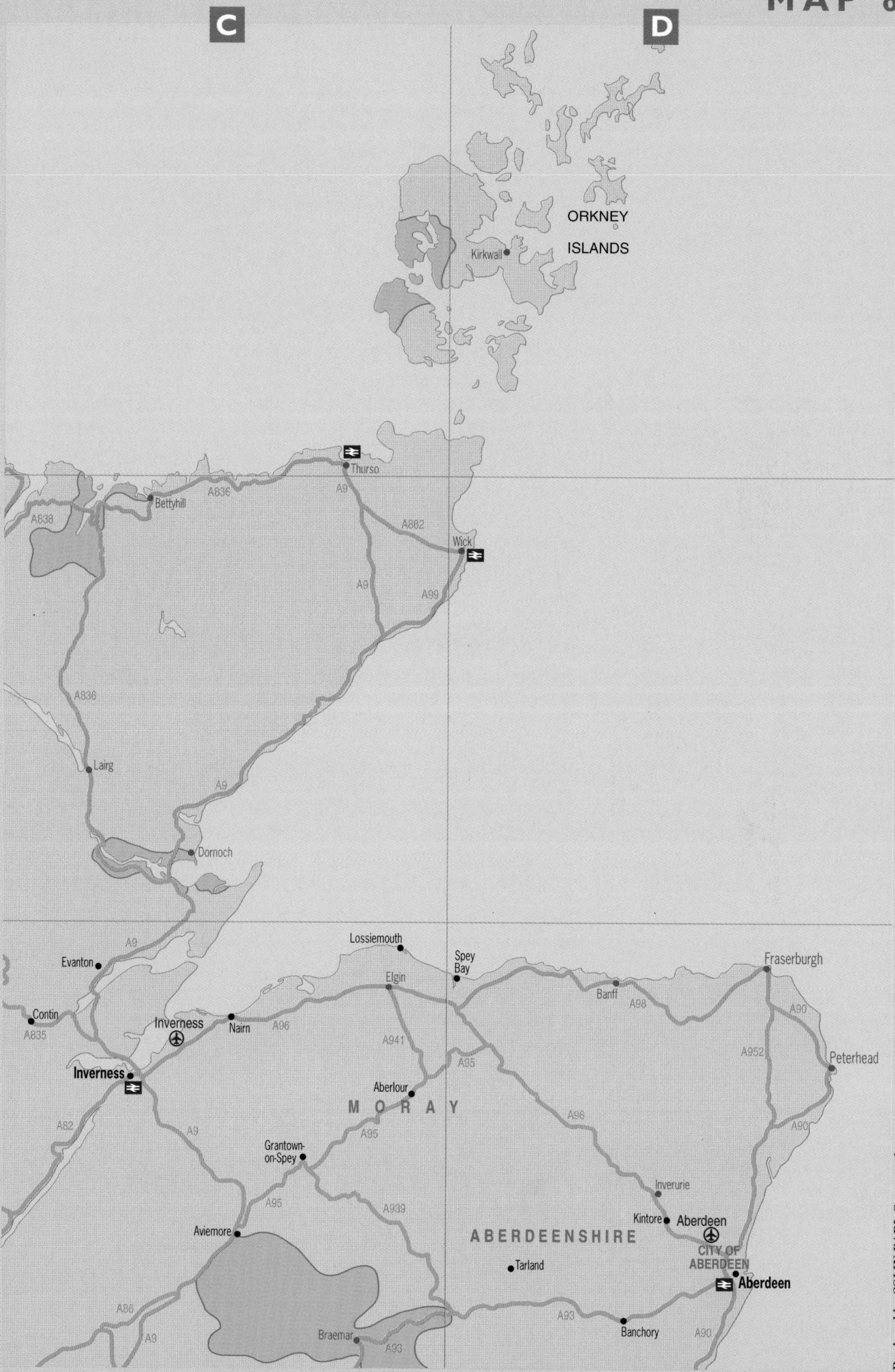

ORKNEY
ISLANDS

Kirkwall

Thurso

Bettyhill   A836
A838   A9

A882

Wick
A9   A99

A836

Lairg

A9

Dornoch

Evanton   A9   Lossiemouth
Contin   Elgin   Spey   Fraserburgh
A835   Inverness   Bay
              Inverness Nairn   A96   Banff   A98   A90
Inverness   A941   A952   Peterhead
                                        A95
A82   Aberlour   A90
              A9   M O R A Y   A96
              Grantown-
              on-Spey   A35
A86   A95   A939   Inverurie
                                                    Kintore Aberdeen
              Aviemore   ABERDEENSHIRE   CITY OF
                                                    ABERDEEN
                                    Tarland
A86   Aberdeen
A9   Braemar   A93   Banchory   A90
                        A93

Produced by COLIN EARL Cartography

MAP 9

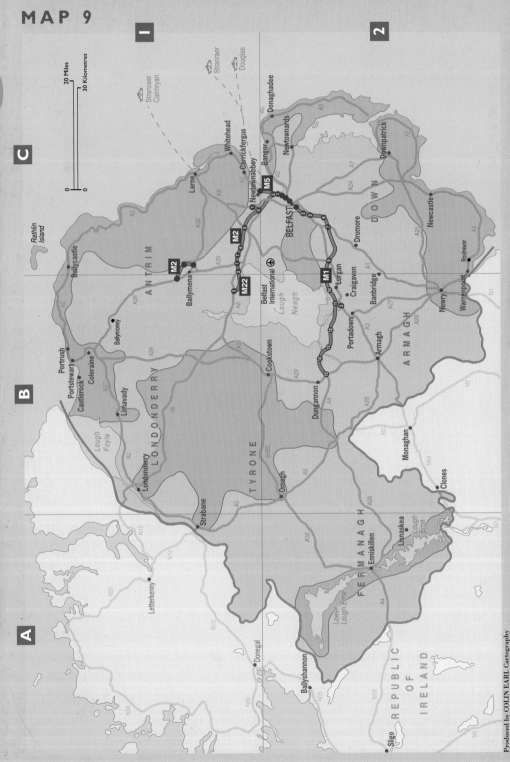

C

B

A

20 Miles
30 Kilometres
0
0

Stranraer
Cairnryan

Stranraer

Douglas

Donaghadee

Newtownards

Bangor

Whitehead

Carrickfergus

Newtownabbey

Larne

M5

Belfast
International

Lough
Neagh

BELFAST

D O W N

Downpatrick

Newcastle

Rostrevor

Rathlin
Island

Ballycastle

A N T R I M

Ballymena

M2

M22

M2

Dromore

Lurgan

Craigavon

Banbridge

Newry

Warrenpoint

M1

Portadown

Armagh

A R M A G H

Monaghan

Clones

Portrush
Portstewart
Castlerock
Coleraine

Limavady

Ballymoney

Londonderry

L O N D O N D E R R Y

Lough
Foyle

Strabane

Cookstown

Dungannon

T Y R O N E

Omagh

F E R M A N A G H

Enniskillen

Lisnaskea

Lower
Lough Erne

Lough
Erne

Letterkenny

Donegal

Ballyshannon

Sligo

R E P U B L I C

O F

I R E L A N D

Produced by COLIN EARL Cartography